AN INTRODUCTION TO
TRANSPORTATION ENGINEERING

an introduction to
TRANSPORTATION ENGINEERING

WILLIAM W. HAY

Professor of Railway Civil Engineering
University of Illinois

JOHN WILEY & SONS, INC., NEW YORK · LONDON

Library of Congress Catalog Card Number: 61–5671

Printed in the United States of America

To Mary, Bill, and Maribeth, who have
contributed more than they realize

PREFACE

I have long been aware of a gap in transportation textbook material regarding those factors and principles that have to do with the technological utility of the various modes of transport in moving persons and goods. Many excellent books have been written on the structural design and formation of plant and equipment. Possibly even more have been written on the economics and regulatory aspects of the industry. The intermediate area of technological use and utility, by which the two are united, has been largely ignored except for portions of an occasional textbook within the area of one mode—such as Wellington's classic *Economic Theory of the Location of Railroads*.

This book has been written, at an introductory level, to fill that gap and to bridge from structural design to economic functioning. It is related to the structural area (including the design of prime movers and equipment) by the conditions of roadway and motive power that must bear and pull the loads imposed by a given traffic pattern and system of operation. It merges in the other direction into the economic and regulatory aspects through the effects of technological characteristics on cost.

The subject matter of this intermediate area is, therefore, the effects of technological factors on movement and the principles involved. Appropriate topics for such a study include the propulsive resistance encountered by all modes of transport and the propulsive force that must be exerted to overcome it. Operating characteristics and criteria determine the suitability of a particular mode of transport for a given situation and traffic. Obviously both route and traffic capacity are of prime importance in determining transport utility. The frequently overlooked factors of terminals, coordination, and operational control must also be considered. The effects of the foregoing characteristics on costs follow in logical sequence.

All of these find their ultimate significance in planning, an element of fundamental importance in developing economical and useful transportation. Planning should, even if it has not always in the past, consider suitability and utility as principal factors in making decisions as to the types of transport to be utilized and developed. Consideration of the nation's transportation resources is another factor frequently overlooked in planning.

Such matters are worthy of the attention of everyone. Not only the engineer but every citizen needs to have some understanding of the significance of these factors to the transportation system, which is the lifeblood of his nation's economy and for which, in one way or another, he must pay.

The student and transportation engineer must be acquainted with these principles as the basis upon which their specialization in one particular mode or area—railroads, waterways, urban transit, etc.—is founded.

An additional value in this presentation is available to the student in engineering. A study of the technological characteristics of transport systems is, in effect, a review of many of the major elements in the engineering sciences and the way these are combined to achieve a desired purpose, a form of systems analysis.

I have attempted to develop a unified approach to these problems, cutting across the conventional boundaries that have separated railways, highways, airways, etc., into unrelated compartments. I have tried to show a common core of problems and principles present in all transport systems.

I am humbly aware of my shortcomings in dealing adequately with any of the foregoing approaches to transportation. It is my hope, however, that this initial attempt will serve to inspire and guide others to a fuller development of the possibilities within this approach. If it does no more than this, the effort will have been worth while.

In the pages that follow, I have endeavored to give full credit to the findings and work of others where these have been knowingly utilized. However, in the extensive reading, study, and contacts that preceded this effort, many ideas and expressions were undoubtedly acquired that I unwittingly now assume as my own. For any such lapses, I hope to receive understanding pardon.

Much of the chronological data on railroad development was obtained from *A Chronology of American Railroads*, compiled and published by the Association of American Railroads. I gratefully acknowledge permission to use these data.

Numerous friends, associates, and students of mine have contributed encouragement and ideas for this work. Space prohibits listing them by name but I am extremely grateful for their valued assistance. I do wish especially to acknowledge the inspiring help and suggestions received from Professor A. S. Lang of the Massachusetts Institute of Technology. Professor Lang conducted a thorough and searching review of the text as it was prepared and made many helpful recommendations for improving the content as well as uncovering an occasional "goof."

Many other mistakes were eliminated through the reading of manuscript and proof by my wife. I am especially grateful for her loyal encouragement and inspiration.

Any errors that remain in the text are of my own doing, and for these I assume full responsibility.

WILLIAM W. HAY

Urbana, Illinois
January, 1961

CONTENTS

PART **I** The Transportation System

1 Transportation's Place and Function   3

2 Development and History   17

Factors in transport development, 17
Development before the nineteenth century, 25
Nineteenth-century transportation, 34
Transportation in the late nineteenth century, 48
Transportation after 1900, 56

3 The Transportation System   70

Components, 70
Carrier classifications, 73
Plant and traffic, 81
Transport routes, 105

II Transport Technology

4 Roadway   113

Subgrade, 113
Drainage, 126
Roadway superstructures, 131
Waterways, 146

5 Technological Characteristics 157

Guidance and maneuverability, 159
Buoyancy and stability, 163
Effects of resistance on transport, 173

6 Propulsive Force, Horsepower, and Elevation 195

Propulsive force and horsepower, 195
Grades and elevation, 217

III Factors in Operation

7 Operating Characteristics 231

Flexibility, 231
Speed and acceleration, 240
Dependability and safety, 246
Land use, 251

8 Operating Characteristics—Continued 255

Performance criteria, 255
Capacity, 262
Summary of operating characteristics, 279

9 Terminals 290

Terminal functions, 290
Characteristics, 295
Terminal facilities, 301

10 Coordination 315

Coordination principles, 315
Types of coordination, 318
Establishment of coordination, 333

11 Operational Control 337

Functions of control, 337
Communications, 338
Interval control, 342
Signals, 344
Navigational aids, 351

12 Costs of Service 357

IV   Planning for Use and Development

13   Planning   377

Planning requisites, 377
Economic justification, 382
Methods of financing, 393
Allocation of cost, 399

14   Planning—Continued   407

Traffic patterns, 407

15   Route Design and Location   432

Effect of traffic patterns, 432
Geometric design, 437
Factors in engineering location, 442

Appendix I   Typical Transport Units   455

Appendix II   Problem Examples   461

Index   485

PART **I**

The Transportation System

CHAPTER 1

TRANSPORTATION'S PLACE AND FUNCTION

General Effects. Transportation is an essential factor in life today. It has been an essential factor in most societies of the past. One can hardly conceive of a future society in which it would not continue to be essential. The adequacy of its transportation system is a fair index of a country's economic development. Just how fundamentally essential transportation has become is the initial consideration of this book.

Transportation has countless specific applications to society, but a few general functions and effects underlie the others. The first is transportation's obvious function of relating population to land use by moving persons and goods from one place to another. It is important to note that the movement of vehicles is of secondary importance. Man and his productivity are thus not bound to his local environment. He has expanded his interests and culture over the whole world and has, in turn, been affected by contacts with other environments. That such contacts have not always been mutually beneficial does not lessen their significance.

Transportation thus makes manifold contributions to the economic, industrial, and cultural development of our country and era.

Transportation is largely concerned with the movement of goods. Goods have little value unless given utility, the capacity for being useful or for satisfying wants. Transportation contributes two kinds of utility to goods—place utility and time utility. These are economic terms which simply mean having goods *where* they are wanted *when* they are wanted. These essential functions of transportation in regard to goods can, without too much strain on the imagination, also be applied to the movement of passengers.

Another economic effect is the increased productivity and lowered costs of production, of which transportation cost is always an element. This is especially true for the United States and accounts in large measure for our present position of power and leadership. Mass production with low unit costs and the increased and more efficient utilization of our natural and national resources may not have developed because of transportation alone, but without transportation they could not exist.

Table 1-1. Improved Transport Techniques versus Cost and Output [1]

Type of Carrier	Output per Man-Ton-Miles per Day	Value of Vehicular Equipment (in dollars)	Accessories Required	Costs per Day [2] (a) Accessory (b) Operating (c) Interest (d) Wages (in dollars)		Total Cost per Day (in dollars)	Costs per Ton-Mile (in dollars)
Man's back (100 lb carried 20 miles)	1	0	Trail and pack rack	(a) (b) (c) (d)	0.01 — — 0.20	0.21	0.21
Pack horse (200 lb carried 40 miles)	4	80	Trail and pack saddle	(a) (b) (c) (d)	0.02 0.20 0.01 0.40	0.63	0.16
Wheelbarrow (400 lb moved 20 miles)	4	10	Path	(a) (b) (c) (d)	0.04 0.02 0.01 0.30	0.37	0.093
Cart, best conditions (1000 lb moved 20 miles)	10	10	Pavement	(a) (b) (c) (d)	0.08 0.02 0.01 0.30	0.41	0.041
Team and wagon (3 net tons moved 40 miles)	120	500	Good road	(a) (b) (c) (d)	0.44 0.30 0.10 3.00	3.84	0.032
Motor truck (10 tons moved 240 miles)	2,400	8,000	Pavement	(a) (b) (c) (d)	2.40 30.60 1.50 20.00	54.50	0.023
Railroad train (2000 net tons moved 40 miles)	80,000	800,000	Tracks and structures	(a) (b) (c) (d)	111.74 424.38 180.00 63.92	780.04	0.010

[1] Based on a suggestion in unpublished papers of the late Dr. E. G. Young, former professor, Railway Mechanical Engineering, University of Illinois.

[2] Costs are those of time and locality where type of carrier was most prevalent. (a) Includes all costs of maintaining and operating facilities, capital costs not included. (b) Fuel (or feed), oil, water, maintenance, etc., except labor. (c) Includes interest on vehicle only, plus simple yearly amortization charge. (d) Direct labor cost of operating vehicle only. (e) Mileage moved is statistical average for all railroads in the United States; obviously a railroad train could run 320 miles ± in 8 hr.

This effect can be seen by the increasing productivity (per man) and the reduction in unit costs as the system of transportation becomes more highly developed and complex. Table 1-1 shows, in a generalized form, the increase in transport productivity as the technological means are improved. The reduction in unit costs, that is, costs per ton-mile (one ton moved one mile, two tons moved one half mile, etc.) follows increased transport productivity. These savings are eventually passed on to the society served.

High productivity is of little value unless the goods produced are utilized and consumed. This is a problem in distribution and involves supplementary problems in financing, advertising, pricing, and merchandising and in an awareness of human wants and their satisfaction. Transportation certainly is necessary for the adequate physical distribution of goods. It has been said that remote areas in China could be experiencing famine, despite a bumper crop elsewhere in that land, because of inadequate transportation. Transportation equalizes opportunities and products. No region with adequate transport need face shortages due alone to remote location. The role of transportation in solving these and other problems is worthy of more detailed consideration.

Specific Economic Functions of Transportation

Utilization of resources. A factor contributing to a nation's wealth and strength is accessibility to and effective utilization of the world's stores of natural resources. Raw materials are seldom consumed where they occur in nature. Iron ore is not reduced to iron and steel in Minnesota or Labrador or Venezuela but must be brought to Gary, Cleveland, Youngstown, Pittsburgh, Birmingham, or Swallows Point. Raw and other materials from diverse sources must often be brought together in one process. See Figure 1-1. Coal and limestone are necessary in conjunction with iron ore to make iron and steel. It was found cheaper to bring iron ore from the lake head to the Cleveland-Pittsburgh area, where coal and limestone were available, than to carry these products to the ore fields. Copper, on the contrary, is reduced at the mines to avoid transporting the useless waste materials that are eliminated in the smelting process. Taconite, a low-grade iron ore, is reduced at the source for the same reason.

Timber has far more utility in consuming areas than standing in the forests or piled in the mill yards of Washington, British Columbia, or Georgia. Most of the grain consumed in the United States is grown in the Midwest, yet only a relatively small percentage of the popula-

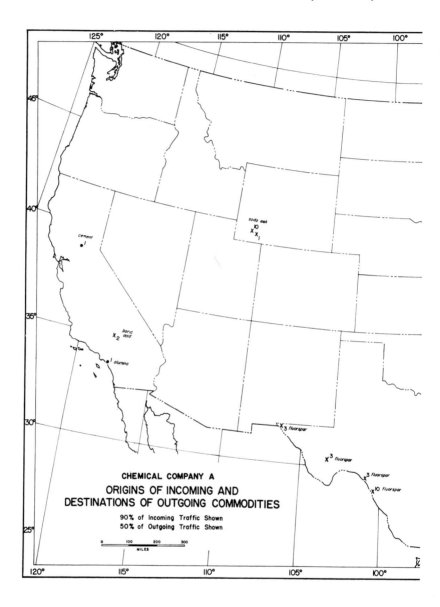

CHEMICAL COMPANY A

ORIGINS OF INCOMING AND
DESTINATIONS OF OUTGOING COMMODITIES

90% of Incoming Traffic Shown
50% of Outgoing Traffic Shown

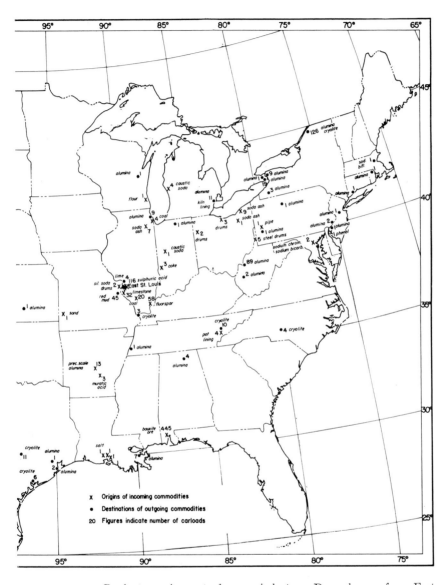

FIGURE 1-1. Product requirements for one industry. Dependence of an East Saint Louis industry upon distant areas. (Courtesy of Dr. Richard L. Day, *Freight Traffic Pattern of East St. Louis,* Ph.D. thesis, 1959, Department of Geography, University of Illinois, Urbana.)

tion lives there.   Analogous patterns exist for coal, petroleum, cattle, lead, and many other products.   By transporting the raw materials to points of processing and consumption, the commodities are given place utility.

As our own natural resources are consumed, we are availing ourselves of iron ore, petroleum, nonferrous minerals, and other vital products from Africa, South America, and Asia by transporting their raw materials to our own shores.   Some countries must depend almost entirely on imports for both raw and finished products.   The United States must depend on faraway sources for products not grown or found in our own land: for example, rubber, coffee, and tin.

Regional specialization.   Transportation makes possible regional specialization both in the production of raw materials and finished goods.   Producing areas are able to concentrate on the output of local resources or specific products.   Labor, which acquires specialized skills and training, is supplied with the necessities, comforts, and luxuries of life.   Specialized production methods, financing, and merchandising lead to quantity output at low unit cost.   Iron and steel production and specialized plants, equipment, and skilled personnel are clustered primarily in the area from Chicago to Pittsburgh.   Chicago, Omaha, Sioux City, and Fort Worth are meat-packing centers. Minneapolis and Buffalo mill flour.   Each region develops the efficiency, economy, and output made possible by the concentrated use of specialized skills, production methods, and equipment.

New markets.   New markets are made available by transportation to and from the foregoing areas of specialization.   Only a small percentage of output can be consumed in the immediate vicinity of production.   Wisconsin cannot possibly consume all the dairy products of that state, nor can Washington consume all its apples and lumber. Transportation again provides place utility by moving the surplus production to all parts of the United States and to seaports for shipment abroad, thereby making the whole world a potential market.

Decentralization.   Many industries are moving away from the traditional centers of specialization.   New manufacturing centers are being established in the South and along the Gulf and Pacific coasts. Proximity to new population and market areas, escape from high taxes and labor costs and from the congestion of older communities, and a dispersion of key industries for national defense are motivating factors.   Regardless of reason, the decentralized areas and industries must be connected with sources of raw materials, equipment, manpower and sustenance for labor and with the market areas.

Time as a factor. Time utility, the delivery of goods and persons at the desired time, is becoming increasingly important. Fresh fruits and vegetables are moved across the continent and even across oceans at such rapid speeds (aided by modern cooling, refrigeration, and concentration) that their original freshness and flavor is available to all. Delays in transit cause spoilage and perhaps loss in market value in the critical market areas. Correspondents and shippers willingly pay premium rates for air mail, air express, or air freight.

A more exacting but less obvious application of time utility in transportation is the supplying of parts to assembly plants. An automobile assembly plant receives car bodies from one city, engines from another, and electrical equipment from a third. Paints, upholstery, and other accessories are secured elsewhere. These components must be available as needed, or the assembly line will slow down or stop entirely. The manufacturer could guard against failure in supply by storing large quantities of parts and materials, but large inventories are expensive and lack flexibility. A current practice is to carry only only three to ten days' supply on hand and to depend for replenishment on continuous rapid delivery by transport agencies. In effect, the production line extends into each producing area, the transport line itself becoming a part of the complete production line. The reduction in inventories saves carrying charges and permits greater flexibility in the introduction of improvements in the assembled product. It also promotes a more ready adjustment to fluctuations in the business cycle.

Other products, such as newspapers, magazines, moving pictures, and recordings, are especially susceptible to the time element, for their sales value depends on their timeliness. Flowers, plants, hatching eggs, and fresh fish also require prompt delivery. Drugs and spare parts are often shipped under emergency demand. Some markets are critical in regard to time of arrival. The first strawberries at northern markets in early spring command higher prices than later arrivals, and this demand gives rise to the expedited strawberry specials run by some railroads.

Power and energy. Command over power and energy is a feature of our society. Unlimited supplies of coal, gas, and fuel oils are necessary to provide power for the factories and heat and light for homes and public and commercial buildings. Transportation itself must have a plentiful supply of fuel. Fuels must be transported, often for long distances and in mass quantities. Much electric energy, it is true, is derived from water power and may eventually come from nuclear fission. However, regardless of its source, the distribution of electricity over power transmission lines is itself a form of transportation.

Other Effects of Transportation. Transportation has far-reaching effects on more than the economic aspects of society. The social order and its culture, government, and military strength have all felt its impact.

Sociological. Progress has been said to follow the lines of communication. Populations (and their problems) have tended to develop adjacent to means of transportation and communication. The shores of rivers, lakes, and good ocean harbors and the crossing of land routes were natural choices. Early civilizations developed along the Aegean Sea, in the Nile Valley, and within the Mediterranean Basin. In the United States the eastern seaboard and the navigable portion of rivers emptying therein served a similar purpose. Later, exploration of the Great Lakes and construction of inland canals and a few westward roads made possible more westerly sites. Population followed the westward development of railroads. Today the rail network, systems of improved roads, and the ubiquity of air travel are developing population centers in the South, Southwest, and West and in other parts of the continent, as well, which but recently were thinly populated.

This has been called an "age on wheels." Transportation has changed the customs and patterns of American life. Trailer courts, hitchhikers, motels, and drive-in theaters are aspects of a migrant population which have accompanied highway-transport development and which in turn, have brought new and difficult problems of health, sanitation, changes in moral standards, law enforcement, and property values. The feared breakup of the American home may be closely related to the instability occasioned by freedom of movement.

City patterns are changing. Shoestring communities border and blight the edges of highways. Shopping centers develop in outlying locations, and stores, banks, and restaurants provide sidewalk service. Surburban living is not new, and the development of peripheral dwelling sites goes on abetted by rapid transit and the automobile. New, however, is the decentralization of commercial and industrial enterprises to suburban and even rural areas to be close to the suburban population centers and to avoid the congestion attending the older centers. The metropolitan area as a population unit is giving way to the regional or metro concept.

Each season brings a great influx of visitors to near and distant vacation spots, and airlines make possible a foreign holiday within the conventional two-week vacation. Businessmen supervise commercial and industrial empires by air travel. The mass-production, low-cost economy, plus widespread distribution, has raised the standard of living for all and given a new concept to comfort. An almost unlimited variety of goods is available to meet the wants of man. No area need be cut off from comforts and luxuries enjoyed by others. Transportation brings them to the door.

Cultural. It is not always easy to distinguish the cultural effects from the sociological. Certainly one sometimes has a determining effect upon the other. Transportation's contribution to cultural patterns includes a decrease in provincialism. World-wide differences have diminished through contact by travel and dissemination of printed matter, pictures, and products of industry. Only political restraints deter the effect. In the United States sectional differences and distinctions are disappearing. No part of the country today can persist in isolated ignorance. A better understanding of other people, their problems, and way of thought is developing.

Not all effects are advantageous. With the disappearance of regional differences, much of the local color and character also disappear, leaving instead a sameness or a drab imitation of local characteristics by others. The easing of tensions from overcrowding in one region frequently means the creation of new tensions at the places to which migration has occurred.

Political. On the political side, transportation has developed a sense of national unity. The administration of so far-flung a nation as the United States would be impossible without adequate means of rapid contact with each part of the country. Sectionalism has declined, and remaining problems are better understood. There is a greater feeling of security. All this develops a sense of oneness under the Federal Government. Development of new routes and means of transport has had far-reaching effects in international politics. Airplanes have eliminated the protection of oceans and forced the United States from its policy of isolationism. British foreign policy was remade and shaped in large part by the construction of the Suez Canal. The historian, Alfred Thayer Mahan, interpreted history largely as a continuing struggle for control of the seas.[1] Sir Halford Mackinder, on the other hand, saw land transportation as enabling land power

[1] Alfred Thayer Mahan, *The Influence of Sea Power upon History, 1660–1783,* 1890, 1911, Little, Brown, Boston.

to outflank sea power.[2] In either theory the role of transportation is decisive. Hundreds of thousands of tons of war machines and equipment, fuel, ammunition, rations, and countless other items of material must be moved, often thousands of miles, to say nothing of the requirements for rapid mass movements of troops. The Panama Canal, long a keystone in United States defense planning and foreign policy, made possible the extension of United States power to the West Coast and across the Pacific. Warfare has moved from the two dimensions of land fighting to a controlling position in the air and into outer space. A prime reason for Hitler's defeat was the collapse of his transportation system under Allied bombs and insufficient maintenance. Submarine attacks on Atlantic shipping almost swung the decision the other way. One of the Allies' most potent "secret weapons" was a submarine pipeline under the English Channel from England to France, which carried precious motor fuels to their armies.

Transportation is fully as important behind the fighting zones. The men and materials of war must be trained and produced. In all of its relations to production, transportation must operate to its utmost speed and capacity because of wartime urgencies.

Other factors. The foregoing is only an example and is far from comprehensive. One could, space permitting, enlarge upon many other ways in which transportation affects modern living—the congestion of cities, competition between regions often widely separated (for example, between Florida and California citrus fruits and resorts or between southern and New England textiles and labor), tax revenues from transport agencies, and the billions of dollars of business that transportation facilities afford to other industries.

The Transportation Industry. The transportation system of the United States represents an extensive and varied complex of industry and comprises various modes, organizations, and types of operation. The most commonplace method, but one of fundamental importance and extent, is the universal use of private automobiles on streets and highways. Small businesses, stores, and industries may also provide their own highway transportation with small trucks. Large industries own and operate private transport systems, often of considerable magnitude—as exemplified by United States Steel's Pittsburgh Steamship Division, National Homes' fleet of trucks, and various lumber, mining, and manufacturers' railroads. Beyond these

---

[2] Sir Halford J. Mackinder, *Democratic Ideals and Democracy,* 1919, 1942, Henry Holt, New York.

private carriers is a vast industry of for-hire and common-carrier operations—railroads, trucks, airline, and pipeline companies, with the single purpose of providing necessary transport service to all or a part of the general public. Typical of this group are the Pennsylvania and the Santa Fe railroads, Greyhound Bus Lines, United Air Lines, Union Barge Line, and the Buckeye Pipeline Company. These agencies, both private and public, in turn help to support an array of supply and equipment manufacturers—steel mills producing rails, pipes, and highway reinforcing and bridge steel; rubber factories making tires for trucks, automobiles, and airplanes and belts for belt conveyors and moving sidewalks; cement plants producing cement for concrete highways and airport runways and for the stabilization of railroad subgrades; and copper manufacturers producing wire for signals, power, and communications for all the carriers. Other industries produce automobiles, barges, locomotives, trucks, ships, and airplanes. One of the nation's prime markets for the products of industry lies in the transportation system and its allied services. Chapter 3 describes in some detail the characteristics of the present United States system of inland transportation and the transport industry.

Transportation and the Individual. Transportation and the transportation industry have significance for every reader of this textbook. The reader might well be amazed at how closely interrelated are transportation and his personal necessities, comforts, and luxuries, as well as those of his family and neighbors; these goods and services are available only because of the transport industries that serve his community. He, and several millions more, may be directly employed by transportation agencies; other millions are indirectly employed in the industries that supply equipment and materials for those agencies.

The cost of almost everything he buys is determined in part by the cost and availability of transportation. A large percentage of Federal, state, and local taxes, which give him roads, schools, fire and police protection, and countless other services, is provided by the transportation industry. As an engineer, the reader may be called upon to design routes or equipment for transport agencies or to plan the use of transport in carrying on some other project. As a manufacturer, he will be required to select the types of transport that will give the most economical and efficient access to raw materials and parts and to markets for his finished products. As a financier, he will find transportation a fertile and demanding field for investment but one beset with many problems. As a lawmaker, he must consider the needs and problems of the country in relation to transportation and the formulation of regulatory policies and measures for transportation companies. As a military leader, he must be aware of the essential role of transportation in national defense. As a city planner, he must know that a city without adequate transportation will wither and decay or strangle in its own traffic congestion. As a sociologist, he must consider the effect upon patterns of life and culture that the freedom to move readily from one locality to another has engendered. As a citizen, he is concerned with all of these manifold functions and relations that are so vital to him and to his country's well-being. Finally as a student, he has the obligation to obtain an understanding of the fundamental principles and relations that govern this essential element in his society. Imperfect understanding of these principles has led at times to misuse of transport potential and to economic loss.

The student of engineering can find in the study of transportation an introduction to the realm of engineering and applications of almost all of the egineering sciences and many of the natural sciences. The design of stable subgrades for railroads and highways draws upon soils engineering and the mechanics of elastic deformation. Roadbed drainage applies the principles of hydrology, hydraulics, and fluid mechanics. Running surfaces involve the student in the field of engineering materials—steel, concrete, bitumens, and timber— and their behavior under load and varying conditions of temperature, moisture, and support. A study of the roadway and roadway structures presents problems of bridge, tunnel, and general-structures design. Motive power applies the principles of thermodynamics, electricity, chemistry, and the specialized fields of fuels and lubricants. Aerodynamics and fluid mechanics govern much of the equipment design and construction of ships and airplanes. The applications of radar and electronics to operational control, signaling, and communications are numerous. The transportation system and its operation exemplify the development of the entire process of engineering and furnish innumerable examples of the engineering application of scientific principles.

In subsequent chapters the reader will learn of the growth and development of transportation, its methods and organization, and of the present system of transportation; he will also learn of the industries that comprise that system. The basic principles, both tech-

nical and economic, that relate all modes of transport to the purposes
of transportation, that is, moving people and goods, are reviewed,
and the application of these relations to each mode or type of transport is shown by example. The relations between technological and
economic principles and the regulatory theories and practices established to insure fair and adequate rates and services to the public are
considered. Finally, planning for transport use and improvement,
including selection of carrier type, location of routes and economic
aspects, impact of traffic patterns, and problems in financing, comprises the remainder of this study.

In Summary. The transportation system may be considered as a
coordinating and integrating agency. See Figure 1-2. It relates

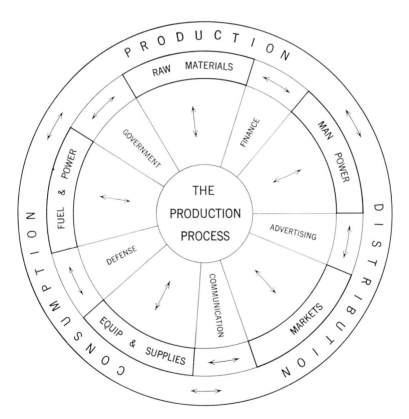

FIGURE 1-2. The "Wheel" of Industry. Arrows indicate integrating and coordinating functions of transportation.

population to land use and integrates the United States and, indeed, the entire world into one vast industrially productive unit. It unites the nation and makes it essentially one people in its economy and culture. It could so unite the world, except for political and social barriers.

QUESTIONS FOR STUDY

1. Explain how you, as an individual, and your local community are dependent upon transportation.

2. What transport facilities do you require and which could you do without? Answer this question first with regard to your immediate pattern of living and then in relation to the over-all pattern of your society.

3. Discuss the dependence of the United States on world trade and world-trade routes.

4. How else, other than as shown in Figure 1-2, might the coordinating and integrating functions of transportation be shown graphically?

5. Develop the cost-per-ton-mile relation, similar to that of Table 1-1, for one specific type of transport, that is, trucks, ships, airplanes, pipelines, conveyors, or cableways.

6. Cite examples of regional specialization and show how transportation helps to make that specialization possible.

7. Prepare an outline or diagram to show the scientific principles that are applied in (a) railroads, (b) highway transport, (c) airlines, (d) waterways, (e) pipelines.

8. Describe the role of transportation in the production and distribution of (a) flour, (b) gasoline, (c) fresh fruits and vegetables, (d) an automobile, (e) other specific commodities.

9. Why did the Allied bombers work so intensively upon the destruction of transport facilities during World War II?

10. Why might industry find it advantageous to be concerned in the maintenance by transport agencies of high purchasing power? Explain in detail.

SUGGESTED READINGS

1. Kent T. Healy, *The Economics of Transportation in the United States,* Ronald Press, New York, 1940, Chapters 2 and 3, pp. 41–46.

2. Stuart Daggett, *Principles of Inland Transportation,* Fourth Edition, Harper and Brothers, New York, 1955, Chapter II, pp. 12–29.

2

DEVELOPMENT AND HISTORY

FACTORS IN TRANSPORT DEVELOPMENT

Problem of Analysis. Any attempt to analyze the factors that have brought about the development of a transport system immediately encounters the difficulty that several of them often combine or overlap to bring about a particular result. The Roman roads, for example, filled both a military and an economic need. The National Road in our own country was built to overcome a mountain barrier and to aid economic development, political unity, and national defense. For purposes of study only, therefore, the factors affecting transportation development are considered under the individual headings of economic, geographic, political, military, technological, and competitive. The reader should always remember that several of these factors were (and are) usually at work at the same time or are otherwise interrelated.

Economic Factors. Basically almost all transport development is of economic origin. Early man's chief preoccupation was the procurement of food, shelter, and sometimes clothing. His initial transportation needs were to transfer the bounty of forest and field to his cave or hut.

As man became more highly developed, the number of his wants increased. He required more of everything and in greater variety. These new wants could often be satisfied only by bringing goods from afar. Even Hiawatha had to travel ". . . to the Land of the Dakotas . . ." to obtain the best in arrows—and in wives!

In some parts of the globe the inhabitants have had to transport almost all their requirements from afar. For others, only a few basic necessities or luxuries thus needed to be secured. The importation of silks and spices from the East, for example, developed the caravan routes to Asia. The small water-bound area of the British Isles forced the islanders to look to other lands for food and raw materials and for markets in which to sell their industrial production. It made Britain a seafaring nation with a citizenry skilled in seamanship and centered world ship building on the banks of the Clyde. Britain established sea routes to her colonial possessions, built ports and fueling stations, and developed bases for a mighty navy to protect these routes and facilities.

As regards the United States, the picture of economic compulsion is equally clear. America was discovered in an attempt to find a new all-water route to the Indies as an improvement upon the overland caravan routes. Much later, exploration of North America stemmed from attempts to find a northwest passage to India. Early highway, canal, and railroad construction had as a major objective the exploitation and economic development of the new territory, especially after the Louisiana Purchase. The need to develop the ore fields of Michigan, Wisconsin, and Minnesota brought forth the most efficient and well-coordinated transportation system in the world: the rail-water-rail movement down the Great Lakes in specially designed railroad cars, ore boats, and ore-handling facilities. A developing market for fresh fruits and vegetables has brought into being elaborate systems of expedited rail and truck movements of those commodities from western and southern farms to northern and eastern markets.

The depletion of natural resources or the initial lack of certain commodities have led to an expanded system of transport to foreign lands. Rubber from Malaya and coffee and bananas from Brazil and Central America have come over ship routes. The iron deposits in Labrador led to the construction of 360 miles of new railroad and contributed to final approval of the St. Lawrence Seaway. American capital has financed rail construction to reach iron ore in Venezuela, to bring chrome and manganese ore to the United States from Mozambique and Rhodesia, and to aid in the general economic development of these countries.

Geography. The foregoing economic examples could as well serve as examples of the effects of geography. The geographical location of natural resources often determines their economic value. In a more obvious way, geography has determined the location of routes through the effects of terrain. Chevalier noted that the destinies of the United States and Canada as great nations could be readily foretold from the geographical features of the terrain that favored excellent transport routes.[1] Great Lakes shipping is a phenomenon of geography in the contiguous placement of natural resources and natural waterways. The Erie Canal and its successor, the New York State Barge Canal, pass through the only natural breaks in the Appalachian Mountains. Construction of the Panama and of the Suez canals was possible because of the peculiar configuration of the land at those sites. The Rocky Mountains have yielded only a few passes through which rail lines and highways might be built and have led to the development of powerful locomotives and of tunnels, snow sheds, snow plows, and other devices to overcome their defenses. River valleys offered natural waterways and provided easy construction for railroads and highways. Trade winds determined the routes of sailing vessels, and today the winds of the stratosphere determine airline routes and schedules. The severe winter climates of northern Europe have contributed to Russia's unending quest for an all-weather port. It is probable that the widespread use of diesel-electric locomotives would have been delayed several years had not railroads in the Southwest found in the diesel engine a solution to the problem of locomotive boiler water.

Political Policies. Political policies have frequently played a deciding part in transport development. Much of the nation's theory and practice of political economy, as well as its foreign policy, is directed toward solving the problems imposed by geographic conditions. The geographic position of Britain as a small island kingdom determined a lack of economic self-sufficiency for that nation. It was, however, the political solution of colonization and free trade that required the setting up of transportation routes and a protective navy with bases scattered over a large part of the world.

The Berlin-to-Bagdad railway was the German counter to Britain's "Lifeline of Empire." Blocked at all principal locations from gaining access to the sea and denied the possibility of meeting British sea power on equal terms, Germany planned a line of land communications, paralleling the British Mediterranean–Suez Canal route to the East, which would not only give economic access to the East but would endanger, in a military sense, the British flank.

Japan's Greater East Asia Co-Prosperity policy would have meant

[1] Michel Chevalier, *Histoire et description des voies de communication aux Etats Unis et des travaux d'art qui en dependent,* Librairie de Charles Gosselin, Paris, France, 1840, pp. 113–114.

little without the Korean and South Manchurian railways. The Trans-Siberian Railway was necessary to give Russia any measure of control over her territories east of the Urals. Russia is again recognizing this principle by developing additional rail routes in Siberia and toward her southern frontiers.

The size and far-flung nature of the United States have always prompted Federal action to bind its isolated areas with lines of communication. In the early days of federation the National Road was designed to unite the lands west of the Alleghenies with those on the east. Later the Land Grant Act and the enabling act for the surveys and construction of a Pacific railroad (the Central Pacific–Union Pacific) united the mid-continent areas and the Pacific Coast with the Atlantic seaboard. The Gadsden Purchase was prompted in part by a desire to gain possession of the mountain passes for a southwestern rail route to the Pacific. Still later the Panama Canal, completed in 1912, made the U. S. Navy a power in the Pacific, as well as in the Atlantic, and brought this country to the forefront in national power. The many transport facilities designed for national defense—air bases throughout the world, shipways and airways for their supply, and the St. Lawrence Seaway, as well as government subsidies to airlines—are planned to give this country the necessary power to support its policies, both national and international.

Military Factors. The military might of a nation is primarily intended to support its political policies and to provide for national defense. Beyond that general concept, military strategy and tactics often have a direct influence on transport development. Earliest history provides illustrations. The Roman roads were routes of conquest for Roman legions. Gibraltar, Malta, Singapore, and other strategically located points served as bases for Britain's navy. The Suez Canal gave Britain and France control over the Indian Ocean routes with a minimum of fleet strength and expense. The railroads of France and Germany radiate to all strategic frontier points to provide quick mobilization and movement of troops. Hitler's autobahns were built for the same purpose. A factor in the Russian selection of the 5-ft gage is said to have been the purpose of making difficult the use of tracks of that gage by invading armies with 4-ft, 8½-in. gage equipment. Countries without domestic oil resources have hesitated to depend on diesel locomotives for fear of being shut off from a fuel supply in time of war.

In the United States many early roads were built to facilitate troop movements. The Civil War provided convincing proof of the vital part transport must play in national defense. It especially highlighted the need of a standard gage for railroad track. A principal aim of the government always has been to keep the transportation system adequate and ready for national emergencies. Development of the inland waterways followed the demand during World War I for more transportation, and the Panama Canal gave protection to the West Coast when we could afford only a one-ocean navy. The Alaska Railroad has been rehabilitated and is maintained to supply our bases in that state. The Soo locks have been enlarged several times to permit the movement of wartime tonnages without delay. Two of the country's biggest pipelines were constructed as national-defense measures during World War II, as were the Alcan Highway to Alaska and the Canol pipeline.

Even more significant are the technological developments in air and highway transportation which resulted from World Wars I and II. The speed-up in new designing made it possible for both agencies to emerge full-fledged from World War I and, in the space of 24 years before World War II, to grow into principal modes of transport. World War II put air transport on a global basis and destroyed forever the geographical isolation of the United States between two oceans. Military necessity now working on rocket propulsion and atomic power may soon bring about new types and dimensions in commercial transport.

Technological Factors. Progress in supporting technologies has played an important role in transport development. It is not proposed to develop here the full story of that relation. Space permits only the citing of a few instances. For example, the invention and use of gunpowder and cannon required heavier and stronger ships to withstand the shocks of firing and to resist the impacts of bombardment.

Far more important to the growth of water transportation were the advances made in celestial navigation. Early mariners were forced to remain close to shore, where the land contours served to guide them. Invention of the astrolabe permitted holding to a straight course when out of sight of land. Discovery of the principle of the compass in the year 1000 and its application to navigation about the year 1400 simplified the problem of keeping on course. The sundial, astrolabe, and compass enabled the navigator to determine his latitude, but the problem of determining longitude was not satisfactorily solved until about 1669, when the Italian astronomer Cacini, working for the Académie Française, suggested the movements of the satellites of Jupiter as an independent clock. More accurate maps and charts were now possible, but errors still existed because of the crude approximations of the circumference of the earth. Once this had been correctly determined, the remaining problem was the perfection of an accurate clock, which was successfully achieved in 1750 in the form of a pendulum clock by the English watchmaker John Harrison. Today a ship or survey party is able to obtain correct time anywhere on the globe by means of radio transmission. Necessary elements in the modern system of train dispatching and railroad operation are a system of standard clocks, a means of checking their agreement and accuracy by telegraph, and accurate individual watches for trainmen.

Hero's knowledge of steam power had little or no practical value. James Watt developed the principles of steam into a workable engine, but it was not until steam power had been successfully adapted to the peculiar requirements of rail and water transport that steam railroads and steamboating became commercially feasible. The fact that Stephenson developed the correct basic steam-locomotive design in his *Rocket* accounts in no small part for the rapid development of rail transportation immediately thereafter.

Even a successful locomotive was not enough. The economies of long, heavy trains moving at high speeds could not have been realized without the development of Bessemer and open-hearth steel production and rolling processes to provide safe, dependable rails, without automatic couplers and draft gears to hold trains together and absorb the impacts of running, and without the automatic air brake to control the enormous momentum and kinetic energy stored in a rapidly moving train. Some of the most desirable locations had to be foregone by early builders because they lacked proper machines for making heavy cuts and fills and for drilling long tunnels. Several such locations have since been utilized with the aid of modern earth-moving equipment—bulldozers, scrapers, power shovels, power drills, and high explosives.

Technology has aided Great Lakes development in numerous ways. Improved locking equipment has made possible the increasing capacity at the Soo. Design of the modern steel bulk-cargo carrier came about as knowledge and skill were acquired in framing the heavy steel members, which were trussed to give strength to the long open holds, a key to the economical loading, movement, and unloading of bulk commodities across the lakes. Ships and locks would have been useless, however, without the invention of rapid loading and unloading facilities and equipment—ore docks, Hulett and bridge crane unloaders, and car dumpers. Radio telephone, radio compass, and radar have removed many of the hazards from Great Lakes navigation—as they have from ocean transport.

Today's system of highway transport exists because of the invention of powerful lightweight gasoline engines, the development of pneumatic tires, and the use of concrete and bituminous materials for highway surfaces. Consider where highway transport would be today without a dependable storage battery or the Edison electric light. And how could women drive as they do today without Kettering's self-starter! Automobiles might still have been a "rich man's toy" had not Henry Ford developed a cheap design of car and the assembly-line process for its mass, low-cost production.

The discovery of oil created the technological need for pipelines. Drawing of seamless steel tubing and electric welding of joints made possible modern lines capable of withstanding high pumping pressures and tight enough to hold highly viscous refined products.

Airplane design has been largely a story of engine design, of obtaining an engine that was powerful, light in weight, and dependable. Other factors are contributing to the safety and expansion of airlines today, notably the new lightweight metals, jet engines, and the various electronic navigational aids, plus a knowledge of soils engineering and of concrete and bituminous materials in pavement design. Thus it is possible to build airport runways capable of withstanding the wheel loads, vibration, and impact of big airliners.

By analogy, the reader can add hundreds of similar examples to this illustrative listing. In so doing, he will include technological advances in all realms of science and engineering—metallurgy, thermodynamics, electricity, electronics, chemistry, optics, prime movers, mechanics, and physics. The list is endless, and the effects are continuous and cumulative.

Competition. One final major factor is that of competition. The competitive urge in Western capitalistic society has given a powerful impetus to transport development. Obviously there is competition between the agencies of transport. Railroads compete with railroads and also with trucks, ships, pipelines, and airlines. All of these compete with each other. Freight service competes with express and express with parcel post. The air conditioning now enjoyed by almost every traveler was developed largely to attract and hold dwindling railroad traffic. High-speed streamlined trains, which cut hours from former schedules, were designed to meet the competition of airplane and automobile. Airlines have counted heavily on speed but have also been forced to extend their efforts in the direction of safety and dependability to meet rail competition and to quiet the fears of a somewhat timid public.

Less obvious, perhaps, but no less real, is the competition between products and industries tributary to transport. The public enjoys the benefits of research and development while bituminous materials compete with concrete as a road surface. Diesel manufacturers are trying to build a truck engine that will be better than gasoline engines. Diesel locomotives have temporarily won the day against steam, but coal producers are backing research to develop a competitive type of steam-powered locomotive. Electrical locomotives are being improved, and an atomic locomotive is on the drafting boards.

Communities and geographical areas are also in competition. Canals were developed to meet the competition of communities enjoying coastal and river traffic, and railroads were built to inland points in an attempt to compete with those on waterways. Competition between East and West, Midwest, Southeast, and Northeast, and Southwest and East has brought about traffic patterns that demand and get new transport routes or improvement of the old.

Other Factors. The foregoing are not the only factors that have been and are continuing to be determining in transport development. The presence or lack of adequate financing has meant life for some routes, failure for others. Many highways and railroads have been forced to inferior initial standards because shortage of capital precluded more expensive location and construction. Steam propulsion might now be the rule on highways had not public sentiment caused legislation in England that discouraged development in that direction. An extensive bulk-cargo overland conveyor system is fighting for public permission to establish a route from the Great Lakes to the Ohio River but has thus far been denied. The high speed of air travel has made that mode of transport attractive to an age that seems always to be in a hurry. The many sides of man's complex nature and society have all played some part, large or small, in transport development.

While reviewing the detailed development of transportation in the following pages, the reader can note how these principles have been effective in determining the transportation system as we now know it.

DEVELOPMENT BEFORE THE NINETEENTH CENTURY

Early History. The beginnings of transportation are lost amid unrecorded events of early history. Primitive man must first have carried things on his back or dragged them on the ground. Dragging was easier, he found, if the ground were smooth and still easier if the object was dragged on a sledlike device or runners. A forward step came with the introduction of rollers under the load or sled. It is speculated that the massive stone blocks used in building the pyramids were transported and put in place by slaves, who dragged the blocks along a smoothed roadway or ramp.

The use of man's back has persisted to present times in the Orient, especially in China. In Tibet and along the northern borders of India it remains a conventional mode of transport. A coolie porter can carry loads up to 100 lb for a distance of 20 to 30 miles per day, or about one ton-mile. The cost ranges from 20 to 30 cents, depending upon load, distance, possibility of return load, and whether or not the carrier provides his own food. (See Table 1-1.) As man domesticated certain of the animals, he shifted some of the burden from his back to theirs. Horses, mules, camels, llamas, elephants, and dogs have thus been utilized and are used today in backward, rugged, or remote sections of the globe.

Man learned that some objects, logs for example, could be floated and thus were easier to move on water than on land. Two logs secured together could support and carry a load. Several lashed together formed a raft capable of moving heavy loads. The log, when hollowed out, gave man a personal means of transport. Wind power later abetted current and paddle, and the raft was transformed into a barge by fashioning planks out of the logs. Water transport was thus under way.

Water-borne carriers. The Egyptians can probably be credited with the first real ships. As early as 3000 B.C. (about the time of the first known roads and four-wheeled land vehicles), the galleys of the Nile used combined sail and oar power (as many as 52 oars), side-paddle steering, and, for fighting purposes, a beak or ram prow. The "aphract bireme" used by the trade-minded Phoenicians was a galley with two banks of rowers, the upper bank being "aphract," or unprotected and visible. With these vessels, they were able to traverse the Mediterranean and, perhaps, even circumnavigated Africa. Fighting vessels were slim and fast. Merchant vessels were broad beamed, to provide cargo space, and slow. The Phoenicians also developed the trireme, which had three banks of oars. More oars, rowing power, and speed were gained by the bank or tier arrangement without increasing the length, and thereby the propulsive resistance, of the vessel. The trireme was further developed by the Greeks and was known to be in use, especially for war, by 700 B.C. Other ships, the quadrireme, quinquereme, and larger, were also developed. The proper spacing of rowers and lengths of oars required great ingenuity and engineering skill, some details of which are still matters of speculation. These galleys were usually equipped with one or more sails. The Norse boats of 1200 to 700 B.C. were single banked and had 30 to 60 oars. One relic of that period measures 78 ft and has a 16-ft beam. Ships of the Middle Ages were patterned after the single-banked galleys, supplemented by sails on two or three masts. A stern rudder replaced steering oars, and higher sides gave more freeboard, thereby permitting their use in storms and heavy seas.

Heavier hull and deck construction was a result of the invention of gunpowder and cannon. Support for the guns and recoil and protection against fire from the enemy were designed. Continuing warfare and the need for self-protection of commercial vessels led to compromises between wartime and commercial requirements of marine architecture in beam, tonnage, and deck design.

By the beginning of the fifteenth century ships depending exclusively on sail power were developed. Spanish and Portuguese caravels, capable of carrying 125 tons of cargo, had broad bows, high narrow poops or stern decks, and three or four masts; the foremast carried a square sail, and the others were rigged with lateen or triangular sails (probably acquired from the Moors during the Crusades). Columbus' ships were caravels. Galleons, used by the Spanish for armed transport of treasure from South America and the West Indies, were larger than the caravels and had three masts and three or four decks. They were first used in the fifteenth century.

In the sixteenth and seventeenth centuries the French and English built "Great Ships" with four and five masts, two or more banks of guns, high poops and forecastles, and displacements of over 1000 tons. Merchant ships varied in size and displacement, and warships varied in the number and position of the guns, but no fundamental changes had become conventional by the beginning of the nineteenth century. An iron passenger ship was launched in England in 1777, and lighters in canal service had iron hull plating in 1787. Iron was also used for some of the framing, but these were the only changes, and wooden ships, wind-driven by sails, continued to be built past the year 1800.

Waterways. Natural waterways—oceans, lakes, and rivers—formed the first water routes. Artificial waterways and canals were used in early Egypt and Assyria and also by the Romans. A system of canals, connecting the Main, Rhine, and Danube rivers, was projected by Charlemagne in the eighth century. In the same period the Grand Canal in China joined the Pai-ho and Yangtze rivers. A problem retarding early canal builders was that of overcoming elevation. Inclined planes over which boats were hauled and lowered were probably used on the Grand Canal.

The use of locks as a means of overcoming elevation is variously credited to the Dutch in the fourteenth century and to the Italian brothers Dominico in 1481. Leonardo da Vinci, in 1487, united the canals of Milan with six locks by using the basic principles now found in lock design.

The Canal du Midi, 148 miles long, connecting the Bay of Biscay with the Mediterranean Sea, was completed across southern France in 1681 from a design by Baron Paul de Riquet de Bonrepos. It used 119 locks to overcome a rise of 630 ft. These early attempts were followed by a network of canals which gradually spread over Europe into Sweden, Russia, and what are now Belgium, Holland, and parts of France. An English canal, engineered by James Brindley, was opened to traffic between the Manchester and the Worsley collieries in 1759. Activity in canal building continued thereafter until the introduction of railroads approximately 60 years later.

In 1785 the first United States canal was built by the James River Company around the falls in the James River between Richmond and Westham, Virginia, and, in 1793, another canal bypassed the falls in the Merrimac River near Pawtucket, Massachusetts. The desire of inland points to enjoy the same commercial advantages as their neighbors who were more fortunately situated on navigable waters and the need for unifying the newly independent colonies gave impetus to the construction of artificial waterways. The James River Company, for example, was organized in 1785 by George Washington and his associates. The company had for its purpose the construction of a canal from the James River tidal basin to Clifton Forge in the Allegheny Mountains to the Kanawha River, a tributary of the Ohio, in what is now West Virginia. The canal was completed a distance of 200 miles from Richmond to Buchanan.[2]

The Great Lakes first became known to white men between 1615 and 1659. La Salle's *Griffin*, built on the Niagara River, began its maiden voyage up the lakes on August 7, 1629. It vanished mysteriously on its return voyage.[3]

Land vehicles. Historians disagree on the time in which the principle of the wheel was discovered and applied to vehicles. The wheel was possibly an adaptation of rollers (or, in earliest times, logs). A single-wheeled vehicle, the wheelbarrow, may have been its first application, but the two-wheeled cart and the chariot must have followed soon after. Under the Romans the chariot obtained a high state of development and ornamentation. Four-wheeled wagons were probably a later development, although they are known to have been used in Mesopotamia about 3000 B.C. The two-wheeled cart is still in common use in some parts of the world. Advent of the four-wheeled vehicle intensified a need for good roads.

Little improvement in vehicles can be noted until about the middle of the sixteenth century, when carriages and coaches came into use by royalty and the rich. A few covered vehicles were used in the fifteenth century but generally only by women; riding in a coach was considered effeminate for men. Their proper transport was horseback. However, coaches, including omnibuses for city traffic, were soon adapted to general and public use. In 1610 stagecoach runs were established between Edinburgh and Leith in Scotland and, in 1658, between London and Edinburgh. Coach development occurred more or less simultaneously in England, France, Germany, and Italy during the sixteenth and seventeenth centuries, and coaching and mail lines were extended across Britain and the Continent during the eighteenth. The use of steel springs was introduced in 1670. Earlier coaches had bodies suspended on leather straps. Improvements in springing, paneling, ornamentation, padding, body design, and mounting continued through the eighteenth century without too radical a departure from early design.

Watt's development of the steam engine early in the seventeenth century gave rise to attempts at steam-propelled vehicles. A Frenchman, Nicholas Joseph Cugnot, invented in 1770 the first successful

[2] Caroline MacGill et al., *History of Transportation in the United States before 1860,* Carnegie Institution of Washington, Washington, D. C., 1917, pp. 269–273.

[3] Harlan Hatcher, *Lake Erie,* Bobbs-Merrill, New York, 1945, p. 31.

self-propelled vehicle, a three-wheeled device for the transportation of artillery. In England working models of steam-propelled wagon-like vehicles were constructed by James Watt and Walter Murdock in 1781 and 1784, respectively, and in 1786 a working model of a steam carriage was built by William Symington.

Highways. The discovery and application of the wheel undoubtedly gave impetus to good road construction. Crude roadways were known to have been in use in Mesopotamia about 3000 B.C. Italy was connected to Denmark by a roadway as early as 2000 B.C., and there is said to be evidence of brick-surfaced roads being used in 1200 B.C. In Switzerland log roads found use in 1500 B.C.

Also in 1500 B.C., the first cut-stone highways were laid along the Mediterranean. Even earlier, about 2000 B.C., the use of oil as a surface hardener and binder began when oil, spilled while being carried from barges on the Euphrates River, was found to possess these useful properties. The Great Wall of China, built in 230–210 B.C., included a highway along its top. The Chinese silk route, in the second and third centuries of the Christian era, extended from Shanghai to Paris to Berlin, a distance of more than 8000 miles.

The year 312 B.C. marked an important period in highway construction: the start of the great system of highways radiating from Rome to provide military and economic access to distant parts of the empire. The first road so constructed was the Via Appia (Appian Way), which led from Rome to Brendice over a total distance of 366 miles and was used for the movement of troops to Greece. A second road, Rome to Naples, was the first stage in the journey of troops to Africa. The fall of the Roman Empire has been attributed in part to the enemy's gaining control of this system of roads, some sections of which are still in existence and use.

Construction started with the excavation of a trench in which were placed foundation layers of heavy, well-compacted stones, building upward in tiers of smaller stones bound together with a crude lime mortar and supporting in turn a wearing surface of heavy cut-stone blocks laid flat. The whole structure was 3 to 4 ft thick. See Figure 2-1. At intervals the interior of the pavement was drained through subdrains into deep ditches paralleling the outside edges of the road.

The paved roadways, 14 to 16 ft wide, were set between raised stone curbings 12 to 18 in. high and 24 in. wide. A graveled shoulder, half as wide as the paved roadway, extended beyond each curb to give over-all widths of 36 to 40 ft. Drainage was considered important. The roadways were raised on low fills when crossing swampy

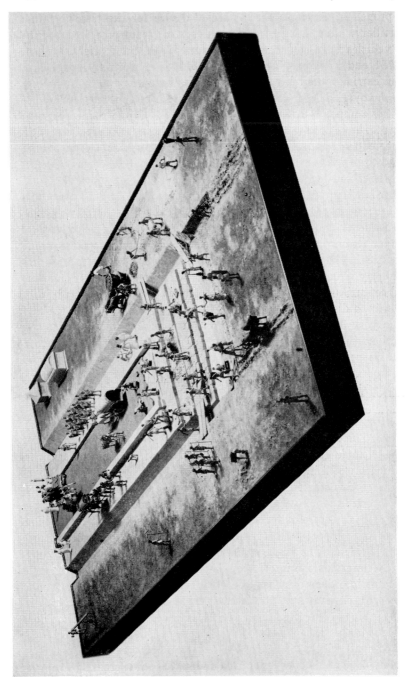

FIGURE 2-1. Model cross section of the Appian Way. Model is permanently located in the National Museum in Washington, D. C. (Prepared by the Bureau of Public Roads, Department of Commerce.)

or poorly drained areas. Route alignments were usually as direct as possible, with few deviations from a straight line, a practice that led to heavy cuttings, masonry arch bridges, and steep grades, gradients of 20 percent not being unusual. The infrequently used curves were of short radii.[4] Construction was probably carried out with slave labor, but little maintenance was required because of the light loads and heavy construction.

The Romans are given credit for being the first real roadway engineers. Their contributions include route planning, preparation of foundation soils and base courses, and, most important, provision for adequate drainage. Their work was characterized by massive construction. They knew the techniques of cement production and use, a "secret" lost during the Middle Ages, which accounts in part for the poor road-building practices of that period. The Roman roads exemplify the combination of economic, geographic, political, and military factors working together to improve road-building technology and to develop routes for transport.

The Great Wall of China gives evidence of excellence in road building possessed by other early peoples. The 1500-mile wall between Inner Mongolia and old China provided a 13-ft roadway 20 to 50 ft above the ground, with brick- or granite-faced side slopes. Another ancient highway used before A.D. 3 was the overland Silk Route from Paris and Berlin to the Orient, via Constantinople, Damascus, north of Tibet, to its terminus at Shanghai on the China Sea. The route is still used by Asians.

Little improvement can be noted in road building after the time of the Roman engineers (roughly 400 B.C. to A.D. 400). Roads built by the Romans continued in use throughout the local areas. As late as the seventeenth and eighteenth centuries Roman methods were followed in France on a few main highways. For the most part the roads of Europe and Britain were miserable dirt affairs. In fact, the feudal system, with its need for defense against enemies, actually placed a premium upon poor road accessibility. In the sixteenth century cobblestone paving was tried on a limited scale both in France and England.

The first principles of modern road building were developed in the eighteenth century, chiefly by Trisaguet in France and Telford and MacAdam in Scotland. The abolition in 1764 of forced road labor necessitated a system of construction requiring a minimum of man-

[4] *Roman Roads,* Bureau of Public Roads, Washington, D. C.

power and the abandonment of the Roman technique of massiveness. Trisaguet (1716–1796) decreased the depth to about 10 in. by setting stones on edge, thereby reducing the labor involved, and cambered or crowned both subgrade and surface. He covered the base with a wearing surface of smaller, hand-placed stones and spread with a shovel a top dressing of small stones. Trisaguet's design is an example of political and social factors leading to improved transport design.

MacAdam stressed the need to keep the subsoil dry by adequate drainage and a waterproof covering, chiefly that formed by small broken stones interlocking through their inherent angularity. Later, roads with waterproof coverings of water-bound, bituminous-bound, or cement-bound materials were termed "macadam" roads.

Both Telford and MacAdam brought principles of good engineering to road construction. They advocated adequate drainage, well-prepared subbase materials, and uniform cross sections, which lacked the excessive crown of contemporary design. Telford emphasized the subbase preparation, MacAdam, the waterproof covering and drainage. Obviously a good road requires both a well-formed base and a waterproof surface.

Road building had evidently attained a high state of development during the time of the Aztec and Mayan civilizations. The Spanish conquistadores, in turn, constructed Los Caminos Reales, the first American highways, northward from Vera Cruz to San Francisco and Santa Fe and eastward to St. Augustine in Florida. These roads were often suitable only for the movement of ox-carts. Their routes, established toward the end of the sixteenth century and in the early seventeenth, are shown in Figure 2-2.

In the American colonies road building was usually primitive in character. Trading posts, and forts to protect them, were established away from the natural watercourses. These posts, depending on the larger communities for trade, export, and supplies, were linked to them by crude roads that often followed Indian and animal trails. Some of the more closely located seacoast communities also were given land connections for protection and communication. The first colonial road of importance, the Boston Post Road, connected Boston with New York in 1711. The Wilderness Road, blazed by Daniel Boone in 1774–1775, was of this primitive type. It extended from the headwaters of the James and Shenandoah rivers through the Cumberland Gap to the Ohio River at the present site of Louisville. In 1795 the Virginia legislature authorized improvement of the Vir-

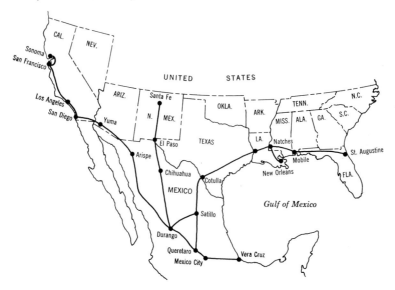

FIGURE 2-2. Early Spanish roads in North America—1836. (Courtesy of the Bureau of Public Roads, U. S. Department of Commerce, Washington, D. C.)

ginia portion to a width of 30 ft. It was always a poor dirt road. Pioneers moved westward across the Alleghenies, and eventually the seaport towns and inland communities were linked by a system of communications traversed on horseback or in stagecoach or wagon. The carrying of mails gave some impetus to road construction. Nevertheless, these early roads, mostly earth surfaced, were poor attempts, dusty and rough in summer, almost impassable because of mud or snow in winter.

Tramways. A different type of roadway came into being in England as early as the sixteenth century. Plankways were laid under the wheels of colliery cars to reduce friction, thereby enabling a horse to pull a heavier load of 10 to 13 tons. The longitudinal planks were usually secured by transverse sleepers or ties, but sometimes cut stones were used instead. Later, iron plates on the timbers reduced plank wear but in turn, caused excessive wear on the wheels. This led in 1734 to the adoption of iron wheels. The iron wheels wore out the iron plates, in 1767 solid cast-iron rails were employed. Here, in brief, is seen the technological battle that has waged continuously ever since between the designers of track and the designers of rolling stock and motive power. The rails of these tramways (named, per-

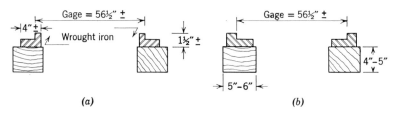

(a)   (b)

FIGURE 2-3. Early rail designs—eighteenth century: (a) inside flanges; (b) outside flanges.

haps, for Outram, a colliery engineer who was instrumental in constructing this type of "way") were plate rails with upright angles
holding the wheels in place. See Figure 2-3.

In 1789 William Jessop, an iron worker near Derby, England, devised a system for placing wheel guides on the wheel itself by means
of a larger wheel concentric wth the running wheel. These first
flanged wheels had the flange outside the rail, but by 1800 Jessop
had reversed the design. He placed the flange directly on and inside
the running wheel, thereby developing the conventional flanged
wheel of today. Tramways are to be considered only as a variation
of highway design, planned for the better movement of horse-drawn
wagons.

Aircraft. The dream of flying above the earth has long attracted
mankind. The first real effort at flight came in 1783 with the experimental balloons of the Montgolfier brothers in France. On June 5
of that year they caused a linen bag filled with hot smoke from burn-
ing straw to make a successful ascent at Annonay. The first man-
carrying ascents were made by Jean Jacques Pilatre de Rozier near
Paris in 1783, first in a captive balloon (October 15) and later in
free flight (November 21). In 1785 the English Channel was crossed
by Jean Pierre Blanchard, a French balloonist, and an American
passenger, Dr. T. J. Jeffries.[5] These and later balloons were filled
with hydrogen gas. Blanchard also made the first man-carrying
ascent in the United States, in 1793 near Philadelphia.

NINETEENTH-CENTURY TRANSPORTATION

Early Nineteenth-Century Transportation. The nineteenth century
opened with water- and road-borne transport as the only means of

[5] *The Universal Standard Encyclopedia,* Vol. II, Unicorn Publishers, New
York, 1955, pp. 635–636.

carriage and with wind, current, animal, and manpower as the only means of propulsion. In the newly formed United States the system was simple and uncomplicated. Early settlers and colonists had sailed their ships in coastal waters and penetrated inland where rivers and bays provided ready-made harbors and waterways. Communities sprang up on the shores of good harbors and at the upper limits of navigable inland rivers. Villages grew into towns and cities because of their strategic positions as potential or actual ports along the Atlantic seaboard. So developed New York, Philadelphia, Boston, Baltimore, Charleston, and the river port of Albany. This rather limited degree of communication was hardly sufficient for a growing country, and other modes of transport developed along with the nation.

Highways. In the United States a somewhat better class of construction came with the turnpike era to replace the crude dirt roads of the late 1700's. Turnpikes were profit-making efforts named for the turning of a pike pole to permit entry of a vehicle after payment of the toll. The Lancaster Turnpike, between Philadelphia and Lancaster, Pennsylvania, chartered in 1792 and completed in 1795, was one of the first and the best. This was a well-constructed all-weather highway, 62 miles long, with a 24-ft surface of gravel overlaying a stone base.[6]

By 1800 charters had been granted to 92 turnpike corporations. The development of canals and railroads, coming soon after, made the turnpikes a losing operation. By 1830–1840 they had passed out of the picture, not to reappear until more than 100 years later as the modern superhighway toll road.

Agitation for better communication with the interior beyond the Alleghenies to bind the new country together was answered by Federal financing and construction of the Cumberland or National Road. See Figure 2-4. Authorized by Congress on March 29, 1806, the first stretch of 130 miles from Cumberland, Maryland, to Wheeling, in what is now West Virginia, was completed in 1818. Good construction characterized the road, with its 66-ft right of way, 20-ft surface, 12-in. base course of rough stones, and 6-in. top course of 3-in. hammer-broken stone. Compaction of the roadway was secured by rolling it with an iron roller and by the heavy traffic moving over it to and from the West. Toll houses, with heavy iron gates to enforce

[6] Public Works Administration, *Highway Practice in the United States of America,* Public Works Agency, Washington, D. C., 1949, p. 1.

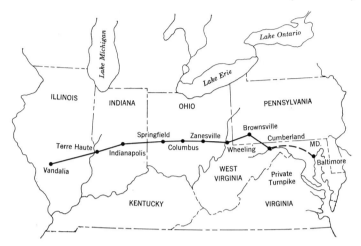

FIGURE 2-4. Route of the National Road—1830.

payment of tolls, were spaced about 15 miles apart. Bridges were of
heavy stone-arch masonry. Cost of the road was approximately
13,000 dollars per mile.[7] By 1852 the road had been extended westward to Vandalia, then capital of Illinois, at a cost of 7 million dollars.
It is said that the cost of freight carriage was reduced approximately
one half and travel time by nearly two thirds. In 1830 President
Andrew Jackson vetoed the Maryland Road Bill, which proposed a
similar road, holding it to be unconstitutional to use government
funds for such purposes. Except for a few military roads in western
territories, the Federal Government engaged in no further road building until 1916. The National Road, now a part of U.S. 40, and roads
of the turnpike corporations were turned over to the states and to
local governments to be incorporated in their systems.

   This period saw the introduction of new construction materials.
Stone-block paving had been tried in Paris as early as 1609. In the
United States stone blocks were used in Philadelphia in 1839. Improvements in joint construction and foundation followed. Wood-
block pavements appeared in St. Petersburg, Russia, in the 1820's and
in London in the 1830's. Beds of sand and later concrete covered with
sand, similar to stone-block foundations, served as base courses.
Joints were filled with sand and covered with boiling wood tar.

[7] *Ibid.*

Longer life was obtained by dipping the blocks in creosote. Wood-
block pavements are generally obsolete today. Asphalt found its
first application to paving between 1820 and 1840 in France. In
1837 it was used as a wearing course on macadam construction between Bordeaux and Bayonne.

Waterways. At the same time, water transportation was developing. Rivers, such as the James and Potomac in Virginia, the Delaware in Pennsylvania and Delaware, and the Hudson in New York,
furnished deep, safe channels inland within the range of tidewater.
Initial canal development, as earlier described, was first aimed at
extending the navigation limits of these rivers, but more ambitious
cross-country channels soon followed.

In 1825 the Erie Canal was completed between the Hudson River,
near Troy and Albany, to Buffalo and Lake Erie 351 miles to the
west. The Erie Canal, crude by modern standards, was an outstanding feat of engineering for those days. It utilized the Hudson and
Mohawk valleys, the only natural break in the Appalachian Mountains. As originally constructed, the canal had a bottom width of
26 ft, a top width of 40 ft, and a depth of 4 ft. It contained 82 locks,
90 x 14 ft of stone masonry with mitered lock gates of oak timbers.[8]
These locks carried the canal over an elevation of 571 ft from tidewater at Troy to the level of Lake Erie at Buffalo. Between 1835
and 1870 the depth was increased to 7 ft, top width to 70 ft, and locks
to a length of 110 ft. In two locations the canal crossed the Mohawk
River on high aqueducts. Towboats were pulled by horse or mule
power. The over-all first cost, borne by the State of New York, was
7 million dollars. The Erie Canal was advertised as placing Buffalo
only "120 hours" from New York.

Farther west, two canals joined Lake Erie and the Ohio River. In
1829 practical completion marked the Miami–Toledo canal from
Cincinnati on the Ohio River via the Miami and Maumee rivers to
Toledo on Lake Erie. In 1833 a canal was completed between Ports-
mouth on the Ohio River and Cleveland on Lake Erie, via the Scioto,
Muskingum, Tuscarawas, and Cuyahoga rivers. This route, 307 miles
long, used 49 locks to surmount the 499-ft Akron Summit. The
canal was 40 ft wide at the top, 26 ft in bottom width, and 4 ft deep.
These dimensions were similar to those of the Erie Canal, on which

[8] Michel Chevalier, *Histoire et description des voies de communication aux
Etats Unis et des travaux d'art qui en dependent,* Vol. I, Librairie de Charles
Gosselin, Paris, 1840, p. 159.

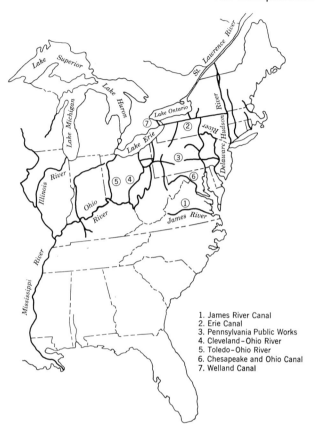

1. James River Canal
2. Erie Canal
3. Pennsylvania Public Works
4. Cleveland–Ohio River
5. Toledo–Ohio River
6. Chesapeake and Ohio Canal
7. Welland Canal

FIGURE 2-5.   Early United States canal routes—1850.

it was patterned.   Upon the completion of the Erie and Ohio canals, traffic that formerly cost 125 dollars a ton to move from the seaboard to the interior could now be brought in for 25 dollars a ton.[9]

Canal construction, financed in large part by state funds, spread rapidly.   See Figure 2-5.   By 1833 indebtedness for canals for more than 60 million dollars had been incurred by 18 states.   Returns, however, were limited, and the panic and depression of 1837 eliminated the idea of deriving large financial returns from state systems.   The Pennsylvania state system of canals and inclined planes over the Alleghenies to the Ohio River at Pittsburgh proved a financial failure but laid the groundwork for the Pennsylvania Rail Road when the

[9] Harlan Hatcher, *Lake Erie*, Bobbs-Merrill, New York, 1945, pp. 113–120.

system was sold to that carrier in 1857–1858. The New York state system, which included the Hudson River, Erie Canal, and Lake Champlain, had a better financial and traffic record. Competition of rail transportation gave the final blow to nineteenth-century canal and river transport in the United States, but canals continued to be important in Europe.

No mention of water transportation in this period would be complete without including the world-famed Baltimore or Yankee clipper ships. The clippers, first built in Baltimore in 1830, were square-rigged and carried a great spread of canvas on raking masts. They had narrow beams and sharp, overhanging bows. Speeds of 18 knots were attained, making them the fastest wind-driven vessels. The largest of these, the *Great Republic*, was 325 ft long and had a capacity of 4500 cargo tons. The high speeds and cargo capacities of these ships gave the American traders an advantage in the long-haul trade with the Orient in silks, tea, and opium. The discovery of gold in California in 1848 intensified the demand for these vessels to provide rapid passage to California around the Horn. Over 160 clipper ships were built in the years immediately following that event, but improvements in steam navigation soon outmoded them, so that few were built after the Civil War.

Steam. Early attempts at steam propulsion were made with the steam barge *Charlotte Dundas* on the Clyde in Scotland in 1767. In the United States John Fitch built a steam-powered oar vessel in 1787 but was unable to convince the public of the possibilities of steam propulsion. Robert Fulton, in 1807, developed the *Clermont*, a practicable steamboat, and placed it in service on the Hudson River. The first ocean voyage by steam, from Hoboken, New Jersey, to Philadelphia, Pennsylvania, was made in 1812, and in 1819 the steamer *Savannah* crossed the Atlantic from Liverpool to New York in 25 days with some use of sail. By 1830 there was regular steam trans-Atlantic service.

Early steamboats were propelled by paddle wheels, driven by single- and later two-cylinder double-acting engines. Requisite shaft speed was obtained by gearing. Still later the oscillating-valve and walking-beam type engines were used. The two-cylinder compound, a big advance in design, was introduced in 1854 by John Elder. The vertical type was the commonest; its steam pressure of 40 psi compares with 10 psi in the *Clermont* and 350 psi today. Ericsson's development of the screw propeller had driven the paddle wheel from the field of ocean shipping by 1850 following the *Rattler-Alecto* tests in 1845. The *Rattler* and *Alecto* were duplicate ships, except that the *Rattler* had a screw propeller, the *Alecto*, paddle wheels. In the tests the *Rattler* towed the *Alecto* astern at 2.5 mph. Paddle wheels continued as the principal mode of river propulsion in this country until the 1930's, when propellers mounted in tunnels or tubes for operation in shallow water came into use.

Advent of the steamboat made necessary a program of deepening and improving river channels. Prior to 1800 river as well as canal commerce was handled by canoes, keel boats, and barges. River obstructions were not important. Regular steamboat service on the Mississippi, begun in 1817, ushered in one of the most colorful eras in transportation history. In 1820, 29 steamboats were plying between Pittsburgh and St. Louis. Steamboat arrivals in New Orleans increased from 21 in 1813–1814 to 2566 in 1859–1860. See Figure 2-6. The later date represented the peak of river transportation. The decline of southern commerce after the Civil War, combined with railroad com-

FIGURE 2-6. Early river steamboat. Side-wheel cotton-boat *J. M. White,* built at the Howard yard, Jeffersonville, Indiana, in 1878: 312 ft, 7 in. keel; 320 ft over-all length; hull width 47 ft, 9 in., over-all width 91 ft; rated tonnage 2027.76. (Courtesy of Dean Emeritus Cyrus E. Palmer and the Ricker Library of Architecture, University of Illinois, Urbana.)

petition, worked to the deterioration of river as well as canal traffic. By the end of the nineteenth century, with the exception of coal traffic on the Monongahela and Ohio rivers and bulk cargos on the Erie Canal, canal and river transportation had become relatively unimportant. During this period of water transport river boats in the United States were principally wood-burning stern wheelers, with deck-loaded freight and often sumptuous quarters for the passengers. Navigation was chiefly the result of the skill of the pilot and his personal knowledge of the river. River transport continued in foreign countries on the Danube, the Rhine, the Elbe, Oise, Seine, Dnieper, and the Volga.

Relatively few vessels sailed the Great Lakes until after Commodore Perry's victory over the British on Lake Erie, September 10, 1813. Thereafter ship building developed rapidly, especially at the south-shore ports of Lake Erie. On August 23, 1818, the lakes' first steamboat, the *Walk on the Water,* made its initial voyage. It was a two-masted, schooner-rigged vessel propelled by two side paddle wheels. The *Vandalia,* a 139-ton sloop, was the first commercial vessel in the world to use Ericsson's screw propeller. By 1860 there were nearly 120 paddle-wheel and 115 propeller-driven steamboats registered on the lakes, in addition to 40 barks, 211 brigs, 608 schooners, and 240 sloops and barges.[10]

Improvement of the waterway itself was necessary to realize the full potential of the lakes. The Welland Canal, authorized by the Canadian Government in 1821, bypassed Niagara Falls, carrying vessels over the Niagara escarpment between lakes Erie and Ontario. The original canal had a 60-ft top width, 40-ft bottom width, 7-ft depth, and 40 locks, 110 x 22 x 8 ft deep.[11] The present canal, as improved in 1930, is 28 miles long and has a 200-ft bottom width; its eight locks are 820 x 80 x 30 ft deep.

Aircraft. The first part of the nineteenth century saw little improvement in aerial navigation. Longer flights and larger balloon bags were the chief items of progress.

Early Nineteenth-Century Railroads. An entirely new form of land transportation appeared early in the nineteenth century. In 1803 Richard Trevithick, an English colliery engineer, designed a self-propelled steam carriage which ran on the highways. In 1804 he constructed the world's first steam locomotive. Running on the col-

[10] Harlan Hatcher, *Lake Erie,* Bobbs-Merrill, New York, 1945, pp. 104–123.
[11] *Ibid.,* pp. 120–121.

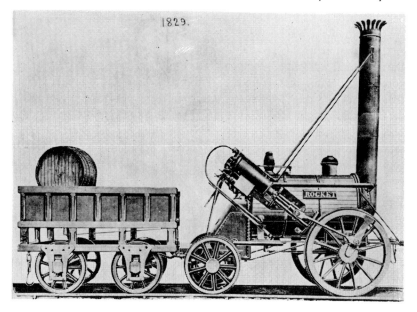

FIGURE 2-7. Stephenson's *Rocket.* (Courtesy of the Association of American Railroads, Washington, D. C.)

liery's tramway, it successfully pulled five cars loaded with ten tons of iron and carrying 70 men. It was not, however, commercially feasible. George Stephenson built his first locomotive in 1814. On September 27, 1825, England's Stockton and Darlington, first public passenger-carrying railway, using both steam and horse-drawn motive power, was placed in service. In 1830 the Liverpool and Manchester went into operation as the first common carrier by rail. It had 31 miles of double-tracked road and, as a result of a contest, selected George Stephenson's *Rocket* as its motive power. See Figure 2-7. This locomotive possessed most of the essential features of a modern steam locomotive, including a horizontal fire-tube boiler, use of exhaust steam for draft, and a variable cutoff.[12]

The first use of rails in the United States is usually credited to Silas Whitney, who in 1607 built a wooden tramway, operated by gravity and horsepower, on Beacon Hill in Boston. However, the

---

[12] Nicholas Wood, *Treatise on Railroads,* Longman, Orme, Brown, Green, and Longman's, London, 1838, pp. 320–326.

first real track is sometimes ascribed to Gridley Bryant; it was built in 1826 to haul granite, used in constructing the Bunker Hill monument, from Quincy, Massachusetts, to the Neponset River three miles away. The tracks were timber stringers secured to stone sleepers 8 ft apart. Straps of iron with a gage of 5 ft were laid on the wooden stringers. Two horses could haul 40 tons at one sixth the cost of using the highway alone! Later improvements used close-spaced wooden ties, transverse to flat-bottomed or Tee-rails, designed in 1830 by Robert L. Stevens, chief engineer of the Camden and Amboy Railroad. Figure 2-8 shows early United States track.

The Stevens' rail has been used all over the United States and in many foreign countries. The Tee-rail did not become an accepted standard in Britain until 1946. The British standard had been the reversible double or bullhead rail set in heavy cast-iron chairs and held in place with wood or metal shims. The first rolling of wrought-iron rails in the United States occurred in 1844.

In February 1825 the first steam locomotive in the United States, a small experimental model designed by John Stevens, was built and operated on a half-mile circle of track. In 1828 John B. Jervis designed one of the first inclined planes in the United States. Its purpose was to haul coal from the mines at Carbondale, Pennsylvania, to the top of a ridge by cable engines, thence by gravity to Honesdale and the canal of the Delaware and Hudson Coal Company, a forerunner of the present Delaware and Hudson Railroad. On these tracks, the *Stourbridge Lion,* imported from England and patterned after Stephenson's earliest Killingsworth colliery model, made the first commercial, full-scale run—of three miles—with Horatio Allen, assistant engineer of the company, at the throttle. The locomotive proved too heavy for the timber stringers of the gravity railroad and was not placed in regular service. Allen went on to become chief engineer of a forerunner of the Southern system.

Jervis, the chief engineer of the Delaware and Hudson, was one of the first great railroad engineers. Among his major contributions was the designing of the swiveled pilot truck, which helps support the weight of the locomotive but provides flexibility and guidance in going around sharp curves. This design had a significant effect in permitting American engineers to use heavy locomotives in conjunction with the sharp curves required by the rough terrain and pioneer construction practiced by the early American builders.

FIGURE 2-8*a*. Early United States track. Part of the original 13 miles of the Baltimore and Ohio Railroad laid between Baltimore and Ellicott's Mills, Maryland, in 1830. (Courtesy of the Association of American Railroads, Washington, D. C.)

FIGURE 2-8*b*. Early United States track. Track on the old Camden and South Amboy Railroad at Jamesburg, New Jersey. The steel rails, designed by Robert L. Stevens in 1831, and manufactured in England, weighed 40 lb to the yard and were attached to stone ties by hooked-head spikes. (Courtesy of the Pennsylvania Rail Road.)

FIGURE 2-9. *Best Friend of Charleston*, pulling a special excursion train, January 1830. (Courtesy of the Southern Railway Company.)

The Baltimore and Ohio, first common-carrier railroad in the United States, was incorporated on February 28, 1827. Construction began on July 4 of that year, and the first 14 miles were opened for service in 1830. Benjamin Latrobe was the engineer in charge of location. So well did he design, that the standards of his railroad, 2.2 percent grades and 6-degree curves, were later incorporated into the Land Grant Acts. On December 25, 1830, the first steam-operated railroad in the United States began operation between Charleston and Hamburg, South Carolina. Horatio Allen here used the first full-sized steam locomotive built in the United States, the *Best Friend of Charleston*. See Figure 2-9.

Railroad construction continued at an accelerated pace, giving inland localities removed from waterways their own transportation. An impetus to rail construction and westward expansion had been given earlier by the Federal Land Grant Act of September 20, 1850. This act provided grants of Federal lands in the form of rights of way 200 to 400 ft wide and alternate sections of land along the rights of way as an inducement to construction. The railroads used these lands for rights of way, as security for loans, for sale to settlers, for industrial sites, and for their natural resources. In return, the railroads granted the government reduced freight and passenger rates. This last feature of the act was repealed on October 1, 1946, after the railroads had thus granted the equivalent of 1.25 billion dollars of savings to the government in reduced rates and fares. The Illinois Central was the first land-grant railroad, but many other railroads in the West and Midwest shared in the grants. The last land grant was made in 1871.

Rail routes were completed from Boston to the Great Lakes at Buffalo on November 24, 1842, between New York and Boston on December 29, 1853, and between Charleston, South Carolina, and Memphis, Tennessee, on April 1, 1857. The Mississippi River was first bridged at Davenport, Iowa, on April 21, 1856. It carried the tracks of the present Rock Island system. By the time of the Civil War there were 30,626 route miles of railroads in the United States. See Figure 2-10.

The general design of American railroads was set by 1860. The Tee-rail was standard, a gage of 4 ft, 8½ in. was commonly (but not universally) used, wooden cross ties had supplanted stone and timber stringers, and iron truss bridges, forerunners of later steel structures, were replacing stone and timber construction. Steam locomotives had the general design and appearance of today, with horizontal fire-tube

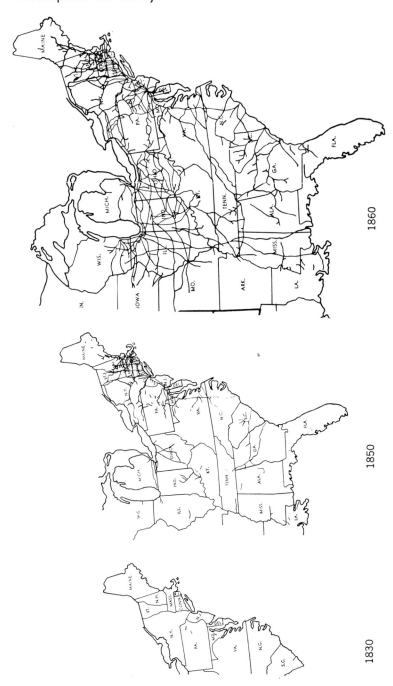

1860

1850

1830

FIGURE 2-10. United States rail routes—1830 to 1860. The nation's railway network increased to a total of 30,626 miles by 1860. (Courtesy of the Association of American Railroads, Washington, D. C.)

FIGURE 2-11a. Early rail equipment. Barrel cars incorporating four-wheeled carriage with link and pin couplers—1837. (Courtesy of the Baltimore and Ohio Railroad.)

FIGURE 2-11b. Early rail equipment. First passenger railway coach in Chicago, July 4, 1849, Galena and Chicago Union Railroad. (Courtesy of the Chicago and North Western Railway.)

boilers and cars featuring the conventional long bodies mounted on two 4-wheeled trucks. See Figure 2-11.

TRANSPORTATION IN THE LATE NINETEENTH CENTURY

Railroads. The value of railroads to our economy was demonstrated in the stress of the Civil War. After the war an era of in-

FIGURE 2-11c. Early rail equipment. Eight-wheeled coal car in use on the Pennsylvania Rail Road about 1863. (Courtesy of the Pennsylvania Rail Road.)

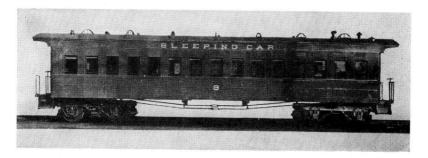

FIGURE 2-11d. Early rail equipment. George M. Pullman's first sleeping car (No. 9, a remodeled day coach) made its first run on September 1, 1859. (Courtesy of the Association of American Railroads, Washington, D. C.)

tensive railroad construction and westward expansion began with the construction of the "transcontinental" route of the Union Pacific–Central Pacific (now the Southern Pacific) railroads from Council Bluffs on the Missouri River to San Francisco on the Pacific Coast. The enabling bill was signed by President Lincoln on July 1, 1862, and a golden spike marking completion was driven at Promontory Point, Utah, on May 10, 1869.

Westward rail expansion continued with the opening of a bridge across the Missouri River at Kansas City on July 4, 1869, but it was not until March 8, 1881, that tracks of a second rail route to the Pacific (the first under one management), the Santa Fe between Chicago and Los Angeles via New Mexico and Arizona, were completed.

See Figure 2-12. Through-passenger service was set up between
Chicago and New Orleans on December 24, 1873 (with a change of
trucks under the cars at Cairo, Illinois, because of a difference in
gage). See Figure 2-13. The Northern Pacific was completed on
September 8, 1883, between the Great Lakes and Puget Sound, and on
January 6, 1893, a second line, the Great Northern, was opened between the same territories. The last spike was driven on November 7,
1885, in the Canadian Pacific at Craigellachie, British Columbia, to
complete the first Canadian transcontinental rail route.

Later chapters present the transporation systems of today. Any
attempt to discuss all the detailed but important developments would
be impracticable. Some features, however, are worthy of note.

Early railroads had been built to a variety of gages. Some approximated the spacing between wheels on the early colliery tramways, which was said to be, in turn, the spacing between wheels on
the Roman chariots or approximately 4 ft, 8½ in. Difficulties of
transshipping freight during the Civil War from tracks of one gage
to tracks of another emphasized the need for a standard gage. The
adoption of 4 ft, 8½ in. as a gage for the Union Pacific practically
confirmed it as the gage to be adopted. All principal railroads were
completely standardized by 1886, and the interchange of cars throughout the country was made possible.

Other important technical developments included the first use of
telegraph and train orders for train direction on September 22, 1851
(on the Erie Railroad), the first Bessemer steel rails in 1855, the
first loading of a petroleum tank car at Titusville, Pennsylvania, on
November 1, 1865, and the adoption of a code of rules to govern the
interchange of freight cars in 1866.

The safety of railroad passengers, employees, and freight was
improved with the introduction of a block system of train operation
in 1865 and of automatic signals in 1866. The first Standard Code
of Train Rules was adopted on April 4, 1887, by a predecessor of the
Association of American Railroads. Additional safety for employees
followed the patenting by Eli H. Janey in 1868 and 1873 and the
adoption in 1887 of standard interchangeable automatic couplers to
replace the dangerous and inefficient link and pin. Safer train operation followed the introduction of air brakes after George Westinghouse
made patent applications in 1868–1869. Adoption of the automatic,
quick-acting, triple-valve brake for freight service followed a series
of tests on the Burlington in 1887. These last two devices and later

FIGURE 2-12. Rail construction for westward expansion. A construction scene during the early days of railroading. (Courtesy of Paramount Pictures.)

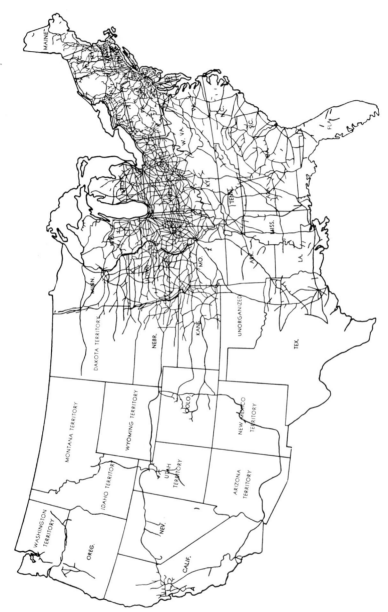

FIGURE 2-13. United States rail routes in 1880. In the ten-year period prior to 1880, some 40,000 miles of railroad were built, bringing the total network up to 93,267 miles. (Courtesy of the Association of American Railroads, Washington, D. C.)

improvements on them have been particularly important in permitting the long 100- to 150-car trains in use today.

The Interstate Commerce Commission was established by the Act to Regulate Commerce of 1887 to regulate the railroads and protect against discrimination and cutthroat competition. Growth and development of the Commission are discussed in a later chapter.

On May 10, 1893, the New York Central's *999* pulled their Empire State Express at a speed of more than 100 mph.

Thomas A. Edison is credited with inventing the electric locomotive. The first steam railroads were electrified in the United States in 1895 in Massachusetts, New Jersey, and Maryland.

By that same year total investment in railroad properties for the first time exceeded 10 billion dollars, with a net capitalization of 9548 million dollars.[13] Route mileage was more than 100,000 miles in 1882. By 1900 it had doubled.

Highways and Highway Vehicles. Since the time of the National Road, highway mileage, built mainly by local governments, had developed slowly and had been of inferior quality. Improvement in materials came with the use of asphalt paving in 1870. In 1890 the League of American Wheelmen, bicycle enthusiasts, joined the Post Office, with its Rural Free Delivery, in urging the construction of better roads. In 1893 the Office of Public Roads Inquiry was opened in the Department of Agriculture.

The greatest impetus to good roads was slowly appearing in the form of the automobile. The early days of the nineteenth century saw a number of steam-propelled vehicles on the road, but public opposition and restrictive legislation, especially in England, retarded development. A law of 1865 required every power-driven vehicle to be preceded on the highway by a man carrying a red flag. This law, which was not repealed until 1896, severely limited highway-vehicle improvement. Nevertheless, in 1841 William Worley built and operated in England the first steam tractor. Two years earlier Robert Anderson of Aberdeen, Scotland, had built and driven an electric carriage.

The modern motor vehicle was made possible in 1860, when the Frenchman Jean Joseph Étienne Lenoir perfected a gas engine with an electric spark for ignition and drove a gas-powered carriage for three miles with the device. In 1866 the Germans Nikolaus Otto

---

[13] *A Chronology of American Railroads,* Association of American Railroads, Washington, D. C., 1957, p. 5.

and Eugen Langen designed a gas engine with a four-stroke cycle—
exhaust, intake, compression, and ignition. A carriage propelled by a
gas engine was driven by Markens of Vienna in 1869. In 1887 Gottlieb Daimler and Carl Benz in Germany began the manufacture of
liquid-gas-driven carriages.

In the United States in 1879 George B. Seldon, sensing the future
of gasoline-powered vehicles, applied for patents covering the general
principles of motorcar design. These patents, granted in 1895, gave
Seldon an almost complete monopoly on United States automobile
manufacture (through patent licensing), until court action broke it
in 1897.

In 1894 the Duryea brothers successfully tried their first gasoline-
driven automobile. Ransom E. Olds had earlier, in 1887, built a
steam-driven carriage but began producing internal-combustion-
motored Oldsmobiles in 1897. These one-cylindered cars, weighing
700 lb, were sold for 650 dollars.[14] Other cars were built in this end-
of-the-century period, including those with electric drive. Attention
became centered on gasoline propulsion when Duryea's car won the
first American Road Race in Chicago on November 28, 1895, defeat-
ing several foreign entries.[15]

Significant automotive improvements of this period included invention of the clutch by MacKenzie of England in 1865 and pneumatic
tires by Thompson in 1867. At the close of the century engines utilizing steam, electricity, and gasoline were in competition as automobile
motive power, with the internal-combustion engine in the lead but
with the issue still undecided.

Waterways. Inland water transport was at a virtual standstill in
the United States after the Civil War, with the exception of coal
traffic on the Monongahela and Ohio rivers and the rapidly expanding traffic of the Great Lakes. The bubble of early canal building had
already burst, leaving only a few principal routes—among them the
Erie Canal, the Welland Canal, and the Chesapeake and Ohio Canal—
in operation. Destruction of the South's economy, coupled with the
desire for westward expansion and development of railroad systems,
reduced river traffic to a nominal quantity.

The first canal to bypass the rapids and falls of the St. Marys River
between lakes Superior and Huron was built at the Soo on the Ameri-

[14] *The Automobile Story,* General Motors Corporation, Detroit, Michigan,
1955, p. 3.
[15] *Ibid.,* p. 4.

can side in 1885. It had two locks 350 ft long, 70 ft wide, and 9 ft deep. In 1895 a second canal was opened on the Canadian side. The rapid growth of ore tonnage and the size of ore boats have led to a continual expansion of lock capacity. In addition to the locks, channels have been excavated and maintained in the St. Marys and Detroit rivers and Lake St. Clair. This work, begun in 1884, must be constantly improved to accommodate larger and larger vessels.

The first of a long line of ore boats was the *R. J. Hackett,* built in 1869. It was 211 ft long, had a 33-ft beam, drew 9 ft of water, and carried a cargo of 1200 tons.[16] Like its modern counterparts, this ore carrier had the machinery aft and navigation quarters forward, leaving an unobstructed hold with hatches spaced on 24-ft centers for ease in handling cargo.

Pipelines. Petroleum transportation became a problem in 1859, when Colonel Drake brought oil to the surface from the first oil well, a shallow 60-ft hole near Titusville, Pennsylvania. Oil was thereafter transported in wooden casks or barrels by team and wagon to the river's edge or to railroad side tracks. Much of it was floated in flatboats or on rafts down Oil Creek to Oil City, thence southwest to Pittsburgh on the Allegheny River.

In 1865 the first railroad tank car, which supplanted the individual barrels and drums previously used, was constructed. The same year marked the initial use of a powerful competitor, the first petroleum pipeline, completed from Pithole, an oil-boom town near Titusville, to a railroad side track five miles away. This first line was constructed of 2-in. wrought-iron pipe with screw joints. It delivered oil at the rate of 500 barrels a day.

Early pipelines were used only for gathering purposes in the field and to transport oil from the fields to railroad side tracks and river landings. The first trunk line, constructed by the Tidewater Pipe Line Company, extended from Coreysville, Pennsylvania, in the Bradford field, to Williamsport, some 150 miles to the southeast. It was laid with 6-in. wrought-iron pipe and used screw couplings. Pumping started at Coreysville on May 28, 1879, and the first flow appeared in Williamsport on June 4, seven days later.

Beginning in 1890, when the petroleum industry was freed from rail domination by the Federal outlawing of rebates, trunk lines were constructed between the Pennsylvania fields and refining centers at

---

[16] Harlan Hatcher, *A Century of Iron and Men,* Bobbs-Merrill, New York, 1950, p. 109.

Warren, Oil City, Bradford, and, later, Pittsburgh and the New Jersey coastal refining and shipping points. Provision for pipeline transportation has now become one of the chief considerations in developing a new oil field.

Pumping was conducted at low pressures, 100 to 300 psi, by steam-driven reciprocating or plunger-type pumps. The screw-type couplings and lap- or butt-seamed pipes did not have the requisite strength for higher pressures or the tightness to hold refined and highly viscous products.

Aircraft. Save for balloon ascensions at county fairs, little was attempted or achieved in the United States toward aircraft development during the late 1800's. Dr. Samuel P. Langley had conducted experiments with his model steam-driven airdrome, but heavier-than-air flight had not yet been accomplished. Balloons were regularly used for observation during the Franco-Prussion War of 1870. The. first powered aircraft was a nonrigid dirigible constructed and flown by Henri Giffard of France in 1852. This craft, a characteristic cigar-shaped bag, was 143 ft long and was driven by a 3-hp steam engine suspended below it in a light gondola.[17] Giffard flew over Paris at a speed of 8 mph. Other builders of power-driven dirigibles included Gaston Tissandier, Charles Renard, and A. C. Krebs of France and Paul Haenlein, David Schwartz, and Dr. Woelfert of Germany. The most noted of this group was a latecomer, a German aeronaut, Count Ferdinand von Zeppelin, who began in 1897 the construction of a rigid dirigible.

Zeppelin's design called for 16 gas-filled bags held in a cigar-shaped, rigid aluminum frame and powered by two 16-hp gasoline motors. Since this craft was not successfully tested until June 1900, the century ended on the threshold of successful aerial navigation. The chief handicap of the early dirigible builders was the lack of a light-weight power plant. Improvements in the gasoline engines available to Woelfert, Zeppelin, and later to Santos Dumont hastened the coming of powered aerial flight.   `

TRANSPORTATION AFTER 1900

Twentieth-Century Railroads. The early years of the twentieth century were a period of combination and consolidation for the rail-

[17] *Universal Standard Encyclopedia*, Vol. 7, Standard Reference World Publishing Company, New York, 1956, p. 111.

roads. Large railroad systems, such as the Pennsylvania, New York Central, Burlington, Illinois Central, and others, were formed by consolidating smaller companies, and are still in operation today. A number of supersystems were also formed, including a combination of the New Haven and the Pennsylvania, the Southern Pacific with the Union Pacific, and the Great Northern with the Northern Pacific. Most of these systems ran afoul of the antitrust laws and were disbanded by court decree.

Technical development included the double-tracking of many routes and detailed improvements in track, motive power, and rolling stock. In 1904 a major improvement in passenger comfort and safety came about by the introduction of all-steel passenger cars. The fastest official train speed in the United States (127.06 mph) was attained during this period on June 12, 1905, by a Pennsylvania Rail Road passenger train near Ada, Ohio. The record is still unsurpassed in the United States, but it was recently exceeded by the French SNCF's *Mistral*, which attained a speed of more than 200 mph on the Paris–Lyon–Marseilles line.

On May 19, 1909, the Milwaukee Road opened its Coast Line extension to form a third rail route between the Great Lakes and the Pacific Northwest. Two additional transcontinental Canadian routes were opened in 1915.

Entry of the United States into World War I in 1917 placed so heavy a strain on rail transport that on December 28, 1917, the Federal Government took actual control and operated the railroads until March 1, 1920. During this period of Federal control the railroad plant deteriorated under the stress of wartime conditions. The next decade saw an intensified effort to improve the physical plant. Improved locomotive types with higher boiler pressures and greater thermal efficiency replaced prewar models. Heavier rails and ties were placed in track, more miles of route were double-tracked, and automatic signaling systems were extended.

A new type of motive power, the diesel-electric locomotive, was placed in yard switching service on the Central of New Jersey on October 20, 1925. In 1934 diesel-electric-powered passenger streamliners made their first appearances on test and regular service runs on the Union Pacific (February 12, 1934) and the Burlington (May 26, 1934). On May 12, 1936, a 39¾-hour passenger service was initiated between Chicago and the Pacific Coast. Diesel-electric locomotives entered regular freight service on the Santa Fe in 1941. This new type of power proved its practicability during World War II. By

May 1952 there were 19,082 diesel-electric units in the United States, compared to 18,489 steam locomotives. Today most railroads are approaching 100 percent dieselization.

Although the introduction of diesel-electric motive power was the most important, it was not the only major engineering development of this period. A system of centralized traffic control (CTC) was placed in operation on the Ohio Central lines of the New York Central on July 25, 1923, between Toledo and Berwick, Ohio. Its application during World War II gave a much-needed increase in traffic capacity to many single-track lines, which otherwise would have been required, in a time of great steel shortage, to build additional main tracks. (It should be noted that the railroads carried the tremendous tonnages of World War II without any need for government control or operation.)

The year 1929 brought improvement in passenger comfort when an air-conditioned Pullman car was placed in service between New York and Chicago on September 9. The first all air-conditioned train began operation between New York and Washington on May 24, 1931.

Improved track materials, mechanization of maintenance work, and stabilization of roadbeds by the application of soils-engineering principles have been other important developments. Rolling stock has been marked by improvements in springing, brake equipment, car-axle bearings, draft gear, couplings, interior bracing arrangements, and by improved interior decor and seating and individual sleeping rooms in passenger cars.

Radio has improved communication and the safety and efficiency of operation. The most recent innovations have included the use of microwave for dispatching in areas in which line wires are subject to storm damage and the use of radar control of the movement of free-rolling cars in freight classification yards. By January 1956 more than 10.8 billion dollars had been spent by the railroads since the end of World War II for these and other improved facilities and equipment. In 1956 the American railroads comprised 221,000 miles of road and 383,000 miles of track.

The Automotive Age. In 1900 there were 150,000 miles of surfaced roads in the United States, 72 percent gravel, 24 percent water-bound macadam, and the remaining 4 percent in miscellaneous materials. These mileages were controlled almost entirely by local governments—towns, cities, and counties. Only six states gave aid to counties in 1900. The first state highway commission was organized in 1903 by the Commonwealth of Massachusetts. Others rapidly followed that lead.

In 1912 the Federal Government assumed active financial participation, to the extent of one third of the cost, in the improvement of roads on which mail was carried. The Federal Road Act of 1916 provided for Federal participation in state-road improvements up to 50 percent of the cost and appropriated funds for the purpose. Initiative was left with the states to determine the roads to be built and to carry on actual construction and maintenance.

World War I halted highway construction temporarily, but the rapidly expanding use of passenger cars and the increase in truck traffic that resulted from wartime development brought an ever-growing demand for better roads. Financing of Federal participation was accomplished by the imposition in 1919 of a tax on gasoline. By 1930 the primary objective of connecting the principal population centers with a system of all-weather, two-lane roads had been met.

World War I provided a proving ground in which the motor truck gave a convincing demonstration of its usefulness. Truck companies developed during the 1920's and 1930's to such an extent that government regulation became necessary to preserve order, competition, and adequate service for th industry and for the public. The Motor Carrier Act of 1935 (Part II of the Interstate Commerce Act) was passed by the Congress for these purposes.

Much of the highway construction was not adequate for the growing volume of traffic, especially truck traffic, with its increasingly heavy axle loads and high speeds. The early-stage construction, in which initially low-cost roads were built to be improved later as funds became available, was not going forward fast enough for traffic demands. Nor were funds available in sufficient quantity. The heavy demand placed upon highways by World War II traffic added to the congestion, rapid deterioration, and obsolescence of all roads.

Following World War II, an intensified effort was made to build highways of modern design with four- and six-lane roadways for each direction, divided as to direction, and with limited access. Financing of these superhighways in many instances depended on tolls as security for revenue bonds. A system of Federal interstate highways between the principal United States centers of population and over direct routes had been proposed for many years. The Federal-Aid Highway Act of 1956, passed June 29, 1956, and supplemented by an amendment of April 16, 1958, authorized the construction of more than 41,000 miles of Federal-aid interstate highways with Federal funds. Again the expenditures and actual construction and maintenance are under state jurisdiction. These new highways are to be of the highest-grade freeway construction, with divided and multiple lanes and with no intersections or cross traffic at grade.

Gravel and water-bound aggregate dust macadam surfaces soon proved unsuitable for the abrasion of fast-moving automobile tires and the suction from their speed. Rutted, corrugated, and dusty roads and bad-weather difficulties made better construction and design imperative. Asphaltic binders for surface and internal use gave greater stability and life to the pavement. Brick pavement had a widespread vogue for the early years of the century. The heavy trucking following World War I made even these improvements inadequate and led to the development and use of concrete as a paving material. In 1909 there were only five miles of concrete highway in the United States. That mileage had increased to more than 30,000 miles in 1925. There are now more than 83,000 miles of concrete-paved highways among the 3 million and more miles of United States roads. The superhighways of today call forth the best in cement- and asphaltic-concrete, heavy-duty pavement construction with a full

FIGURE 2-14. Modern superhighway and interchange—east shore exit from San Francisco's Oakland Bay Bridge. (Courtesy of *Highway Magazine,* Armco Drainage and Metal Products, Inc., Middletown, Ohio.)

application of the principles of soils engineering and drainage. See Figure 2-14.

The bringing in of the fabulous Spindletop oil well near Beaumont, Texas, on January 10, 1901, assured an ample supply of fuel for internal-combustion engines. This, coupled with the lightness, cleanliness, simplicity, and ruggedness of that engine, made it the favored means of automotive propulsion.

By 1904 there were 55,000 cars on the road, and the automotive industry was already tending to center around Detroit. Two important manufacturing techniques led to the large-scale production of a car at a price the general public could afford. In 1908 Henry Leland introduced Eli Whitney's interchangeable parts in his Cadillacs, and Henry Ford designed a simple standardized car produced on a moving assembly line. See Figure 2-15. Another important development which helped to popularize motor cars was the invention of the self-starter in 1910 by Charles F. Kettering. Standardization of parts was introduced in 1910 by the Society of Automotive Engineers (S.A.E.), a factor that contributed economy of manufacture and interchangeability of parts.[18]

Improvements in automotive design have moved rapidly forward, with the development of more efficient and powerful motors, streamlined bodies, quick-drying lacquers, and an ever-simplifying control system and panel board. By the end of World War I in 1918 there were 5.5 million passenger cars registered. In the next ten years registration increased to more than 23 million. It has since risen to more than 47 million passenger vehicles and 9 million trucks (1955). By 1925 used-car lots were appearing to blight the landscape, and gasoline filling and service stations were beginning to occupy the busiest street corners and rural intersections.

Flight. The nineteenth century ended with Count Ferdinand von Zeppelin at work on the first rigid dirigible. This cigar-shaped craft made its first successful flight in 1900. It was approximately 416 ft long and had a rigid aluminum frame. Buoyancy was obtained from 16 hydrogen-gas-filled bags contained in aluminum compartments within the frame. A speed of 20 mph was attained from the thrust of two 16-hp Daimler engines. Total weight was 9 tons. Zeppelin built several dirigibles with financial assistance from the German Government. During World War I the zeppelins engaged

[18] *The Automobile Story,* General Motors Corporation, Detroit, Michigan, 1955, p. 3.

(a)

(b)

(c)

(d)

FIGURE 2-15. (a) Early Model-T Ford automobile (courtesy of the Ford Motor Company, Dearborn, Michigan). (b) Twentieth-century automobiles and trucks —the first Cadillac, 1902 (courtesy of the General Motors Corporation, Detroit, Michigan). (c) Twentieth-century automobiles and trucks—the first GMC trucks, 1912 (courtesy of the General Motors Corporation, Detroit, Michigan). (d) Twentieth-century automobiles and trucks—a modern automobile, 1959 (courtesy of the General Motors Corporation, Detroit, Michigan).

in aerial reconnaissance and bombardment of England. Following the war, Germany built a few zeppelin-type dirigibles for the United States as a part of her war reparations. The United States Navy, in cooperation with the Goodyear Tire and Rubber Company, also built rigid and semirigid dirigibles. Others were constructed by the British. Although numerous intercontinental flights were made, including one over the North Pole and another around the world, the lighter-than-air craft proved expensive to build and operate and difficult to control in rough weather. After a series of spectacular disasters had wrecked all but one of these airships, efforts to develop the design were abandoned.

Alberto Santos Dumont, a Brazilian, conducted numerous flights during the first years of the century in his 14 designs of semirigid and nonrigid dirigibles. The nonrigid type have had a continuing minor use in naval operations, especially for observation purposes. Santos Dumont in 1906 went on to make the first heavier-than-air flight in Europe.

Although many experimenters had strived to produce a heavier-than-air flying machine during the last part of the nineteenth century, successful flight was not attained until 1903. On December 17th of that year at Kitty Hawk, North Carolina, the Wright brothers, Orville and Wilbur, successfully launched and flew a heavier-than-air craft for three wobbly minutes. It was powered by a 16-hp gasoline engine designed by the Wrights and weighed only 7 lb per horsepower. The pilot lay stretched out full length on the lower wing. See Figure 2-16.

Other models and longer flights, both in the United States and Europe, especially in France, soon followed that first flight. An English Channel crossing was made in 1909 by Louis Blériot in his own monoplane design.

The slow, steady improvement in airplane design was given impetus by World War I. Airplanes were used for observation and reconnaissance, bombing, attack, and pursuit. Experimentation and development accompanied a sharply increased demand for maneuverable planes, dependable engines, and skilled pilots and mechanics. The box-kite design took on a fuselage, and, aerodynamic design was improved, but probably the most important development was the designing of dependable, lightweight motors.

The close of the war made available a surplus of wartime airplanes and engines as well as many trained pilots, some of whom later engaged in barnstorming, air acrobatics, and stunt flying with military

FIGURE 2-16. The Wright brothers airplane. The start of it all! The first flight took off from the sands of Kitty Hawk, North Carolina, on December 17, 1903. The flight covered 120 ft in 12 sec. (Courtesy of United Air Lines.)

surplus planes. The more conservative and imaginative turned their attention to commercial flying. Long-distance flights were accomplished by civilian pilots and by military personnel of this and other countries. Coast-to-coast flights in the United States, intercontinental, and around-the-world flights became realities.

Airmail service was established in 1916 by the Post Office Department, and regular service was being flown in several locations by 1918. Scheduled transcontinental airmail between New York and San Francisco became operative in 1924. The Kelly Mail Act of 1925 authorized mail-carrying contracts between the Post Office Department and commercial airline operators, which led to the establishment by 1926 of 14 domestic airmail lines. These lines in turn developed into today's commercial carriers of passenger, mail, express, and freight.

The Air Commerce Act of 1926 was passed to promote and hasten the development of commercial aviation. It provides, among other things, for safety, licensing, and air-traffic control. The Civil Aeronautics Act of 1938 combined and placed under the Civil Aeronautics Authority all of the functions of aid and regulation of the aircraft and air-transportation industries. Economic regulation, establishment of airways, and air-traffic control are among the important aspects of C.A.A. supervision. Under the revisions of the Federal Aviation Act of 1956, most of these activities are now carried out for a Federal Aviation Authority by the Civil Aeronautics Board (C.A.B.).

By the time of World War II improved fuels and engines, radio communications and navigational aids, lightweight metals, and other developments made possible a dependable and comfortable airplane for commercial service, best exemplified by the still-active DC-3. The DC-3, with two engines, a capacity of 21 passengers and 3 crew members, and a cruising speed of 180 mph, became the standard for main-line operation. Today it serves equally well in feeder-line service. It was a forerunner of the four-engined DC-4 and the latter-day DC-6 and DC-7 airliners.

The vital role played by aircraft in World War I was repeated on a higher level and with greater intensification in the development of aircraft that stemmed from World War II. Planes designed to carry heavy bomb loads for long distances held equal opportunity as cargo carriers. Troop carriers presaged the high-load capacities of the DC-6, DC-7, and Constellation classes. High-octane fuels, superchargers, and pressurized cabins made flight in the stratosphere a reality. Radar provided added safety and comfort. Improved knowledge of soils and paving materials made possible the runways for these craft.

The war also introduced possibilities in jet propulsion now being adapted to commercial use in the Boeing 707 and similar ships. The German V-1 and V-2 rockets were forerunners of the modern rockets with which man is probing outer space—and which offer intriguing future possibilities in earth-to-earth movement of mail, express, and even passengers.

Another highly significant result of World War II was the development of the use of nuclear fission with its repercussions on policies of defense and political economy. Because it no longer lies protected by two oceans, the United States has become deeply concerned with world affairs and with the nation's systems of defense. This objective has caused a tremendous federally directed effort to be expended in the development of various types of aircraft and navigational aids as well as in programs of jet propulsion and rocketry.

Waterways.   Inland-water transport, with the exception of a developing coal traffic on the Monongahela and Ohio rivers and the rapidly expanding traffic in coal, ore, grains, and aggregates on the Great Lakes, was at a virtual standstill in the United States after the Civil War.

An International Waterways Convention was held in Cleveland in 1900, and the first Rivers and Harbors gathering was held that same year in Baltimore. These conventions created a new interest in inland-water transportation, which led in 1902 to passage by the United States Congress of the Rivers and Harbors Act. This act established a Board of Army Engineers to receive all recommendations for inland-waterways projects.

By 1903 New York State had voted 101 million dollars for the improvement, including relocation, of the Erie Canal and had changed its name to the New York State Barge Canal. Increased transportation requirements during World War I led to a public demand for river and canal transport. Under President Hoover, a strong inland-waterways program was carried forward, supported in turn by suceeding administrations. October 23, 1929, marked the official completion of a 9-ft channel in the Ohio River (begun in 1907) from Pittsburgh, Pennsylvania, to Cairo, Illinois, and the Mississippi River. Later years saw increased slack-water development of the upper Mississippi and its tributaries, notably the Missouri and Illinois rivers.

Larger barges and more powerful towboats were developed during the early years of the century, but relatively minor improvements marked the industry until after World War I. Steel barges then came into common use, and in the late 1930's diesel-driven tugs and towboats or rams began to replace the steam vessels. At the same time the paddle wheel gave way to propeller drive. The propellers are mounted in grooves or tunnels in the ship's hull to permit operation in shallow water. The steam-driven stern-wheeler has been largely replaced by 1000- to 4800-hp diesel craft, 117 to 202 ft long, 30 to 40 ft in beam, and drawing 7.6 to 9.8 ft of water. See Figure 2-17. Steam- and diesel-driven tugboats and self-propelled tankers and barges are seen on the coastal-waterways system. Present-day vessels are equipped with radio ship-to-shore telephones and with radar that permits safe operation when visibility is impaired by rain or fog. Steel barges, 2000 tons or more in capacity, have replaced the earlier wooden barges. Some of these can be integrated so that two together form a single *rigid* unit. Mechanization of loading and unloading at terminals and wharves is adding speed and economy to river transport. Larger locks are being built to accommodate the increasing dimensions of rams, barges, and tows. Completion of the Calumet Sag project in Chicago will integrate the inland-river system with the Great Lakes–St. Lawrence Seaway system.

The opening of the Panama Canal in 1912 had great domestic and

FIGURE 2-17. Modern river towboat and barges. (Courtesy of the Dravo Corporation, Pittsburgh, Pennsylvania.)

international significance, linking, as it does, the east and west coasts by an all-water route suitable for deep-sea draft vessels.

On the Great Lakes, a notable vessel, the *Seeandbee*, was placed in service in 1913 by the Cleveland and Buffalo Line. Built for 4.5 million dollars, the *Seeandbee* was a side-wheeler 500 ft long, 22 ft, 10 in. deep, and 97 ft, 6 in. in beam. It was powered by 12,000-hp engines and carried 6000 passengers on seven decks at a speed of 22 mph. After an eventful career as a passenger boat, the *Seeandbee* was converted in World War II into an aircraft carrier for training purposes at the Great Lakes Training Station. The *Seeandbee* marked the peak and the virtual end of passenger traffic on the Great Lakes.[19]

Ore carriers have become larger with the demand for steel, especially during two world wars, when military needs required the utmost in productive capacity. Today's steel freighters, 600 ft long, carry 15,000 to 20,000 tons at a time. A major factor in the development of the ore fleet was the invention of rapid unloading devices. Brownhoist and Hulett unloaders, familiar at southern lake ports,

[19] Harlan Hatcher, *Lake Erie*, 359, Bobbs-Merrill, New York, 1945, pp. 134–135.

permit a vessel to be unloaded and turned around in a few hours instead of several days or weeks.

Pipelines. Prior to 1928, most pipelines were operated with the same equipment and traditional methods that marked the beginnings of the industry. The introduction of welded joints to replace screw joints, a major step, permitted the development of high pressures and long-distance pumping. The first oxyacetylene welded line for gas flow was 1000 ft long and was laid in Philadelphia in 1911, but the first successful high-pressure, electrically welded line was not completed until 1920. This line, constructed by the Prairie Pipe Line Company, extended 15 miles from the Cherokee pump station to Bartlesville, Oklahoma. In 1928 electric welding and the manufacture of seamless steel tubing reached a state of technical excellence that permitted a combination of the two in high-pressure pipelines. The tight joints and pipe necessary to retain high-viscosity liquids and gases became a reality. Since then, there has been rapid expansion of high-pressure, long-distance pipelines, not only for the transportation of petroleum but for the flow of gasoline, kerosene, and natural gas.

Pumping facilities have reflected improvements in line and related technologies. High-pressure turbine and centrifugal pumps and electric and diesel-fueled prime movers have replaced cumbersome steam equipment in most stations. Various forms of radio and microwave transmssion have been installed to permit communication between stations, which is a vital part of pipeline operation.

The placement in commercial operation in April 1958 of a 108-mile pipeline to carry powdered coal in suspension from Georgetown, Ohio, to Cleveland, Ohio, perhaps marked another milestone in pipeline transportation. An earlier line, built in 1957, carries Gilsonite in suspension 72 miles from Bonanza, Utah, to Gilsonite, Colorado.[20]

QUESTIONS FOR STUDY

1. What were the contributions of the Romans to transportation engineering?
2. Develop significant illustrations, other than those used in the text, for each of the several factors affecting transport development.

[20] A. S. Lang, "The Use of Pipe Lines for the Long Distance Transportation of Solids," *Proceedings of the A.R.E.A.*, Vol. 60, America Railway Engineering Association, Chicago, 1959, pp. 240–244.

3. Contrast the contributions of Trisaguet, Telford, and MacAdam. What engineering principles did their work exemplify?

4. Why does the beginning of the nineteenth century stand as an approximate milestone and dividing line in the development of transportation?

5. Early United States railroad development was said to be "pioneering" in character. Explain the technological meaning and significance of the statement and the factors that permitted and/or required that type of development.

6. Using a modern transport unit (automobile, airplane, ship, etc.), outline the technological developments not connected with transportation that make that unit possible.

7. Why did the end of the Civil War mark the decline of steamboating and the rise of western railroads?

8. What technological developments make possible a 150-car freight train running at 50 mph?

9. Account for the rapid growth of gasoline, kerosene, and benzine pipelines after the late 1920's.

10. On what technological basis can one account for the rapid popularization and use by the general public of private automobiles?

SUGGESTED READINGS

1. Caroline MacGill and a staff of collaborators, *History of Transportation in the United States before 1860,* Carnegie Institution of Washington, Washington, D. C., 1917.

2. Nicholas Woods, *Treatise on Railroads,* Longman, Orme, Brown, Green, and Longman's, London, 1838.

3. Charles Francis Adams, Jr., *Railroads: Their Origin and Problems,* G. P. Putnam's Sons, New York, 1878.

4. Michel Chevalier, *Histoire et description des voies de communication aux Etats Unis et des travaux d'art qui en dependent,* Librairie de Charles Gosselin, Paris, 1840.

5. Harlan Hatcher, *Lake Erie,* and others in his Lakes and Rivers series, Bobbs-Merrill, New York, 1945.

6. Kent T. Healy, *The Economics of Transportation in America,* Ronald Press, New York, 1940, Chapters 1 through 9.

7. Franz von Gerstner, *Report on the Interior Communication of the United States,* Vienna, 1843.

CHAPTER 3

THE TRANSPORTATION SYSTEM

COMPONENTS

The outline of the transportation system and industry in this chapter is based primarily on that of the United States. The patterns thus defined are typical of the way transportation can develop but are not necessarily those that have actually developed in other countries. They would vary with the geography and economic state of those lands.

Transport Agencies. The conventional modes of transport are known to everyone. Railroads, highways, ships and barges on rivers, lakes, and oceans and airplanes flying the airways are commonplace. Pipelines as transporters of petroleum products and natural gas may not be so well known but are highly important. The quantities of freight and passengers transported by these principal units in the transportation system are given in Figures 3-1 and 3-2.

In the foregoing systems there are numerous variations. Within the railroad group are street railways and interurban lines, elevateds, and subways. Highways include not only the modern superhighway but also town and city streets, access roads, and country lanes carrying trucks, buses, and automobiles of private and commercial ownership. Waterways include rivers, canals, lakes, and oceans and the freighters, passenger liners, excursion boats, barges, car ferries, and submarines in or under those waters. Along the airways are flown commercial, private, and armed-forces aircraft for freight and passengers, taxi planes, and helicopters, both land- and water-based. Pipelines handle water, crude oil, refined petroleum products, natural and manufacturer's gas, sulfur, and, in suspension and on an experimental basis, ore and coal.

Added to these are fringe or experimental types of transport not usually included in the transport system—elevators, conveyors, cable

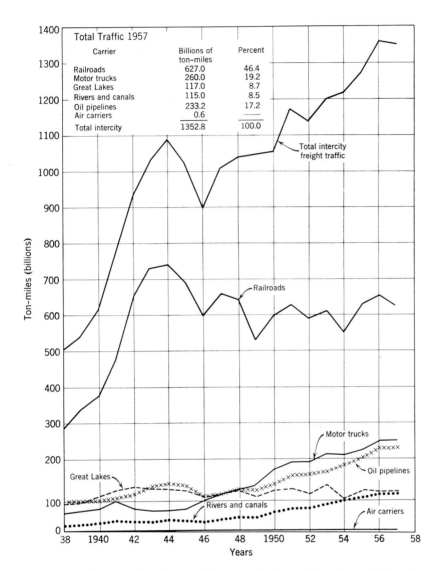

FIGURE 3-1. Comparative volumes of intercity freight traffic. (Compiled by the Bureau of Railway Economics, *Railroad Transportation: A Statistical Record*, Association of American Railroads, Washington, D. C., 1958, p. 34.)

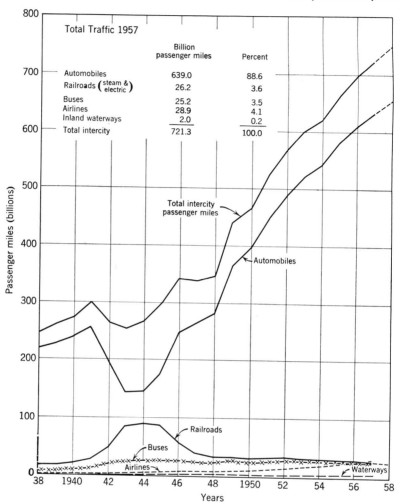

FIGURE 3-2. Comparative volumes of intercity passenger traffic. (Based on *Railroad Transportation: A Statistical Record*, Bureau of Railway Economics, Association of American Railroads, Washington, D. C., 1958, p. 35, and *Bus Facts*, Twenty-seventh Edition, National Association of Motor Bus Operators, Washington, D. C., 1958, p. 8.)

cars, aerial tramways, inclined railways, moving stairs and side-walks, monorails, tractor trains, and motor sleds.

Finally, there is a group of quasi-transport agencies, which do not move actual goods or persons but perform or supplant a transportation function. Power transmission lines carry electrical energy made from coal rather than the coal itself. Central heating and refrigerating plants and conduits perform similar functions. By stretching the imagination, one can even think of television as supplanting the transportation of films and newsprint and of people on their way to movies, concerts, theaters, and athletic events.

Transportation Needs. Each element in society has its own characteristic transport requirements. A family unit will utilize one or two automobiles for pleasure, shopping, going to and from work or school, and for personal business. The owner services and maintains the cars at his own expense. The children often have individual bicycles. Access to a system of public transit contributes a desirable flexibility. Fuel, milk, grocery, and mail deliveries and the collection of garbage are made in privately owned trucks by those who sell the articles or services.

A large corporation, by contrast, may require fleets of automobiles and airplanes for its personnel; it may operate its own private railroad and steamship line and have its own trucks on the highways. Again the costs of acquisition, operation, and maintenance are borne by the owner-corporation. Between these extremes lie all sizes of enterprises that depend in varying degrees on thir own private means of transport.

Regardless of size, however, each unit—family, farm, small business, contractor, large corporation—will make some use of for-hire transportation, whether by special contract or by utilizing common-carrier services available to all at established and government-regulated rates. Costs of operation are, theoretically at least, borne by the carrier that provides the service. The user pays for that service in the form of freight and passenger charges. For-hire carriers offer an extent of movement and variety of equipment that would be uneconomical and usually impossible for the individual user to provide.

CARRIER CLASSIFICATIONS

To meet the needs thus specified, no other part of the world, with the exception of western Europe and Great Britain, has a system of transportation so widespread and complex as that found in the United States. All major transport elements are present in abundance. A brief summary and cross section of that transport system are presented in this chapter. Included in them are the various types and classifications, physical facilities, and statistical sizes, without inquiry into the reasons for the existence or design and operating practices of an individual carrier. An understanding of the technological and economic characteristics that are responsible for the system in its present form is the purpose of this entire book and is developed in later chapters.

Railroad Classifications. Railroads may be classified initially into *private* and *common* carriers. The private group is relatively small and unimportant. Lumbering, mining, and industrial plant facilities comprise most of it. Railroads used as plant facilities, however, often establish a common-carrier status whereby their services are available to the public.

Railroads are further designated by use as *line-haul, switching* or *belt-line*, and *terminal*. The first group handles intercity traffic and is exemplified by the Santa Fe, Pennsylvania, Illinois Central, Reading, Milwaukee, and others. Switching or belt-line carriers offer sidetrack services at wharf and waterfront areas, industries, warehouses, etc., to line-haul railroads, for a switching charge that is included by the line-haul carrier in its total charges. Examples are the New Orleans Public Belt Railroad, owned by the City of New Orleans, and the Port Terminal Railroad Association of Houston, owned jointly by the Navigation District and the user railroads.

Terminal railroads supply terminal services to line-haul carriers and are usually owned by one or more of the railroads served. Several railroads can thereby gain access to city and terminal areas without the expense of providing costly duplicate terminal facilities. The Kansas City Terminal Company, the Belt Railway of Chicago, and the Cincinnati Union Terminal Company are examples of this kind of rail carrier.

A commonly used classification is that established by the Interstate Commerce Commission according to gross operating revenues. Class I carriers are those with gross annual operating revenues of 3 million or more dollars. There are between 115 and 125 (119 in 1957) Class I rail carriers. These railroads in 1957 hauled more than 99 percent of the United States rail freight traffic (1308 million originated tons), employed 93 percent of all railroad workers (986,001 workers, earning 5,385 million dollars), and operated 95 percent of total line-haul mileage (209,965 route miles). There are also approximately 431 Class II carriers, those with revenues less than

3 million dollars. Added to these are some 225 small terminal, switching, and industrial carriers.

Highway Carriers of Freight. The variety of trucking operations poses difficulties in selecting any one or two as typical. A review by categories and classifications, including those promulgated by the Interstate Commerce Commission, is helpful. As with railroads, a distinction can first be made between private and for-hire operators. The for-hire operators may be further subdivided into common, contract, and exempt carriers. For-hire carriers in 1956 accounted for 26.80 percent of the truck miles on main rural roads; private trucks accounted for 73.20 percent.[1]

Common carriers. These for-hire agencies serve the general public by hauling traffic as offered over regular or irregular routes. They are subject to close control by the I.C.C. and must have a certificate of public convenience and necessity from that body in order to operate if engaged in interstate commerce. There were 15,000 certificated common carriers in 1956. For purely intrastate operation, the state body for regulating utilities would exercise the same supervision.

Contract carriers. These carriers are for-hire agencies that engage under individual contract for motor-freight transportation. Contract carriers are subject to modified regulation by the I.C.C. (and the state authority). Permits to operate were issued to more than 26,000 such carriers in 1956. Contract carriers may contract for freight distribution from warehouses or rail or water terminals (pickup and delivery) or may furnish vehicles and drivers for the exclusive use of designated shippers to operate under the shipper's jurisdiction. Others may serve several shippers within a specialized commodity area (haulers of petroleum products, for example) by guaranteeing to have available a minimum number of vehicles and drivers when needed. Contract carriers usually handle volume tonnage in truckload lots directly between the shipper and the consignee. Therefore, few if any terminal facilities need be furnished by the carrier.

Exempt carriers. These would fall within the foregoing categories if they were not specifically exempted by statute from the economic regulatory features of the Interstate Commerce Act. Exempt carriers are operators of for-hire vehicles that transport agricultural products, farm supplies, livestock, and fish; that distribute newspapers; that are

[1] *Motor Truck Facts,* 1957 edition, Automobile Manufacturers' Association, Detroit, Michigan, p. 34.

operated by farmers' cooperative marketing organizations; that are used in transport incidental to airline operations (freight and express service); and that are used in occasional or casual service by persons not regularly engaged in the transportation business. Citrus fruits move in quantities via these carriers. Certain exempt carriers operate over a fixed route or series of routes. Others may move from area to area picking up a load wherever available for any destination suitable to the operator. Sometimes the vehicle is leased to a certificated carrier in order to obtain a return load. Many exempt carriers, haulers of fish, for example, must provide refrigeration service and may have terminal or traffic loading and concentration points. Many others have no terminals at all and operate directly from farmyard or field to destination. Runs of 1000 to 2000 miles are not uncommon. These carriers are often owner-operated, but several trucks may be owned by one operator. Many loads are obtained from freight brokers. About 243,000 vehicles are engaged in exempt service, 50 percent more than are engaged as common and contract carriers.

Private carriers. Private carriers, also exempt from all but safety regulations, are those transporting the owner's goods or goods for which the truck owner is lessee or bailee. They are not for hire. Merchandising and industrial firms with sufficient business find many advantages in this system. They can assure flexibility of service, prompt delivery of goods without delays en route or in terminals and without the excessive crating or packaging required by common carriers.

In 1956 there were six private fleets (including Railway Express, Bell System, and National Dairy), containing more than 10,000 trucks each of various types and sizes, ten companies operating more than 5000 trucks, 46 with 1000 or more truck vehicles, and 48 companies with 100 or more trucks in their private fleets.[2]

The I.C.C. has further classified carriers as to types of service and routes:

A. Regular route, scheduled service (point to point)
B. Regular route, non-scheduled service (point to point)
C. Irregular route, radial service (operating point to point over radial lines from a fixed or base point)
D. Irregular route, non-radial service (no established pattern)
E. Local cartage service

[2] *Motor Truck Facts,* 1957 edition, Automobile Manufacturers' Association, Detroit, Michigan, pp. 50–51.

A further I.C.C. classification is by type of commodity.

1. Carriers of general freight
2. Carriers of household goods
3. Carriers of heavy machinery
4. Carriers of liquid petroleum products
5. Carriers of refrigerated liquid products
6. Carriers of refrigerated solid products
7. Carriers engaged in dump trucking
8. Carriers of agricultural products
9. Carriers of motor vehicles
10. Carriers engaged in armored truck service
11. Carriers of building materials
12. Carriers of films and associated commodities
13. Carriers of fruit products
14. Carriers of mine ore (excluding coal)
15. Carriers engaged in retail store delivery
16. Carriers of explosives or dangerous articles
17. Carriers of commodities not otherwise designated

By combining these classifications, any carrier may be specifically designated. A contract carrier of building materials over an irregular route, nonradial, would be designated as a Contract Carrier, Class D-11.

The I.C.C. also has an operating revenue classification for common and contract carriers. Class I carriers are those with annual gross operating revenues of 1 million dollars or more. There were 933 in this class in 1957. Class II carriers have operating revenues of less than 1 million dollars but greater than 200,000 dollars. There were 2055 in this class in 1957. Class III carriers have gross operating revenues of 200,000 dollars or less. In 1957 Class I, II, and III carriers produced 85 billion ton-miles of intercity highway-freight transportation, approximately 33 percent of the total of 260 billion produced by all highway carriers.

Highway Passenger Carriers. In the United States the principal carrier of passengers is the privately owned and operated automobile. In most communities and rural areas almost every family has a car, and a large percentage has two cars or more. In 1955 there was in the United States approximately one car to every three persons.[3] In that same year 73.5 percent of all families in the United States owned

---

[3] *Automobile Facts and Figures*, Thirty-sixth Edition, Automobile Manufacturers' Association, Detroit, Michigan, 1956, p. 20.

one or more cars, 10.3 percent owned more than one car, and 10.1 percent had no car at all.[4]

This does not represent the total use of cars by individuals. The renting of cars on a drive-it-yourself basis has been steadily increasing, especially at airports and railroad terminals. The net effect of this trend on general travel habits and car ownership is still to be determined, but it is likely to be significant. The ownership of passenger cars by commercial and industrial concerns and other agencies for the business use of their employees is long standing. Car renting is also entering this field of use.

Taxicabs represent a for-hire service largely confined to urban areas. Statistics on taxi operation are incomplete, but a compilation by the American Taxicab Association showed a total cab ownership in 1955 of 48,370 units in 50 of the nation's largest cities (including 11,789 in New York, 9500 in Washington, D. C., and 3700 in Chicago).[5] Another compilation by the National Association of Taxicab Owners showed 78,191 cabs in operation throughout the country in 1954. These cabs carried 1404 million passengers a distance of 4748 million miles.[6]

About 269,000 buses were registered in the United States in 1957.[7] Bus operation is largely on a for-hire basis. Some large companies, government agencies, institutions, and traveling groups, such as dance bands and professional ball teams, have their own private buses. More often, arrangements are made on a contract basis with a bus company (which may also be providing a common-carrier operation) for the service required. Sight-seeing buses account for a considerable number. Approximately 10 million school children are carried, and about 5.5 billion rides are provided each year on the local bus systems of cities and metropolitan regions.[8]

The I.C.C. has divided interstate-bus companies into three classes. Class I carriers are those with annual gross operating revenues of 200,000 dollars or more. In 1957 153 such companies carried 226.7 million passengers, over two thirds of all the estimated intercity passenger traffic.[9] Class II carriers have revenues of less than 200,000

[4] *Ibid.,* p. 30.

[5] *Ibid.,* p. 58.

[6] *Ibid.,* p. 58.

[7] *Bus Facts,* Twenty-seventh Edition, National Association of Motor Bus Operators, Washington, D. C., 1958, p. 5.

[8] *Ibid.,* pp. 5–6.

[9] *Ibid.,* p. 12.

dollars but greater than 50,000 dollars; Class III are those with revenues less than 50,000 dollars. The trade journal, *Bus Transportation*, uses the following four classifications by type of operation.

1. City—operating exclusively within city limits
2. City-suburban—operating within the city and to the suburban areas surrounding it
3. Intercity, short-haul—the operation is between two or more cities where the average fare is under 35 cents
4. Intercity, long-haul—operating between two or more cities where the average fare is more than 35 cents

A majority of group 4 is combined or integrated into one of the large systems, several of which operate from coast to coast and from the Great Lakes to the Gulf of Mexico.

Water Carriers. The system of domestic waterways may be roughly divided into three groups; the Great Lakes, coastal waters and canals, and inland rivers and canals. Each of these areas includes private, contract, and common-carrier shipping. In 1956, 237 carriers reported to the I.C.C.

Inland-waterways carriers reporting to the I.C.C. are classified according to average gross operating revenues: Class A with revenues of more than 500,000 dollars, Class B with revenues of more than 100,000 dollars but no more than 500,000 dollars, and Class C with revenues of 100,000 dollars or less. Eight Class A and seven Class B carriers on the Great Lakes constitute the bulk of those reporting to the I.C.C. as reported by the I.C.C. Bureau of Statistics.[10]

The Corps of Engineers lists 24 common carriers, no contract carriers, and 319 exempt (including private) carriers for the same period.[11] Only 11 of the common carriers are in bulk-cargo trade, and, of these, no more than five are Class A or B. The major percentage of Great Lakes traffic moves in private and exempt ships.

On the Mississippi River and its tributaries the foregoing I.C.C. tabulations show 21 Class A and 4 Class B carriers.

The corresponding count of the Corps of Engineers (but including the Gulf Intracoastal carriers among which there is a preponderance of common carriers) is 34 common carriers, 10 contract carriers, and 890 exempt and private carriers. Here, also, the relatively small area of control exercised by the I.C.C. is indicated.

[10] *Transport Statistics of the United States, Part 5, Carriers by Water,* Interstate Commerce Commission, Washington, D. C.; year ending December 31, 1956.
[11] *Transportation Lines on the Great Lakes System, Transportation Series 3,* U. S. Army, Corps of Engineers, 1957, pp. VII–XIV.

There were, for the same period as well, 25 Class A and 19 Class B Atlantic and Gulf Coast reporting carriers, 15 Class A and 13 Class B Pacific Coast lines, and one intercoastal line.

Pipelines. Nearly all pipelines for petroleum products have common-carrier status under the law. As a fact of operating practice, most pipelines are gigantic plant facilities, owned by the petroleum industry, which transport the owner's oil from field to refinery or refinery to market. There were 83 pipeline companies reporting to the I.C.C. in 1957. These lines transported in trunk-line movement 3056 million bbl of crude petroleum and 876 million bbl of refined products. They produced thereby 930,558 million barrel miles of crude-oil transportation and 248 million barrel miles of refined-products transportation.

Gas pipelines have common-carrier status in some localities, but others operate as private facilities. The status of gas lines is not so clearly defined as that of petroleum lines.

Airways. Air transport is generally divided into private and for-hire flying. The private category includes both pleasure craft and those used by private industry and commerce for transporting equipment, supplies, and personnel. The use of private planes by business executives has shown a rapid increase. Typical of these is General Motors, which has a fleet of 20 planes, Magnolia Petroleum, 15, and Magrobar, 18. A special group of for-hire planes includes those not specifically a part of scheduled transportation but which engage in crop dusting, aerial reconnaissance and photography, skywriting, fire fighting, timber inspection, and other nontransport activities.

For transportation purposes, the Civil Aeronautics Board, which has the same relation to air transport as the I.C.C. has to other types of transportation, has divided airlines into seven general categories:

1. *Domestic trunk lines* are certificated carriers holding permanent operating rights within the continental United States; they include the major transcontinental carriers. Twelve lines in 1957 produced 78 percent of all revenue passenger miles, or 24,500 million, and 74 percent of total revenue miles, or 2720 million.

2. *Domestic local-service* carriers operate on routes of light traffic density on short flights between small traffic centers and provide a *feeder service* for trunk lines. Some operate on temporary permits. Thirteen domestic local-service carriers in 1957 flew 747 million revenue passenger miles and 78 million revenue ton-miles in serving more than 600 cities.

3. *International and overseas lines,* 20 in all, are United States flag carriers between the United States and foreign countries other than Canada. Some of these companies are also engaged in domestic trunk and local service. In 1957 they flew 5752 million revenue miles and 855 million revenue ton-miles.

4. *Territorial lines* are in two groups. The *Insular* group serves United States island possessions in the Pacific and Caribbean areas; in 1957 they produced 89.5 million revenue passenger miles and 9 million revenue ton-miles. The *Alaska* lines operate within Alaska and between Alaska and the rest of the states. In 1957 they produced 152 million revenue passenger miles and 33 million revenue ton-miles.

5. *All-cargo lines* operate scheduled freight and express service, usually under temporary permits, between points in the United States. These lines are not authorized to carry mail or passengers. In 1957 six companies flew 245 million ton-miles of freight.

6. *Helicopter airlines* carry mail between the airports and central post offices in New York, Chicago, and Los Angeles. In New York and Chicago the use of helicopters has been extended to the carrying of freight and passengers between major airports; the Los Angeles line carries air express. As an experimental service, helicopter airlines operate on temporary permits. In 1957 they flew 3273 revenue passenger miles and 450 revenue ton-miles.

7. *Noncertificated air carriers* operate on letters of authorization and are not allowed to engage in scheduled service (exceptions: air-taxi operators and air-freight forwarders). In 1957 this group included 43 supplemental and irregular transport carriers and 65 freight forwarders.[12]

PLANT AND TRAFFIC

The network of routes over which goods and persons are moved, the equipment devoted to those movements, and the amount of traffic carried thereby are here summarized.

Railroads. The American railroad system is a far-reaching network of tracks serving virtually every community in the United States. A shipper in any part of the country has direct rail access to any other part of the United States, Canada, and Mexico and, via car

---

[12] This and foregoing airline data are from *Air Transport Facts and Figures,* Nineteenth Edition, Air Transport Association of America, Washington, D. C., 1958, pp. 15–16, 31.

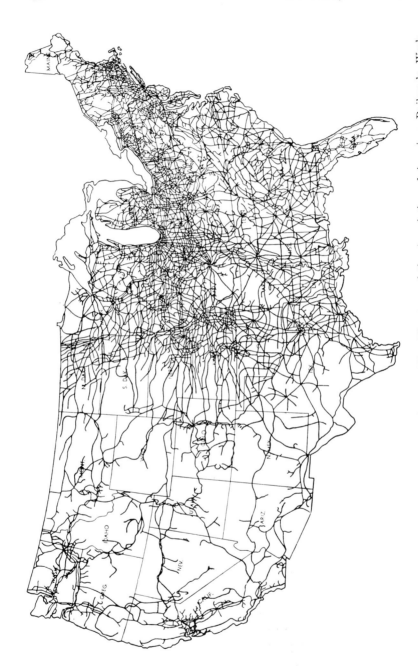

FIGURE 3-3. Railroad network of the United States—1958. (Courtesy of the Association of American Railroads, Washington, D. C.)

Table 3-1. Railroad Mileage in the United States, 1957 [a]

Tracks	Class I	All Other [b]	Total
Road (first main track)	209,965	9,102	219,067
All other main tracks	30,758	6,365	37,123
Yard track and sidings	105,109	12,569	117,678
Total all tracks	345,832	28,036	373,868

[a] Derived from mileage tables, *Railroad Transportation—A Statistical Record, 1958*, Bureau of Railway Economics, Association of American Railroads, 1958, pp. 1, 5.

[b] Includes some duplication of mileage operated under trackage rights by two or more railroads.

Table 3-2. Railroad Equipment, All United States Railroads, 1957 [a]

Locomotives		32,391 [b]
Freight train cars (railroad owned)		
Freight carrying	1,777,557	
Caboose	20,908	
Total railroad-owned freight cars		1,798,465
Private-line cars		
Railroad-owned refrigerator-car lines	77,919	
All other	198,835	
Total railroad and private refrigerator cars		276,754
Total freight cars, private and railroad		2,075,219
Passenger train cars		
Railroad owned	29,564	
Pullman Company	3,970	
Total passenger train cars		33,534
Company service cars		76,679

[a] *Railroad Transportation—A Statistical Record: 1929–1957*, Bureau of Railway Economics, Association of American Railroads, Washington, D. C., 1958, pp. 2, 13.

[b] Class I railroads owned 22,092 locomotive units, 18,493 diesel-electric, 3045 steam, 523 electric, and 31 others.

ferry, to Cuba and Caribbean points. With the minor exceptions of trackage rights and joint operations agreed between individual roads, only a railroad's own trains operate on these tracks. There is no intermingling of private and public, commercial and pleasure vehicles on a railroad's tracks. The occupancy of its roadway and tracks is exclusive. Even when cars of nonrailroad ownership, such as refrigerator, tank, and other special-purpose cars, are hauled by a railroad, they are moved by the railroad's locomotive in trains manned by its crews under full railroad control and direction.

The extent and completeness of the system of railroads in the United States are illustrated in Figure 3-3. The total mileage in the railroad system and its distribution between classes of rail carriers is given in Table 3-1.

Table 3-2 summarizes the equipment operated by United States

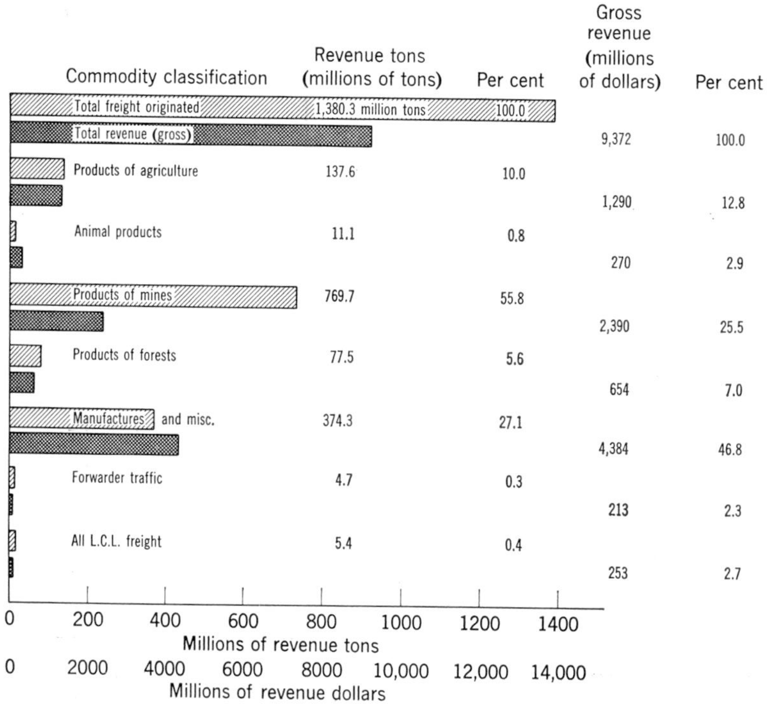

Commodity classification	Revenue tons (millions of tons)	Per cent	Gross revenue (millions of dollars)	Per cent
Total freight originated	1,380.3 million tons	100.0		
Total revenue (gross)			9,372	100.0
Products of agriculture	137.6	10.0		
			1,290	12.8
Animal products	11.1	0.8		
			270	2.9
Products of mines	769.7	55.8		
			2,390	25.5
Products of forests	77.5	5.6		
			654	7.0
Manufactures and misc.	374.3	27.1		
			4,384	46.8
Forwarder traffic	4.7	0.3		
			213	2.3
All L.C.L. freight	5.4	0.4		
			253	2.7

```
0     200    400    600    800   1000   1200   1400
            Millions of revenue tons
0    2000   4000   6000   8000  10,000  12,000  14,000
            Millions of revenue dollars
```

FIGURE 3-4. Total revenue freight originated by Class I railroads. (Courtesy of *Railroad Transportation: A Statistical Record,* Bureau of Railway Economics, Association of American Railroads, Washington, D. C., 1959, p. 18.)

railroads over the trackage listed in Table 3-1. These railroads in 1957 represented a net capitalization of 14,682 million dollars; operating revenues were 10,625 million dollars, operating expenses were 8,322 million dollars, and 1,091 million dollars in taxes were paid. Net income was 765 million dollars and 5,442 million dollars were paid to 999,000 employees.[13]

The total revenue tons of freight, according to the I.C.C.'s seven principal categories, carried in 1957 by Class I railroads is shown in Figure 3-4.

Highways. The highway system of the United States is even more elaborate and ubiquitous than is the rail network. In 1956 the highway system was comprised of the mileage given in Table 3-3. These figures include more than 1200 miles of superhighway construction.

All primary rural routes are built and maintained by the states. An approximate 156,000 miles are designated as national highways because the Federal Government contributes to the cost of their construction and maintenance. A total of 7,060 million dollars was contributed by the Federal Government in the fiscal years 1917–1955. National highways bear the Federal shield marker and route number. East-west highways are given even numbers, from U.S. 2 between Boston and Seattle on the north to U.S. 90 between Jacksonville, Florida, and El Paso, Texas, on the south. North-south highways receive odd numbers beginning with U.S. 1 on the eastern seaboard between Maine and Key West, Florida. Basic numbers are one or two digits (except U.S. 101 on the West Coast). Three-digit numbers are for main highway branches. For example, U.S. 224 is a branch of U.S. 24.

The Federal Highway Act of 1956 and the supplementary act of 1958 introduced a new dimension to highway planning that will have far-reaching significance. Recognizing the inadequacy of the highway system for present as well as future traffic, the Congress of the United States has appropriated more than 40 billion dollars to be used principally for the construction in the next 16 to 20 years of more than 41,000 miles of a National System of Interstate and Defense Highways. Of this mileage, approximately 70 percent will be new route locations connecting some 90 percent of all cities with populations of 50,000 or more, including 42 state capitals. See Figure 3-5. Construction will be to superhighway standards, with easy curves

[13] *Railroad Transportation—A Statistical Record, 1958,* Bureau of Railway Economics, Association of American Railroads, 1958, p. 3.

Table 3-3.   United States Highway Mileage, 1956 [a]

(in thousands of miles)

System	Nonsur-faced Mileage	Surfaced Mileage			
		Low Grade	Medium Grade	High Grade	Total
Rural mileage					
Under state control					
State primary system	5	33	134	217	389
State secondary system	7	26	37	24	94
County roads under state	27	56	39	10	132
State parks, forests, etc.	6	2	1	3	12
Total state control	45	117	211	254	627
Under local control					
County roads	708	782	181	57	1728
Town and township roads	207	283	58	14	562
Other local roads	35	4	1	—	40
Total local control	950	1069	240	71	2330
Under Federal control					
National parks, forests	71	18	3	2	94
Total rural mileage	1966	1204	454	327	3051
Municipal mileage					
Under state control					
Extension of state primary system	—	—	6	30	36
Extension of state secondary system	—	1	3	3	7
Total state control	—	1	9	33	43
Under local control					
City streets	41	77	104	114	336
Total municipal mileage	41	78	113	147	379
Total rural and municipal mileage in the United States	1107	1282	567	474	3430

[a] *Highway Statistics, Table M-2,* Bureau of Public Roads, U. S. Department of Commerce, Washington, D. C., 1958, p. 102.

FIGURE 3-5. The National system of interstate and defense highways. (Courtesy of the Bureau of Public Roads, Washington, D. C.)

Table 3-4. Vehicles in Highway Transportation, 1956

Vehicle Type	Private Vehicles	Public Vehicles	Total Vehicles
Automobile registration (all types excluding military) [a]	51,989,027	184,207	52,173,234
Motor trucks [b]	10,310,000	443,000	10,753,000
Farm ownership (28.4 per cent of all trucks registered)			2,702,811
Trailers, commercial (5 tons and up) [c]		Percent of Total	
Total, all trailers			632,259
Vans (including insulated, refrigerator, furniture, and others)		58.0	366,710
Platform (cattle, grain bodies, etc.)		17.0	107,484
Tanks (petroleum and others)		9.0	56,903
Poles and logging		4.5	28,451
Low beds for heavy loads		4.5	28,451
Dump trailers		3.0	18,968
All other truck-trailers		4.0	25,292
		100.0	632,259
Bus registration [d]			
Total, all buses			255,249
Private ownership			142,335
Public ownership			112,914
Intercity service			25,000
Local transit service			51,400
School buses			143,600
Others: sight seeing, government agency, etc.			35,149

[a] *Automobile Facts and Figures*, Thirty-Sixth Edition, Automobile Manufacturers Association, Detroit, Michigan, 1956, p. 20.

[b] *Motor Truck Facts*, Automobile Manufacturers Association, Detroit, Michigan, 1957, pp. 20, 23, 24, 35.

Note: Single-unit trucks accumulated 76.8 percent of truck vehicle miles and produced 25.0 percent of the ton-miles. Truck tractor and semitrailer combinations accumulated 29.9 percent of all truck vehicle miles and produced 67.5 percent of all ton-miles.

[c] *Ibid.*, p. 36 (author's estimate based on total and annual truck-body production as given therein).

[d] *Bus Facts*, Twenty-Sixth Edition, National Association of Motor Bus Operators, Washington, D. C., 1957, p. 5.

designed for speeds of 70 mph, separate lanes for opposing directions with a wide median strip between, and no cross roads. The Federal Government will pay 90 percent of the costs (collected from gasoline, tire, and other excise taxes) and the states, 10 percent. Initiative for instituting a section of the system rests with the states and, as with other national highways, is carried out by forces under the supervision of the states. The Bureau of Public Roads establishes general standards and policies. This system will carry approximately 20 percent of the nation's highway traffic. As of December 1, 1957, some 4400

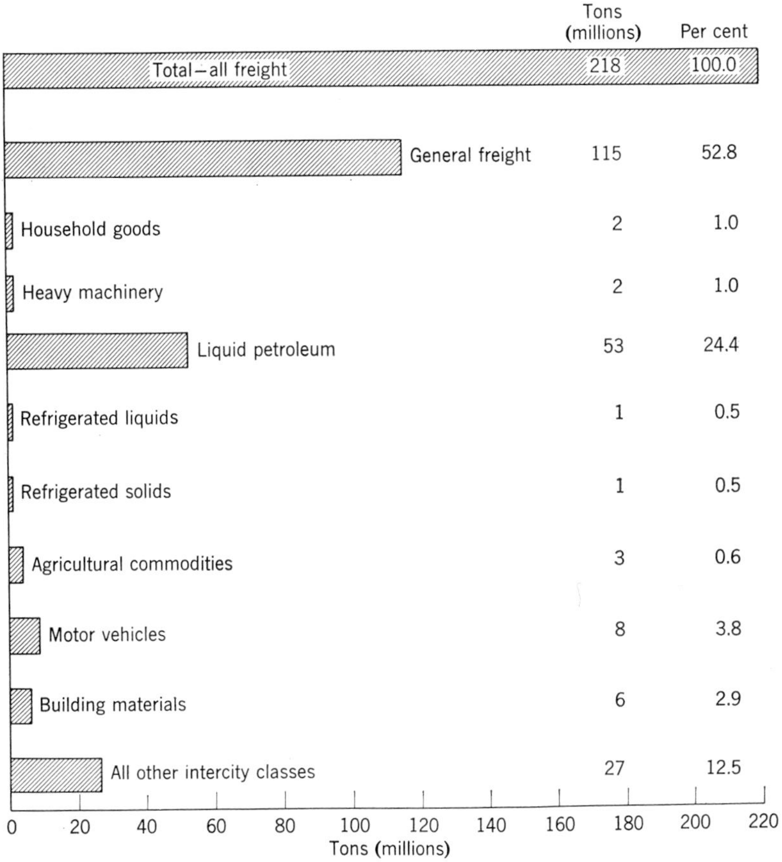

	Tons (millions)	Per cent
Total—all freight	218	100.0
General freight	115	52.8
Household goods	2	1.0
Heavy machinery	2	1.0
Liquid petroleum	53	24.4
Refrigerated liquids	1	0.5
Refrigerated solids	1	0.5
Agricultural commodities	3	0.6
Motor vehicles	8	3.8
Building materials	6	2.9
All other intercity classes	27	12.5

Tons (millions): 0 20 40 60 80 100 120 140 160 180 200 220

FIGURE 3-6. Intercity motor freight tonnage—1957. Classes I and II common and contract carriers. (Based on 1957 tonnages and 1957 indices of the American Trucking Associations, Inc.)

odd miles had been programed; considerably less had been actually constructed.

The number of vehicles by types moving upon this system of streets and highways is set forth in Table 3-4. The distribution of freight-traffic commodities by classes carried in interstate trucks is shown in Figure 3-6.

Waterways. The system of domestic or inland waterways may be divided roughly into three groups: the Great Lakes, coastal waters and canals, and inland rivers and canals. The Great Lakes provide one of the most efficient routes of transport known to man, equaled only by the Mediterranean Sea. The Lakes system includes the five Great Lakes—Superior, Huron, Michigan, Erie, and Ontario. It also includes the connecting channels of the St. Marys River and the Soo Canal between Superior and Huron, the Straits of Mackinack connecting lakes Huron and Michigan, the St. Clair River, Lake St. Clair and the Detroit River between Huron and Erie, and the Welland Canal between lakes Erie and Ontario around Niagara Falls and the Niagara River. See Figure 3-7. In a broader sense the Great Lakes system also includes the St. Lawrence River from Lake Ontario to tidewater and the 350 miles of New York State Barge Canal between Lake Erie, via a small part of the Niagara River, and the Hudson River at Troy, New York. Duluth, at the head of the lakes, is 986 miles from Buffalo at the eastern end of Lake Erie, more than 1200 miles from the eastern end of Ontario, and 1334 miles from Montreal at deep water on the St. Lawrence River. The Great Lakes provide an up-bound channel depth of 20 ft and a down-lake channel depth of 24 ft. The New York State Barge Canal has a 14-ft open-channel depth and a 12-ft lock-sill depth. The St. Lawrence provided a minimum depth of 14 ft over the sills of the locks but now has a depth of 27 ft since the completion of the St. Lawrence Seaway. Plans also call for increasing all channel depths in the lakes to the same 27 ft. A majority of ocean shipping will thus be able to sail up the St. Lawrence to inland points, and existing Great Lakes ports will become world ports engaged in international trade. Total cost of the seaway portions of the project (1952 levels) is said to be more than 263 million dollars.

The coastal system includes the east, west, and Gulf coasts and the protected channels and canals along the coasts and across the Florida peninsula. Intercoastal shipping in deep water follows a somewhat longer route through the Panama Canal. Part of the coastal trade moves in deep-water vessels with characteristics similar to those in

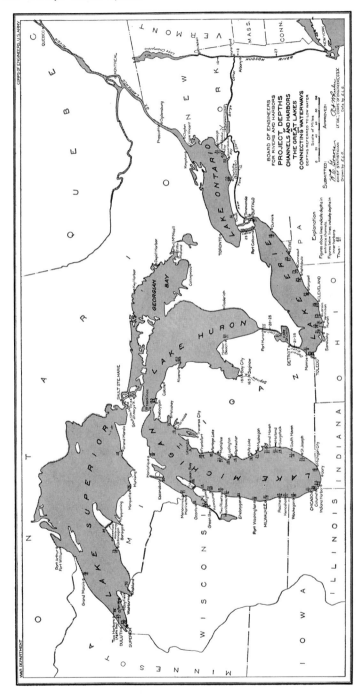

FIGURE 3-7. Great Lakes system. (Courtesy of the U. S. Army Corps of Engineers.)

Table 3-5.   Navigable Lengths and Depths of United States Inland Waterway Routes [a]

Length in Miles of Waterways

Group	Under 6 ft	6–9 Ft	9–12 Ft	12–14 Ft	14 Ft and Over	Total
Atlantic coast waterways (exclusive of Atlantic intracoastal waterway from Norfolk, Va., to Key West, Fla.) but including New York State Barge Canal System	1563	1445	589	965	1241	5,803
Atlantic intracoastal waterway from Norfolk, Va., to Key West, Fla.	—	158	65	1104	—	1,327
Gulf coast waterways (exclusive of Gulf intracoastal waterway from St. Marks River, Fla., to Mexican border)	2174	819	2095	270	372	5,730
Gulf intracoastal waterway from St. Marks River, Fla., to Mexican border (including Plaquemine-Morgan City Alternate Route)	—	—	—	1173	—	1,173
Mississippi River system	4829	1491	5008	755	268	12,351
Pacific coast waterways	733	515	237	27	461	1,973
All other waterways	100	148	14	8	369	639
Total of all systems	9399	4576	8008	4302	2711	28,996

[a] *The Inland Waterways and Mass Production,* map and statistical insert, The American Waterways Operators, Inc., Washington, D. C., 1956.

ocean trade. These companies report to the U. S. Maritime Commission rather than to the I.C.C.

Canals and rivers form routes of limited extent. Many parts of the country have no access to navigable waters, for few reaches of water have a naturally sufficient depth of channel, 9 to 14 ft. Rivers must be deepened by dredging or by dam construction and canalization. The lower Mississippi River has 840 miles of 9-ft (or deeper) channels (much of it is 12 ft in depth), the Ohio has 980 miles, and the upper Mississippi has 650 miles of 9-ft depth. The United States now has almost 30,000 miles of improved inland waterways, of which the Mississippi and its 30 navigable tributaries comprise more than 12,000 miles. The Gulf Intracoastal Canal extends over 1100 miles from Florida to the Mexican border. See Table 3-5.

Navigation aids—channel markers, lights, and some harbor facilities—must be provided. These facilities, in addition to the actual channels, are furnished or maintained by the Federal Government free to all users. River, lake, and canal operators are spared the cost and responsibility of channelway construction and maintenance; they make no user payments, equivalent, for example, to the high-

Table 3-6. Number of Vessels on Inland Waterways of United States (Exclusive of Great Lakes) for Transportation of Freight as of December 31, 1954 [a]

Types of Vessels	Mississippi River System	Atlantic, Gulf, and Pacific Coasts	Total
Self-propelled			
Towboats:			
Number of vessels	1,748	2,270	4,018
Horsepower	963,880	975,978	1,939,858
Nonself-propelled			
Barges and scows, dry cargo:			
Number of vessels	7,002	4,982	11,984
Cargo capacity (net tons)	5,847,894	762,232	2,934,126
Total barges and scows (all types):			
Number of vessels	8,482	5,610	14,092
Cargo capacity (net tons)	8,019,884	3,826,665	11,846,549

[a] *The Inland Waterways and Mass Production*, map and statistical insert, The American Waterways Operators, Inc., Washington, D. C., 1956.

Table 3-7. Freight Tonnage and Revenue for Class A and B Inland Waterways and Maritime Carriers Reporting to the I.C.C., 1956 [a]

Commodity Group (2000-lb tons)	All Navigation Areas		Maritime Carriers		Navigation Area								
					Inland and Coastal Waterways		Atlantic and Gulf Coast		Great Lakes Area [b]		Mississippi River System [b]		Pacific Coast	
	Tons	Revenue	Tons	Revenue	Tons	Revenue	Tons	Revenue	Tons	Revenue	Tons	Revenue	Tons	Revenue
				(Revenue tons and gross revenues in millions)										
Products of agriculture	6.39	$ 20.16	0.20	$ 4.47	6.18	$ 15.70	0.34	$ 1.08	1.82	$ 4.76	3.65	$ 8.70	0.38	$ 1.16
Animals and products	0.09	0.78	0.02	0.40	0.07	0.39	0.03	0.11	—	—	0.03	0.09	0.02	0.18
Products of mines	52.63	59.38	0.78	3.09	51.85	55.40	8.30	7.96	14.60	15.35	27.58	31.11	1.37	1.00
Products of forests	13.85	44.30	2.03	34.29	11.83	10.01	0.13	0.17	0.12	0.45	0.10	0.09	11.39	7.54
Manufactures and Miscellaneous	33.34	177.45	4.39	85.38	28.96	92.07	5.82	15.56	2.41	9.11	16.00	56.44	4.75	10.96
Forwarder traffic	0.04	1.09	0.04	1.09	—	—	—	—	—	—	—	—	—	—
Total, carload	106.34	$303.16	7.46	$129.60	98.89	$173.56	14.62	$24.87	18.93	$28.67	47.33	$96.43	17.92	$20.82
LCL freight	0.22	6.67	0.10	5.19	0.13	1.47	0.08	1.10	0.01	0.04	—	0.02	0.04	0.32
Total, all Traffic	106.56	$309.83	7.56	$174.79	99.02	$175.03	14.70	$25.97	18.94	$29.71	47.33	$96.45	17.96	$21.14

[a] *Transport Statistics in the United States, Part 5, Carriers by Water,* I.C.C., Washington, D. C., for the year ended December 31, 1956, Table 3, pp. 40–64.
[b] Passenger revenues: Great Lakes, $2,121,040; Mississippi River and tributaries, $1,310,568.

Table 3-8. Traffic and Revenue by Carrier, 1956 [a]

Class of Carrier	Number of Carriers	Operating Revenue (in millions)		Revenue Freight Carried (in millions)		Revenue Passengers Carried (in millions)	
		Dollars	Tons	Tons	Dollars	Number	Dollars
Inland and coastal waterways							
Class A	70	$218.03	84.63	89.37	$167.29	2.63	$ 7.77
Class B	43	17.13	6.65	9.64	7.74	1.08	1.20
Class C	103	22.46	8.72	8.51	7.44	6.18	4.32
Total	216	$257.62	100.00	107.52	$182.47	9.89	13.29
Maritime carriers	32	$555.72	—	7.55	$134.80	0.001	0.71

[a] *Transport Statistics in the United States, Part 5, Carriers by Water*, I.C.C., Washington, D. C., for the year ended December 31, 1956, Table 3, p. 1.

way fuel tax. All types of traffic—pleasure and commercial, private, contract, and common carriers—share the canals, rivers, lakes, and coastal waters. Most of the commercial traffic moves in private vessels. An exception to the foregoing free use of the waterways are the tolls charged over the St. Lawrence Seaway. The amount of toll to be charged is presently a matter of sharp debate. The number of vessels using the inland waterways, exclusive of the Great Lakes, is given in Table 3-6.

Tables 3-7 and 3-8 show the revenue tons of freight carried on these several systems of inland and coastal waters and the revenues therefrom. The routes are shown on the map of Figure 3-8.

Airways. Airplanes have introduced the third dimension into transportation. Nevertheless, airway routes are closely related to the ground on which both visual and radio guides are established in designated patterns. A system of Federal airways was established by the Civil Aeronautics Authority (C.A.A.) of the U. S. Department of Commerce. These airways are policed, controlled, and maintained by the Civil Aeronautics Board (C.A.B.), which presently operates under the authority of the F.A.A. Low- or medium-frequency radio-range-controlled, color-designated airways extended over 59,762 miles in 1956 (67,783 miles including Alaska and Hawaii).[14] These routes consist of 10-mile-wide air lanes between principal cities. East-

[14] *Statistical Handbook of Civil Aviation*, U. S. Civil Aeronautics Administration, Washington, D. C., 1957, p. 18.

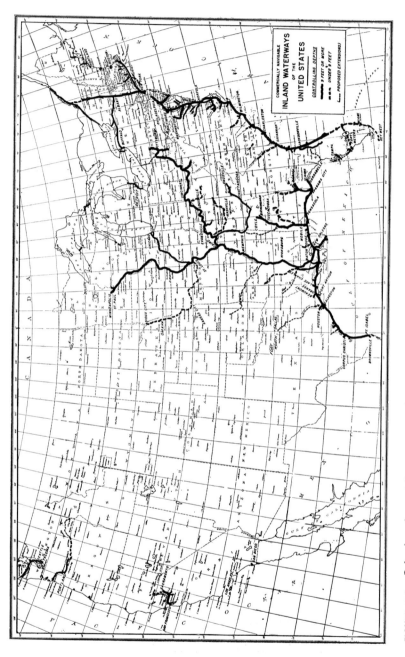

FIGURE 3-8. Inland and coastal waterways of the United States—1960. (Courtesy of The American Waterways Operators, Inc., Washington, D. C.)

west routes are designated red and green; green for main routes, red for local routes. North-south routes are correspondingly amber and blue. Colored airways are numbered north to south and west to east. These routes are equipped with visual markings for day and night flying, low-frequency radio-range stations, and emergency landing fields. The number of visual stations is decreasing as more dependence is placed on radio-range stations, particularly those of very high frequency, and as commercial landing fields become more numerous. Flight separation is provided laterally, horizontally, and vertically (in 1000-ft layers) by rules and by the supervision of traffic-control centers located in 31 principal cities.[15]

Closely paralleling the colored airways is another 89,244 miles (90,268 miles including Alaska and Hawaii) of direct VHF (visual very high-frequency omnirange) airways, which will eventually supplant the colored airways as the high-frequency radio equipment is installed in range stations and aircraft. Two skyways, 40-mile-wide strips with ground markings for day and night flying of private planes, have been established: Skyway No. 1, between Los Angeles and Washington, D. C., and Skyway No. 2, between Seattle and Boston. These are not heavily traveled. There is, in addition, considerable cross-country flying by private operators. Routes of the Federal airways are shown in Figure 3-9.

In 1956 there were totals of 64,688 active certificated civil aircraft and 669,079 pilots—15,295 air transport, 221,096 commercial, and 432,688 private.[16] The number of aircraft by number of engines and other types in the United States is shown in Table 3-9.

The traffic distribution of air transport carriers is given in Figure 3-10. Trunk, local, and insular routes in 1956 employed 103,489 persons and international airlines employed 28,014. The average domestic passenger trip in 1956 was 536 miles; the average international trip was 1298 miles.[17] Airlines have engaged primarily in passenger business and in carrying mail but are developing a traffic in freight and express. Most line-haul carriers fly mail, express, and some freight. In addition, there are several all-cargo lines.

Pipelines. Systems of pipelines for the transportation of petroleum products in the United States are shown in Figure 3-11. Petroleum pipelines may be divided into three categories: gathering lines, which

[15] *Ibid.*
[16] *Ibid.*, p. 35.
[17] *Ibid.*, pp. 25, 92, 81, 90.

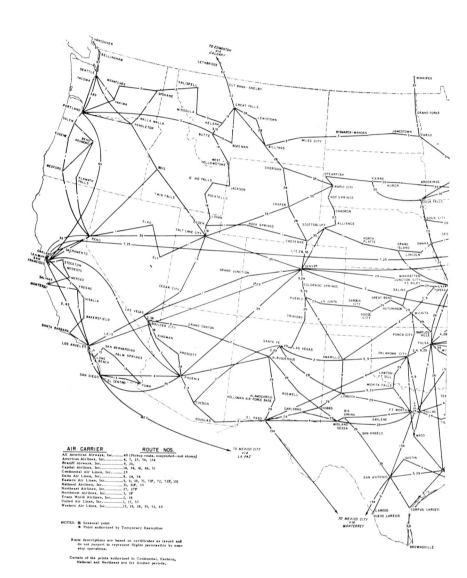

AIR CARRIER   ROUTE NOS.

All American Airways, Inc.——49 (Pickup route, suspended—not shown)
American Airlines, Inc.——4, 7, 25, 56, 134
Braniff Airways, Inc.——9, 26,
Capital Airlines, Inc.——14, 34, 41, 46, 51
Continental Air Lines, Inc.——29
Delta Air Lines, Inc.——8, 24, 54
Eastern Air Lines, Inc.——5, 6, 10, 71, 71F, 72, 72F, 131
National Airlines, Inc.——31, 31F, 39
Northeast Airlines, Inc.——27, 27F
Northwest Airlines, Inc.——3, 3F
Trans World Airlines, Inc.——2, 38
United Air Lines, Inc.——1, 17, 57
Western Air Lines, Inc.——13, 19, 28, 35, 52, 63

NOTES: ⌶ Seasonal point
        ⋆ Point authorized by Temporary Exemption

Route descriptions are based on certificates as issued and
do not purport to represent flights permissible by nonsstop operations.

Certain of the points authorized to Continental, Eastern,
National and Northeast are for limited periods.

FIGURE 3-9a. Principal Federal air routes—trunk-line carriers (United States air transportation system, routes certificated to trunk-line carriers, March 31, 1959). (Courtesy of Routes Division, Bureau of Air Operations, Civil Aeronautics Board.)

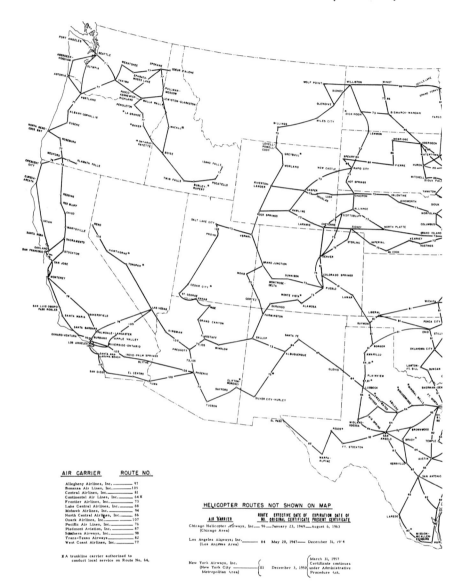

AIR CARRIER   ROUTE NO.

Allegheny Airlines, Inc. ———— 97
Bonanza Air Lines, Inc. ————105
Central Airlines, Inc. ———— 81
Continental Air Lines, Inc. ——— 64 X
Frontier Airlines, Inc. ———— 73
Lake Central Airlines, Inc. ——— 88
Mohawk Airlines, Inc. ———— 94
North Central Airlines, Inc. ——— 86
Ozark Airlines, Inc. ————107
Pacific Air Lines, Inc. ———— 76
Piedmont Aviation, Inc. ———— 87
Southern Airways, Inc. ———— 98
Trans-Texas Airways ———— 82
West Coast Airlines, Inc. ——— 77

X A trunkline carrier authorized to
conduct local service on Route No. 64.

HELICOPTER ROUTES NOT SHOWN ON MAP

		ROUTE	EFFECTIVE DATE OF	EXPIRATION DATE OF
AIR CARRIER		NO.	ORIGINAL CERTIFICATE	PRESENT CERTIFICATE

Chicago Helicopter Airways, Inc. ___ 96 ___January 23, 1949___August 6, 1963
(Chicago Area)

Los Angeles Airways, Inc. ___ 84   May 20, 1947— December 31, 1974
(Los Angeles Area)

New York Airways, Inc.   { March 31, 1957
(New York City ———{ 111   December 3, 1951{ Certificate continues
Metropolitan Area)   { under Administrative
                                                               { Procedure Act.

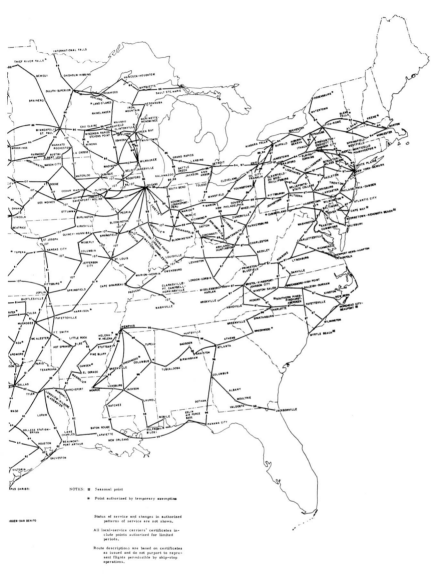

FIGURE 3-9b. Principal Federal air routes—local-service carriers (United States air transportation system, routes certificated to local-service carriers, March 31, 1959). (Courtesy of Routes Division, Bureau of Air Operations, Civil Aeronautics Board.)

Table 3-9. Aircraft Certificated in the United States, 1956 [a]

	Type of Airplane				
Type of Line	Twin Engines	Four Engines	Four Engined Turbo- Prop	Heli- copter	Total
Domestic airlines	691	582	54	20	1,347
International airlines	20	176	—	—	196
Total: Scheduled United States airlines	711	758	54	20	1,543
Total registration: All uses					64,688
Single-engined			58,404		
Twin-engined			5,015		
Three-engined			13		
Four-engined			867		
Experimental and unknown			132		
Balloons and dirigibles			14		
Gliders			243		
Total			64,688		

[a] *Statistical Handbook of Civil Aviation*, U. S. Civil Aeronautics Administration, Washington, D. C., 1957, pp. 33, 73, 91.

carry crude oil from the fields to the initial pumping station, crude trunk lines for pumping crude petroleum, and product trunk lines for handling gasoline, kerosene, and distillate fuel oils. There were 83 common-carrier pipeline companies reporting to the I.C.C. in 1957. The mileage and traffic of those lines are presented in Table 3-10.

The pipeline routes generally lead from the oil fields to refining centers or to river or Gulf ports for water transport to the eastern seaboard or abroad.

Natural-gas lines totaled more than 400,000 miles in 1957. Principal lines (see Figure 3-12) run to population and industrial centers, where the gas constitutes about 24 percent of the nation's fuel supply. An increasingly large amount is used in the production of petrochemicals.

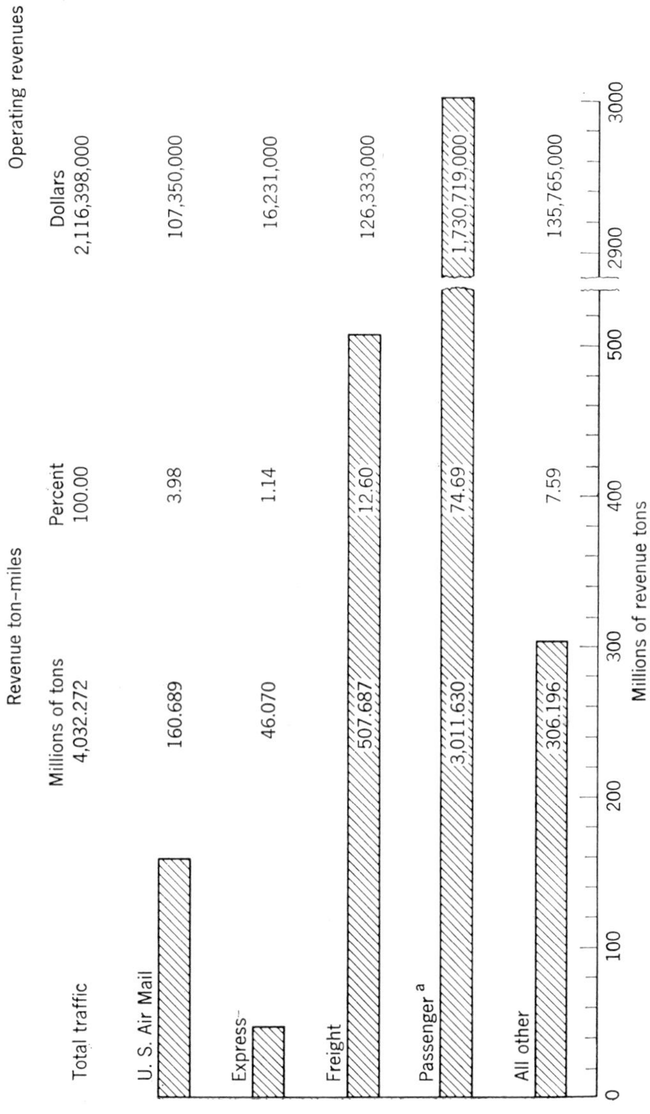

[a] Passenger miles are converted to ton-miles on the basis of about 10 to 1

FIGURE 3-10. Traffic distribution: certificated United States airlines—1957. (From *Air Transport Facts and Figures*, Nineteenth Edition, Air Transport Association of America, Washington, D. C., 1958.)

Table 3-10. Mileage and Traffic of United States Petroleum and Petroleum Products Pipelines, 1957

Pipeline mileage [a]		
Trunk lines:		
Crude petroleum	58,552 miles	
Refined products	30,293 miles	
Total trunk lines		88,845 miles
Gathering lines:		51,611 miles
Total petroleum pipeline mileage		140,456 miles
Pipeline traffic [b]		
Total barrels having trunk line movement:		
Crude petroleum	3,056,065,958	
Refined products	876,234,678	
Total	3,932,300,636	
Barrel miles having trunk line movement:		
Crude petroleum	930,558,064,000	
Refined products	248,318,537	
Total	930,806,382,537	

[a] *Transport Statistics in the United States, Part 6, Oil Pipelines,* I.C.C., Washington, D. C., for the year ended December 31, 1957, p. 1.
[b] *Ibid.,* p. 1. [b]

Conveyors. Conveyors have generally been limited to use as plant facilities in factories and mines or as carriers of aggregates for distances up to eight miles in connection with large construction projects. However, their adaptation for hauling coal and ore between the Great Lakes and the Ohio River is being strongly urged and indicates a possible future development.

Cableways. Aerial tramways, cableways, or ropeways offer a specialized type of transportation. They are used primarily for moving products of mines relatively short distances over terrain that is too rough for economical construction and operation of other types of transport. They are also used as a plant facility in operating gravel pits and quarries and in moving aggregates from nearby sources of supply to large construction projects.

Cableways have been used extensively in the rugged terrain of the Alpine countries for hauling freight and passengers. It was there that this type of transport originated and has reached its fullest development.

There are only a few major cableway installations in the United States; each of the two largest is 13 miles long. There is a 20-mile cableway in the Andes, one 54 miles long in Colombia, another 8 miles long in the Philippines for hauling gold ore, and still another that moves asbestos a distance of 12 miles from Swaziland to a railhead of the South African Railways.

Summary of Mileage. In summary, the total route mileage of the five major elements in the United States transportation system is approximately that shown in Table 3-11.

TRANSPORT ROUTES

Lines of Flow. A study of the maps in this chapter will show that certain rather well-defined transportation routes, usually served by several carrier types, have developed in this country. Such development has arisen from the geographical pathways and barriers formed by lakes, rivers, valleys, mountain ranges, and mountain passes and from the sites of natural resources and patterns of economic activity and population density.

1. The *Atlantic Seaboard* route extends along the east coast from Maine to Florida. It is served by highways (for example, U.S. 1), railroads (New Haven, Pennsylvania, Atlantic Coast Line), airways (American, Eastern, National, and Capital), and by coastal shipping. This route features the movement of perishable farm products north and south into the heavily populated Washington–New York sector,

Table 3-11. **Approximate Route Mileage of the United States Transportation System**

Carrier	Route Mileage
Railroads (main line)	219,067
Highways (paved roads)	2,148,000
Inland waterways (authorized navigable lengths)	28,996
Pipelines (crude oil, petroleum products, natural gas)	440,000
Airways (color-designated and VHF under Federal control)	158,051
Total transport route miles	2,994,114

New York-to-Miami vacation travel, forest products (newsprint, building materials, etc), and petroleum and its products in barge and tanker from the Gulf coast.

2. The *North and Middle Atlantic–Gulf Coast* route provides rail, highway, and air connections southwestward between New York and vicinity and the Gulf coast and intermediate points. It also serves as a portion of the transcontinental route for traffic moving between the northeastern seaboard and the West Coast via the southern transcontinental route. Water connections are made around and across the Florida peninsula. Pipelines carry gas and petroleum from the Gulf area. Manufactured products from the north move southwestward and farm produce, cotton and textiles, sulfur, and forest products flow northeastward.

3. *Trunk Line Territory* routes are the most numerous and extensive and carry the densest traffic flow of any in the United States, if not in the world. Airlines (TWA, United, and American) provide frequent service between Boston-New York-Washington points and Detroit-Chicago-St. Louis points as well as between intermediate centers via Buffalo and Pittsburgh. All types of traffic move over these routes, but manufactured products, products of mines, and foodstuffs prevail. The Great Lakes–New York State Barge Canal combination also serves this route. Ore, lumber, grain, and aggregates move down the lakes; coal, petroleum, and some manufactured products compose the return traffic. Most of the iron ore terminates on the south shore of Lake Erie for rail movement to consuming centers. The Ohio River, which forms the southern route boundary, carries bulk cargos of raw materials and forms a link connecting these routes with the Mississippi River and Gulf of Mexico. Pipelines from the mid-continent and southwestern-Gulf oil- and gas-producing regions find their eastern extensions in this group.

4. *Pocohontas* routes are adjacent to the Trunk Line routes on the south and may indeed be considered a part of that group. Coal from Virginia and West Virginia is hauled by rail from the interior mines to tidewater at Norfolk and Baltimore and to the Great Lakes at Toledo and Sandusky. Air service is provided principally by feeder lines. Bituminous coal from Kentucky also moves eastward over this route.

5. *Mississippi Valley* routes generally parallel the Mississippi River, which in itself furnishes a key mode of transport for coal, petroleum products, grains, aggregates, and other bulk commodities. These routes extend from the Gulf to the Twin Cities, Chicago, and the

Great Lakes; they also reach Pittsburgh via the Ohio River. The Illinois Central, the Gulf, Mobile, and Ohio, the Missouri Pacific, and the Frisco railroads connect Chicago, St. Louis, and intermediate points with the Gulf coast. North-south highways (U.S. 41, 45, 51, and 67), airways (Delta and Ozark), and pipelines to refining and consuming points at Whiting, Indiana, Cleveland, and Pittsburgh and to gas-consuming industrial areas share this route. An important part of the traffic flowing over this path is that between Chicago and St. Louis.

6. The *Eastern Gulf* routes extend from the Mississippi River as far north as Memphis to eastern and Florida points. Pipelines, airways, railways, the Gulf itself, and the Intracoastal Canal serve this region. Traffic includes a portion of the Chicago–St. Louis to the southeast rail and water flow and the coal, iron, and steel of the Birmingham district.

7. *Pacific Northwestern* routes originate in the Chicago, Minneapolis–St. Paul, and Duluth-Superior regions and extend westward to the Pacific Coast at Seattle and Tacoma via points in Montana and Spokane. Railroads (Milwaukee, Great Northern, Northern Pacific) predominate here in long-haul freight, and airlines (TWA, Northwest) move passenger traffic. Highways are active, mostly for shorter hauls, and a few pipelines serve the fields in Wyoming and Canada to the north. Imports from Japan, Hawaii, and Alaska, lumber from the Pacific Northwest, grains and cattle, fresh fruits and vegetables, and nonfuel minerals are carried eastward to processing, manufacturing, and consuming centers. Manufactured products, coal, and exports to the Pacific area move to the west. This route also serves as a continuation of a longer *East Coast–North Pacific* route.

8. *Central or Overland* routes extend from Chicago and from Mississippi and Missouri river crossings and gateways (St. Louis, Kansas City, Omaha, and Peoria) to Los Angeles and San Francisco via Denver, Cheyenne, and Salt Lake City. Rail, air, and highway traffic predominate, but there is some crude-oil pipeline flow from the Wyoming fields to Kansas City, St. Louis, and eastward. American, United, and Western airlines fly this route. The Union Pacific– Southern Pacific, the Denver and Rio Grande Western, and the Western Pacific are typical railroads. Cattle, grains, fresh fruits and vegetables, and mineral products move eastward; coal and manufactured goods, especially car parts, flow to the west. There is con-

siderable passenger traffic over this route, especially between New York and the West Coast via Chicago.

9. The *Southwestern* routes originate at Mississippi and Missouri river crossings and gateway points (St. Louis, and Kansas City) and extend southwestward into Arkansas, Oklahoma, and Texas and westward to the Pacific Coast. A heavy pipeline network, which carries petroleum and natural gas to mid-continent refining and consuming centers, is a part of this route. Pipelines also terminate at Mississippi River system transfer points. Air passenger traffic flies in planes of TWA, American, and Delta. Railroad lines include the Santa Fe, Frisco, Cotton Belt, Kansas City Southern, and the Missouri Pacific. Cattle, fruits, vegetables, chemicals, petroleum products, and some lumber move east and north; manufactured goods and foodstuffs flow west and south.

10. The *Gulf–Pacific Coast* or *Southern Transcontinental* routes extend from Mobile, Birmingham, New Orleans, and Shreveport, in the Gulf coast area, westward to points in Texas and on the Pacific Coast. Rail, air, highway, and water-borne traffic are heavy, as is the pipeline flow from producing ponts to river and tidewaters.

11. *Pacific Coast* routes extend north and south from San Diego and Los Angeles to Seattle and Tacoma. Pipeline operation is limited to short hauls from producing areas to the coast. Rail and highway networks are light, but traffic over those that exist is heavy, especially between Los Angeles and San Francisco. Motor freight is extensive on the highways of this area.

12. *Panama Canal* routes connect the Pacific Coast with Gulf and eastern seaboard cities. This is deep-water shipping, with little or no barge movement. Lumber, petroleum products, and manufactured goods move via the canal.

The foregoing routes are generalized and by no means include all of the many minor paths between key cities and regions. A specific traffic-flow pattern exists, for example, between Houston and Dallas, Chicago and St. Louis, New York and Boston, and Kansas City and the Twin Cities. Also, these groupings have been made by route concentrations rather than by the modes of transport specific commodities usually follow, although the two frequently coincide. It will be noted that the transport network thins out from east to west. This can be attributed to (a) present relative scarcity of population and industry west of the Mississippi (owing in part to the time lag in westward expansion), (b) the greater availability of waterways east of the Mississippi, (c) the geographic suitability of the Midwest for agricultural purposes, (d) the natural barriers imposed by the Great Plains, Rocky Mountains, and the desert regions, (e) the location of petroleum and iron-ore deposits in the general vicinity of the mouth and course of the Mississippi River, and (f) cattle raising in the Far West with its demands for open country.

Gateways. An interesting feature of route location is the concentration of routes through certain limiting zones. These zones may arise because of rates and tariffs whereby certain desirable rates and connections are quoted only via a few key points. Peoria, St. Louis, Omaha, and the Twin Cities have traditionally served as such gateway points, and traffic has tended to flow and routes to concentrate accordingly.

Terrain and topography are other important limiting factors. A river valley provides easy grades and locations for railways and highways as well as for water-borne commerce. The industry and population which then congregate along the river intensify the traffic needs and production of that area. The Great Lakes and their adjacent coastal plain similarly provide a natural location for shipping, railways, highways, pipelines, and a route for airways to follow. Mountain passes have long been a limiting factor in route location. The Delaware Water Gap, Cumberland Gap, Mohawk Valley, Donner Pass, and others are occupied by one or more railroads and highways. A thorough study of the effects of geography on transport would be far too extensive to attempt in this book.

QUESTIONS FOR STUDY

1. Present in graphic form the various components of the United States transportation system.
2. Distinguish between the services performed by (a) a belt line or switching railroad, (b) a terminal railroad, (c) a line-haul railroad.
3. Give a complete I.C.C. designation for (a) a Class II contract carrier serving an irregular route, nonscheduled service, and carrying petroleum products, (b) a Class I common carrier hauling motor vehicles over a regular route with scheduled point-to-point service.
4. Explain the advantages and disadvantages of private systems of transport for (a) private individuals, (b) small companies, and (c) large companies and corporations.

5. Indicate the position in the United States system of transportation and the significance of (*a*) the St. Lawrence Seaway and (*b*) the Federal System of Interstate and Defense Highways.

6. Discuss the relative significance of the various components of transport in the carriage of persons.

7. What implications for the future does the drive-it-yourself system of automobile and truck rental offer?

8. Along how much of the United States coastline is it possible to sail a small boat in protected waters?

9. Name the several freight classifications promulgated by the I.C.C. for railroads and waterways. Wherein do these differ from that used for highway carriers?

10. Why have several well-defined transportation routes developed? Name these and give their location and general characteristics.

SUGGESTED READINGS

1. Wilbur G. Hudson, *Conveyors and Related Equipment*, Third Edition, John Wiley and Sons, New York, 1954.

2. Harold M. Mayer, *The Port of Chicago and the St. Lawrence Seaway*, University of Chicago Press, Chicago, 1957.

3. *Transportation on the Great Lakes*, Transportation Series No. 1, 1937 revision, Corps of Engineers, U. S. Army, U. S. Government Printing Office.

4. Charles A. Taft, *Commercial Motor Transportation*, 1955 revision, Business Publications, Chicago.

5. *Transportation of Oil*, Supply and Transportation Division, Petroleum Administration for Defense, Washington, D. C., December 1951.

6. Lloyd G. Wilson and Leslie A. Bryan, *Air Transportation*, Prentice-Hall, New York, 1949.

PART **II**

Transport
Technology

CHAPTER

4

ROADWAY

The physical facilities devoted to transportation are varied and extensive. One can make an arbitrary grouping of roadway, motive power, rolling stock, signals and communications, and terminals— facilities that are concerned directly with the movement of persons and goods and the vehicles in which they are transported. There is, in addition, an array of supporting services and facilities—shops, accounting and statistical machines, stores, medical and recreational facilities, and sometimes hotels, restaurants, and resorts.

This and subsequent chapters survey the principles and functions of the most important elements of the first category.

SUBGRADE

Function of the Subgrade. Every carrier moves in, on, or over a route having a direct or indirect relation to the land surfaces. That portion of the land area devoted to the route and facilities of railroads, highways, canals, pipelines, cableways, and conveyors is the right of way. Natural waterways have their own basins and river beds. Airways are related to the terrain only by visual or radio-range route markers and at airport runways.

Between the vehicle and the natural terrain of land-based carriers a bearing and running surface is interposed. Rails, ties, and ballast form a track or superstructure laid upon a subgrade for railroad trains. Trucks, buses, and automobiles are borne upon a smooth, paved surface also supported by a subgrade. Airplane runways perform a similar function as airplanes take off and land. Pipelines are laid within the earth itself, preferably below the frost line. Cableways and conveyors are supported on towers and trestlelike structures, which in turn are based on the soil beneath. In its conventional use a subgrade serves to bear and distribute the imposed loads with di-

113

minished unit pressures, to facilitate drainage, and to provide a smooth platform on which the running structure can be laid.

Action under Load. For railroads, highways, and runways, the track and pavement provide continuous elastic support for static and dynamic wheel loads and distribute them with diminished unit pressure to the subgrade. (Track also provides guidance for the railroad vehicles.) The subgrade in turn distributes track and pavement pressures with diminished unit pressure to the subsoil.

Concepts of the transmission of pressures through pavement, base courses, ballast, and subgrade are founded upon principles of elasticity modified in practice by simplifying assumptions and test results. Two general cases can be identified for wheel-load distribution; a pneumatic tire on a more or less flexible pavement (base courses and wearing surface) and a railroad wheel, usually of steel, on a steel rail supported on a wooden (sometimes concrete or steel) cross tie in a base course or ballast section.

An initial simplifying assumption for the first example is the distribution of a load from each wheel of a vehicle in the form of a cone supported by surrounding materials having a slope of approximately 45 degrees. The subgrade reaction is assumed to be uniform with a value of p psi. See Figure 4-1. The wheel load shown in Figure 4-1a is concentrated at a single point of application. Actu-

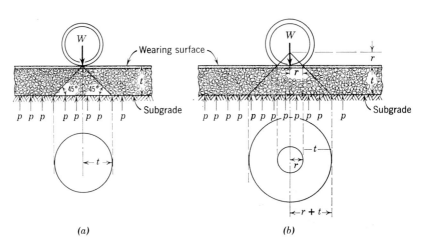

(a)   (b)

FIGURE 4-1. Cone theory of wheel load distribution: (a) tire assumed unflattened; (b) tire assumed flattened.

ally the load is spread over a small area because of the flattening of the tire, thereby lessening the unit intensity. For light trucks and passenger cars, the area is generally assumed to be a circle of radius r. The altitude and (for a 45-degree cone) the base are then equal to $t + r$. Equating the imposed load W to the support at the base of the cone, that is, at the subgrade, the supported load = supporting area $\times$ unit supporting reaction, or $W = \pi(t + r)^2 p$ and $t = 0.546\sqrt{W/p} - r$. This is the Asphalt Institute Formula given by Sharp, Shaw, and Dunlop in *Airport Engineering*.[1] Modifications of the foregoing applied to heavy trucks and airplanes are derived from the same source.

The value of r varies with the nominal tire width and degree of inflation. A conservative value is probably r = nominal width of tire divided by 4. In any event, the tire load on the pavement (and therefore on the subgrade) is somewhat decreased. Obviously the pavement thickness and the bearing capacity of the soil have a significant interdependence.

For the heavier wheel loads of large trucks and airplanes, the area of contact is assumed to be an ellipse with a width approximately equal to the nominal width of tire. The length of the ellipse may be computed by assuming the actual tire load = inflation pressure $\times$ area of the ellipse = inflation pressure $\times$ πab. See Figure 4-2.

In Figure 4-2 the elliptical loading area, assumed pressure distribution, and uniform reaction are shown diagrammatically for a single wheel. Again, applied total load equals area of support $\times$ unit supporting reaction, or

$$W = \pi(a + t)(b + t)p$$

and

$$t = \sqrt{W/\pi p - ab + [(a + b)/2]^2} - (a + b)/2,$$

where a and b have the values shown in Figure 4-2.[2]

However, the assumption of uniform pressure distribution and reaction is not actually true. Figure 4-2 also shows an actual pressure curve, developed by Goldbeck, which uses pressure cells placed in the subgrade to measure the intensity of transmitted load. The support that the subgrade must offer is that of the maximum pressure p_m. The relation between maximum and calculated uniform

---

[1] H. Oakley Sharp, G. Reed Shaw, and John A. Dunlop, *Airport Engineering*, John Wiley and Sons, New York, 1944, p. 67.

[2] *Ibid.*, p. 68.

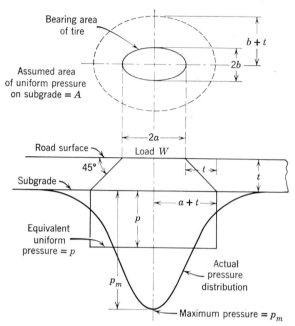

FIGURE 4-2. Area of contact for heavy wheel load. (Courtesy of H. O. Sharp, G. R. Shaw, J. A. Dunlop, *Airport Engineering,* John Wiley and Sons, 1944, p. 68, Figure 94.)

equivalent pressure is given by the factor $k = p_m/p$. Tests have shown an average value of $k = 2$ for stable surfaces and $k = 4$ for unstable surfaces. In terms of k and p_m,

$$t = \sqrt{kW/\pi p_m - ab + [(a + b)/2]^2} - (a + b)/2.$$

When dual tires are used, the assumed and actual distributions are as shown in Figure 4-3. The area of equivalent subgrade pressures equals $2S(a + t) + \pi(a + t)(b + t)$, $W = \text{area} \times p = \text{area} \times p_m/k$, and pavement thickness becomes

$$t = \sqrt{kW/\pi p_m - 2Sa/\pi - ab + [(2S + a + b)/2\pi]^2} - (2S + a + b)/2\pi,$$

where $S = $ center to center spacing of the dual wheels in inches.[3]

The actual impact loading for airplanes at landing may not greatly exceed the static load because of the gradual descent to the runway

[3] *Ibid.,* pp. 70–71.

and the additional flattening of the tires (as much as 100 percent or more) owing to the initial impact. An impact factor of 1.5 to 2.0 will cover most cases, and 3.5 will provide for the rarest and severest landing effects. Impact augments can also arise from irregularities in the pavement surface and from poor springing of the wheels. The most exacting airport conditions are likely to come from vibration caused by warm-up of piston-engined planes and to require a safety factor of 1.5 to 2.0.

The foregoing principles for elastic pavements apply with important modifications to rigid concrete pavements, where the pavement itself has a bridging effect that absorbs some of the load. These modifications are noted in the section on rigid pavements.

Although there is some flattening of the steel wheel of a railroad car or locomotive (the bearing contact is probably less than $\frac{1}{2}$ sq in.), such deformation has no significance at this point because the entire axle load (two-wheel loads) is supported and distributed by the

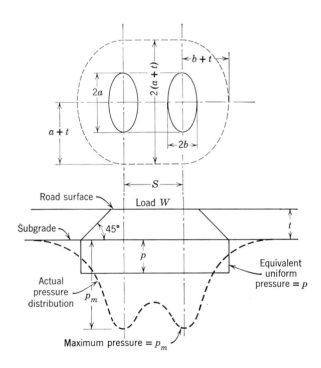

FIGURE 4-3. Load distribution under dual wheels. (Courtesy of H. O. Sharp, G. R. Shaw, J. A. Dunlop, *Airport Engineering*, John Wiley and Sons, 1944, p. 70, Figure 95.)

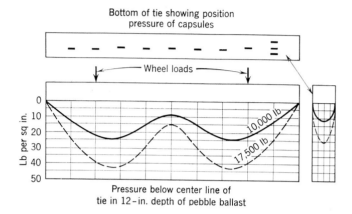

FIGURE 4-4. Pressure distribution across face of tie. (A. N. Talbot, "Second Progress Report of Special Committee to Report on Stresses in Railroad Track," *A.R.E.A. Proceedings*, Vol. 21, American Railway Engineers Association, Chicago, 1920, pp. 645–814.)

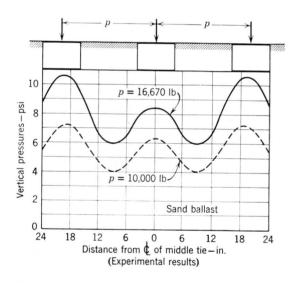

FIGURE 4-5. Lateral pressure distribution from three ties. (A. N. Talbot, "Second Progress Report of Special Committee to Report on Stresses in Railroad Track," *A.R.E.A. Proceedings*, Vol. 21, American Railway Engineers Association, Chicago, 1920, pp. 645–814.)

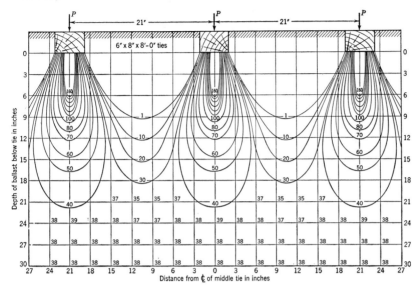

FIGURE 4-6. Pressure distribution from three ties (in percent of unit pressure on face of ties). (A. N. Talbot, "Second Progress Report of Special Committee to Report on Stresses in Railroad Track," *A.R.E.A. Proceedings,* Vol. 33, 1933, Figure 97, p. 807.)

cross tie. As will be shown later, the girder action of the rail distributes the wheel load over more than one tie. However, in considering ballast and subgrade loads, the entire wheel load is usually taken as concentrated on one tie, as it sometimes might be under conditions of nonuniform tie and ballast support. It is, therefore, the distributed load due to the area of the tie that must be considered. Such distribution, however is not uniform but varies over the face of the tie from the point of load application, as shown in Figures 4-4 and 4-5. Figures 4-4, 4-5, and 4-6 are derived from pressure-cell laboratory and field studies of actual track loadings, made by the Special Committee on Stresses in Railroad Track, of which the late Dr. Arthur N. Talbot was chairman.[4] Figure 4-5 represents the pressure distribution under one tie. The combined effects of loads on two or more adjacent ties are found by superposition and lead to the diagram of Figure 4-6.

[4] A. N. Talbot, Second Progress Report of Special Committee to Report on Stresses in Railroad Track, *A.R.E.A. Proceedings,* Vol. 21, American Railway Engineering Association, Chicago, 1920, pp. 645–814.

From these and similar diagrams, Dr. Talbot derived the conclusion that a uniform distribution of pressures in the ballast occurs at a depth approximately equal to the center-to-center spacing of the ties plus 3 to 4 in.

The actual pressure values in Figures 4-5 and 4-6 are expressed as percentages of the average pressure over the face (bottom) of the tie in pounds per square inch, or $p_a = 2P$ divided by bl, where $P =$ the wheel load in pounds, $b =$ breadth of tie in inches, and $l =$ length of tie in inches. The maximum pressure is seen to occur approximately 6 in. below the face of the tie. By methods not here reproduced, Dr. Talbot developed a formula for the pressure directly under the center line of an 8-in. tie, the point of maximum pressure intensity, as $p_c = 16.8 p_a/h^{1.25}$, where $p_c =$ pressure in pounds per square inch on any horizontal plane at a depth of h in. below the center of the tie face. For the vertical pressure at any point x in. to the right or left of the center of the tie and in a horizontal plane h in. below the face of the 8-in. tie,

$$p = 1.23(p_a/h)10^{-2.06(x/h)^{-}},$$

where p is the intensity of pressure in pounds per square inch.[5] This empirical expression is accurate for depths between 4 and about 30 in. For a graphical solution to this problem, which draws more closely upon the principles of elasticity for individual tie loads, the reader is referred to the Newmark influence charts.[6]

From the foregoing figures and equations, the pressure intensity or load in pounds per square inch on the subgrade under a given depth of ballast can be approximated. Conversely, given a bearing capacity for the subgrade, the depth of ballast necessary to distribute the load within the capacity of the subgrade can be calculated. Accuracies of 1 to 5 percent were obtained by the Committee on Stresses, when uniform ballast materials were used and the track was properly tamped. However, such accuracies cannot always be expected because of nonuniformity of ballast materials, tamping, and wheel loads. These nonuniformities make the problem considerably more complicated than this analysis would indicate. Nevertheless, the foregoing outlines the factors involved.

The Track Committee found little difference in size of ballast particles for load distribution. However, the ultimate bearing ca-

[5] *Ibid.*
[6] N. M. Newmark, Influence Charts for Computation of Stresses in Elastic Foundations, *Engineering Experiment Station Bulletin, Series No. 338,* University of Illinois, Urbana, May 1951.

pacity of large base-course materials, for example, broken stone in contrast to sand or ¾-in. stone as opposed to 2½-in. stone, is greater. The coarser materials with greater load-bearing capacities are usually recommended for the top base course and ballast sections, where the load to be borne is at a maximum. Subbase and subballast materials can be finer and lighter.

Track and pavement loads are usually much greater than the bearing capacity of the subgrade material. See Table 4-1. The load transmitted by the ballast or base course depends upon the depth of

Table 4-1. Typical Wheel Loadings for Various Modes of Transport

Transport Vehicle	Total Wheel Load (lb)	Area of Contact (sq in.)	Load on Support (psi)
Locomotives			
Diesel-electric			
Road engines	25,000	0.3 ± sq in.	83,333
	30,000		100,000
Switchers	10,000	0.3 ± sq in.	33,333
	20,000		66,667
Steam			
Heavy freight	30,000	0.3 ± sq in.	100,000
	35,000		116,667
Passenger	25,000	0.3 ± sq in.	85,000
	30,000		100,000
Railroad cars (loaded)	15,000	0.3 ± sq in.	50,000
	25,000		83,333
Automobiles (loaded)	1,000		
	1,200	20–30 sq in.	50–60
Heavy pneumatic tire loads [a]			
Single tires			
Gross load per wheel	60,000	527 sq in.	114
	100,000	798 sq in.	125
	140,000	1080 sq in.	130
Dual tires			
Gross load 60,000	30,000	325 sq in.	92
100,000	50,000	464 sq in.	108
140,000	70,000	612 sq in.	114

[a] H. O. Sharp, G. R. Shaw, and J. A. Dunlop, *Airport Engineering*, 1944, John Wiley and Sons, New York, 1944, p. 71.

ballast or base course under the tie or pavement as well as the type of materials. If the subgrade were of bedrock, no ballast would be needed for load distribution. A subgrade of dense, well-compacted soil with bearing capacities of 40 psi or higher could withstand a high intensity of pressure. Weak soils may, on the contrary, have a bearing capacity of 10 to 20 psi or less. The weaker the subgrade or the heavier the loads imposed, the deeper and heavier the ballast or base course and the rails or pavement must be. Similarly, if the subgrade is strong or the loads light, both subgrade and track or pavement structure can be lighter. For very heavy loads both subgrade and superstructure must be the heaviest and strongest.

Under the conditions of elastic support, the structure and its support will deflect slightly under load but return to their initial positions when the load is removed. Each element in the roadway structure is subject to a repetitively applied deflecting and bending load as wheels of trains or automotive vehicles pass. These repetitive loadings are likely to initiate fatigue failures and plastic deformation in underdesigned structures. The supports will not return to their initial positions when the load is removed. Common examples are ruts in earth roads and low spots in railroad track surface.

In summary, the primary requirements of the subgrade are adequate bearing capacity and stability under repetitive loadings. There must be freedom from plastic deformation (ruts, pockets, settlements), from foundation failures (subsidence under the subgrade), and from slips, slides, and soft spots within the subgrade. Stability is especially critical for highways. Irregularities in subgrade support under a railroad track can be adjusted in the ballast sections and failures repaired with a minimum effort. A highway pavement, on the contrary, can be severely and permanently damaged if given inadequate subgrade support.

Soils. Soils are the construction material from which the subgrade is built. Soils possess characteristics of grain size, internal friction, cohesion, shearing strength, capillarity, permeability, porosity, elasticity, compressibility, liquid and plastic limits, and mineral content, which determine their bearing capacity and stability when properly placed in the fill. These *index properties* for proposed subgrade soils must be established according to the principles and by methods of soils engineering to determine their suitability.

Modern roadbed design, departing from traditional rule-of-thumb methods, requires an evaluation of *load-bearing capacity* for safe and economic proportioning of over-all design. Unfortunately, such evaluations are still largely empirical, and the degree of accuracy is limited. Load-bearing characteristics vary greatly with combinations of the index properties. A design or procedure for one soil or climate might not be adequate for another soil or climate. A major cause of uncertainty is the frequent nonuniformity of soils.

There are many ways of determining a measure of bearing capacity, none of which is precise. It may be computed from the data of soils tests performed in the laboratory. Field tests give quicker if less refined values. For transportation subgrades, field-test methods are more in favor than laboratory tests and usually some form of loading or penetration test. The reader is referred to standard works on soils engineering, especially those listed at the close of this chapter, for more detail on such tests and on the principles of soils engineering.

Soils surveys are a necessary part of reconnaissance and location studies and a means to the proper selection or rejection of soils. The survey should include these steps:

1. A study of all data already available in the form of reports and records of governmental agencies, universities, railroads, highway departments, and canal and pipeline companies. The geological history of the area under study should be determined.

2. Soil profiles as visible in existing railroad, highway, and canal cuts and embankments, sites of slides, and local borrow pits.

3. Earth auger borings to determine the general profile along the proposed center line of the route and to determine the general character, uniformity, or nonuniformity of the soils to be encountered.

4. Taking of sufficient soil samples to make required field and laboratory tests, depending in detail upon the soil encountered, proposed construction methods, climate, and importance of the proposed structure.

5. Making the tests mentioned earlier to determine bearing capacities of the soils to be used.

6. Coordinating observed data with soil characteristics and recommended use in one or more of the several systems of soil classification.

Design for Stability and Adequate Bearing Capacity. The requirements for stability and bearing capacity as stated and implied in the foregoing paragraphs may be summarized in the following:

1. Proper location will, insofar as practicable, avoid difficult ground—swamp muck, muskeg, false shales, unstable side-hill cuts and fills, and beds of soft or swelling clays.

2. Proper soils will be selected for construction purposes. Desirable soil characteristics include high internal friction and shearing strength, low capillarity, low elasticity, high compressibility, low tendency toward volume change with changes in moisture content, and low plasticity.

3. Soils must usually be used as they occur along the route, with only a limited opportunity for selective choice. Therefore, the cross section must be designed to compensate for unfavorable soil characteristics. Compensating methods include flattening the slopes from the conventional 1½:1 to as little as 2–2½:1 for rounded-particle sands and 3:1 at the base of fills more than 20 ft high containing a large percentage of clay. Soils with a tendency to swell should be placed on the shoulders beyond the loaded area of the fill or buried near the bottom of the fill, so that the weight of better materials above will restrain the swelling forces and absorb any swelling that does occur. Capillary rise is reduced or prevented by an underlying bed of granular materials, which insulates against it, or, if there is muskeg, permafrost, etc., by placing an insulating bed of peat that is already saturated over the possible source of moisture. Slides in weak foundation materials can be restrained by counterweight masses of soil at the toe of the fill.

4. The fill material should be kept dry, especially under the load-carrying areas. A core of impermeable clay is helpful. Excess moisture is diverted from the subgrade by side and intercepting ditches. Subdrainage may be necessary to divert subsurface flow, seepage, or percolation and to dry out pockets in established subgrades.

5. Proper construction procedures must be specified and carried out. Organic materials are stripped from under the proposed subgrade, and the exposed surface is rolled and compacted. Fill material is spread in thin layers and compacted to a maximum density at the optimum moisture content consistent with the soil and equipment. Routing of earth-moving equipment over the face of the fill may give sufficient compaction, but better results obtain if special compacting equipment—vibrator rollers and sheepsfoot rollers—are used.

6. Protection against wind and water erosion, wave wash, and sloughing is given by planting root-mat-producing vegetation or blanketing the slope with riprap, cinders, crushed slag, or other similar granulars held in place by cement grout or asphaltic compounds.

7. Along with the problem of subgrade stability there is that of slope stability in cuts. Generally, the factors contributing to stability of fills also apply to slope stability. Practically, stability is usually obtained by making the slope flat enough to hold the materials in repose. Additional width (to provide for sloughing), terraces, and setbacks for every 25 to 30 ft of height and sodding, planting, or otherwise blanketing the slope also help. The stability or resistance to sliding of proposed slopes can be analyzed mathematically when the internal friction has been obtained by laboratory tests or field comparisons with other slopes. Inspection of suspected slopes, removal of the overburden to reduce sliding tendencies, and drainage (both surface and subsurface) to prevent slope saturation and plastic flow are recommended practices.

Canals. The foregoing principles are also applicable to waterway design and construction with some differences in emphasis. A canal has no load-bearing problems as such. The two primary soil objectives in "subgrade" design are stability of side slopes and retention of water. As with railroads and highways, much can be gained by including the factor of soils in location planning.

Side slopes in canals involve no additional problems to those common to other routes, with the exception that the toe of the slope is always immersed and subject to saturation. Wherever an artificial embankment must be built to provide a canal channel or wherever a levee is required to restrain channel waters, the problem is essentially one of earth-dam design and construction. One solution is to place earth materials, as available, along the route without any special compaction effort beyond that afforded by the hauling and spreading equipment, depending upon flat slopes of 3:1 to 6:1 for stability. With controlled design and construction, an impermeable, well-compacted clay core aids in water retention. The slopes should be protected against wave wash by coarse granular materials, riprap, or grouted blanket. The solution becomes critical if failure of the embankment can cause loss of life and damage to adjacent property. Then a full application of the more detailed principles and methods of soils engineering is in order.

To prevent water loss, porous soils and fissured and jointed limestone should, if possible, be avoided in the initial location. Cracks and fissures can sometimes be sealed with concrete or cement grout, and porous soils can be made less permeable by injections of clay, cement grout, or asphalt or by covering with clay, grout, or asphaltic blankets.

Pipelines. The problems of stability and support for pipelines are less critical than for other carrier types. Usually the natural ground gives sufficient support in the trench, and the rigidity of the pipe will carry it over soft spots a few feet in length. However, consideration should be given to soil conditions for access roads, which must often be constructed to bring in equipment and materials along the route.

Location reconnaissance and surveys seek to avoid troublesome ground. A unique soil characteristic in regard to pipelines is the corrosive quality of some soils. A combination of ground water and soil chemicals is likely to corrode the pipe and calls for expensive protective coverings and cathodic devices to prevent electrolysis. Sulfur, for example, may combine with water to form sulfuric acid. Not only naturally corrosive soils but those made corrosive by seepage of industrial wastes, which often contain corrosive substances, must be avoided if possible.

In swamps and small streams there should be a minimum depth of cover of 4 to 5 ft and a 10- to 20-ft minimum coverage under large streams and rivers. In addition, the pipe may have to be weighted with a concrete casing to aid in resisting forces of stream flow and scour.

Proper compaction of the backfill is desirable (but often neglected) to insure a return to normal supporting strength of the natural ground. Soil compaction is especially desirable when a surcharge might be placed over the line, a likelihood in built-up areas or areas of potential development. Mechanized tamping procedures and control of moisture to insure maximum density should be followed. The first 6 to 8 in. of backfill should be moderately fine material free of large lumps and rocks to prevent damage to the pipe and its protective covering as coarser, heavier backfill is added and compacted.

DRAINAGE

Relation to the Subgrade. The section on soils has indicated the need for adequate drainage as a means of stabilizing subgrades. Drainage is undoubtedly the most important single factor contributing to stability. The first prerequisite is to keep water away from the subgrade structure. This involves a system of ditches and culverts. Roadside and track ditches border the ballast section and pavement shoulder through cuts and level country to give immediate drainage to track or pavement. Intercepting ditches collect runoff before it reaches the subgrade. Culvert openings are necessary at intervals in the subgrade to conduct runoff and drainage channels to the other side. Figure 4-7 shows schematically these several drainage features.

Drainage Design. A design problem, basic and common to culverts and ditches, is to determine the cross-sectional area of ditch or culvert that will provide sufficient capacity for the quantity of flow that must be handled. Expressed mathematically, $Q_c = A \times v = Q_r$, where Q_c = capacity of channel or opening in cubic feet per second, A = cross-sectional area of opening or channel in square feet, and v = rate of flow in feet per second. From hydraulics, the Manning formula gives a value for flow velocity as $v = (1.486/n)R^{2/3}S^{1/2}$, where R = the hydraulic radius = area of the cross section divided by the wetted perimeter, S = slope in feet per foot, and n = coefficient of roughness varying from 0.02 for ordinary earth smoothly graded and for cor-

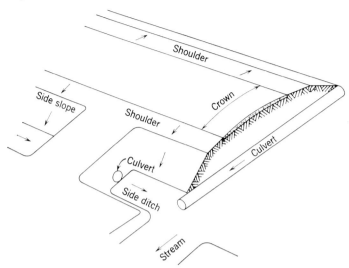

FIGURE 4-7a. Roadway drainage—surface water. (Courtesy of Eugene Y. Huang, *Manual of Current Practice for the Design, Construction, and Maintenance of Soil-Aggregate Roads,* Engineering Experiment Station, University of Illinois, Urbana, June 1959, p. 57, Figure 3.8.)

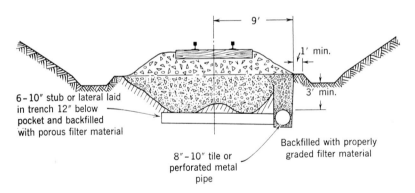

6 - 10″ stub or lateral laid
in trench 12″ below
pocket and backfilled
with porous filter material

9′

1′ min.

3′ min.

Backfilled with properly
graded filter material

8″ - 10″ tile or
perforated metal
pipe

FIGURE 4-7b. Roadway drainage—subsurface water.

rugated metal pipe to 0.016 for concrete paved and smooth tiled channels. An average value of 0.04 may be used for stream channels when other data are lacking and 0.06, for weed-grown ditches. The value of v, the velocity, should not exceed 10 fps in culvert pipes to prevent scour at the outlet and should preferably be no more than

4 to 6 fps. Concepts of critical flow from hydraulics lead to the equation of $S = 2.04/D^{\frac{1}{3}}$, where D is again the diameter of the pipe in inches and $S =$ slope in feet per foot $=$ that critical slope at which a pipe must be placed so that the water may be taken away without any backwater effect, the condition of maximum flow.[7] The pipe or channel capacity Q_c must, of course, be equal to the runoff Q_r, the amount of water coming from the drainage area. By assuming a value for A and determining corresponding values for S and v, the pipe capacity Q_c is determined and compared with Q_r. If the first comparison is not in close agreement, a second value for A is chosen, the choice being guided by the error in the first assumption.

The rational method of determining Q_r is based on the hydrology formula $Q_r = AIR$, where $Q_r =$ rate of runoff in cubic feet per second $= 1$ acre-in. per hour. $A =$ area of watershed or drainage area in acres, $I =$ intensity of rainfall in inches per hour for a selected storm of given duration and frequency (the maximum design storm, see Figure 4-8), and $R =$ the runoff factor. R is a difficult value to determine accurately, depending as it does on topography, vegetation, permeability and other soil characteristics, and extent of paved and built-up areas. It will vary from 0.10 to 0.15 for flat, vegetated, or gently rolling country, from 0.3 to 0.5 for built-up sections, from 0.8 to 0.9 for completely built-up sections or rocky, hilly, or mountainous areas, and will be 1.00 (or even more when snow is melting) for frozen ground. This formula has been further modified to account for the time of rainfall concentration at the culvert, that is, the time for maximum runoff to reach the opening. $Q_r = AIR/f$, where $f =$ a factor to compensate for surface slope, which in turn affects the time of concentration. For slopes of 0.50 percent or less, $f = 3.0$; for slopes between 0.5 and 1.0 percent, $f = 2.5$, and for slopes greater than 1.0 percent, $f = 2.0$.[8]

Empirical Formulas. Simple empirical formulas have also been developed to compute the quantity of runoff from a given area and/or the cross-sectional area of ditch or pipe to handle it. These formulas have been determined in local areas and given attempted universal application by introducing a variable coefficient to compensate for changes in topography. Rainfall and time of concentration

[7] *Handbook of Drainage and Construction Products*, W. H. Spindler, Editor, Armco Drainage and Metal Products, Middletown, Ohio, 1955, p. 215.
    [8] *Ibid.*, pp. 350–351.

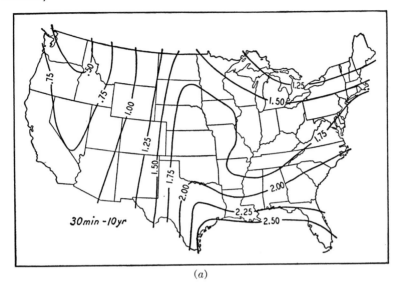

(a)

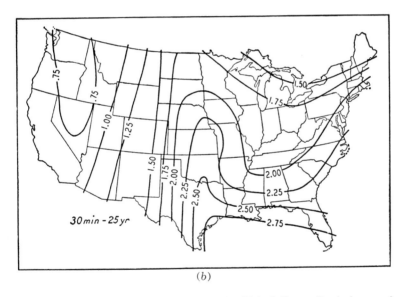

(b)

FIGURES 4-8 a and b. Rainfall intensity in the United States (typical examples of depths of precipitation of various durations): (a) 30-minute rainfall, in inches, to be expected once in 10 years; (b) 30-minute rainfall, in inches, to be expected once in 25 years. (Courtesy of C. O. Wisler and E. F. Brater, *Hydrology*, Second Edition, John Wiley and Sons, 1959, p. 90, Figures 33 and 34.)

are usually ignored. Such formulas are obviously inaccurate and should be used with caution and understanding.

Of the several empirical equations in use, the Talbot formula, developed in Central Illinois by A. N. Talbot, is widely used by railroads and highway departments for small areas requiring openings of 60 in. in diameter or less. It has a value of

$$A = c\sqrt[4]{A_d{}^3} \, ,$$

where A = area in square feet of required opening, A_d = drainage area in acres, and c = a coefficient having a value of 1 for steep rocky ground with abrupt slopes, $\frac{1}{2}$ for uneven valleys that are long in comparison with their width, $\frac{1}{3}$ for rolling agricultural country with a valley length three to four times the width, and $\frac{1}{5}$ for flat, level land. The required pipe diameter given by this equation is on the high side for small openings and thereby contributes to the safety of its use. Because the openings are small, the excess size does not constitute a severe economic handicap. More accurate methods are employed when openings exceeding 60 in. in diameter are contemplated.

Subdrainage. Soils that are kept excessively wet by subsurface flow, seepage, or percolation may require some form of subdrainage to lower the water table and dry out the soil. Large, flat areas, such as airfields, railroad yards, and parking lots, also benefit from drainage. A subdrain usually consists of tile laid with open joints or of perforated corrugated metal pipe laid in a ditch and backfilled with a porous, well-graded material (usually sand or gravel). The drain may be a short stub laid transversely under a railroad or highway embankment and discharging down the slope of the subgrade, a similar pipe in a cut draining into a longitudinal header, or a long header and series of stubs through a large, flat area. The success of the drain will depend on its location with respect to the water table, source of percolation or underground flow, or bottom of water or ballast pocket. The type of soil is also important. Impervious clays will not drain readily, and subdrainage is then useful primarily to drain pockets and intercept underground seepage. There must be sufficient fine material in the backfill grading to prevent fine-grained silts and clays from entering and clogging the drain. The water table may also be lowered by digging ditches to a depth below it alongside the subgrade and draining away moisture from the upper levels of the soil.

ROADWAY SUPERSTRUCTURES

Railroad Track. Railroad track is formed of parallel steel rails which bear and guide the flanged wheels of cars and locomotives. The rails are held to proper gage, 4 ft, 8½ in. in the United States (meter, 42 in., 5 ft, 0 in., 5 ft, 3 in., and 5 ft, 6 in. in various other countries), on timber cross ties. The rail is manufactured from open-hearth steel in 39-ft lengths (which just fit inside a 40-ft gondola for shipment) and is referred to by the weight per yard and the design of the cross section. Thus 132 RE rail weighs 132 lb per yard of rail length and was designed by the A.R.E.A.

Ties vary from 7 x 8 in. to 8 x 9 in. in cross section and from 8 to 9 ft in length (for 4 ft, 8½ in. gage). Ties are usually treated with a creosote-oil preservative to retard decay and insect attack and are protected with steel tie plates and rubber or fiber tie pads placed between the ties and the base of rail. The rails are secured end to end by bolted joint bars or by welding the ends together to form long continuous welded rails. Rails are held to the ties and tie plates by nail spikes, screw spikes, or spring clips. Thermal expansion and contraction of continuous welded rails is restrained by anchoring the rails to the ties and by the compression of spring clips.

The ballast section, in addition to distributing the wheel loads, must also anchor the track. The interlocking between the ballast particles and between the ballast and the ties serves to resist longitudinal and lateral movement of the track. Additional anchorage is obtained by filling the ballast section to the top, or nearly to the top, of the ties and by extending it 6 to 12 in. beyond the ends of the ties. A tie in crushed stone ballast offers a resistance to movement per rail of 500 to 800 lb.

Because of the close 19- to 24-in. spacing of the ties, the rail may be analyzed as a flexible continuously and elastically supported beam. The primary vertical deflections and bending moment relations are indicated in Figure 4-9. A wheel load applied at any point in the track structure causes a deflection of the rail and an upward reaction accompanied by a downward movement and compression of the ties and ballast immediately under and adjacent to the load. Beyond the point of load application, a reverse bending occurs in the rail, with downward components of force acting in the rail. In effect, the wheel continually runs uphill. The energy expended in compressing the track and pushing the reverse bending wave ahead of the wheel re-

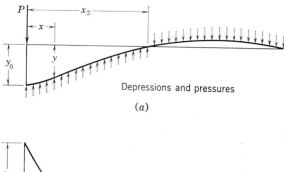

Depressions and pressures

(a)

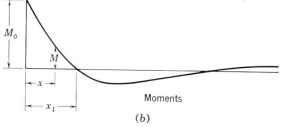

Moments

(b)

FIGURE 4-9. Deflection and bending.

duces by a small amount the energy available to accelerate the train and to haul payload.

With a constant proportionality factor u and the assumption of elastic, continuous support, the track depressions and upward pressures resulting from the applied wheel load P are proportional to each other, so that $p = uy$. See Figure 4-9a. The maximum deflection $P = uY$ occurs under the point of load application. The proportionality factor u is the modulus of track elasticity that depends upon the stiffness of rails, ties, ballast, and subgrade. It is the load-per-unit length of rail required to depress that unit length an equal unit distance. The value of u must be determined by test, assumed by comparison, or computed when other related factors are known. Typical u values as determined by the Special Committee on Stresses in Track are given in Table 4-2. The larger the value of u, the stiffer the track will be, with a corresponding reduction in track deflection, bending moment, and stress.

In developing this concept of an elastically supported continuous beam, the Special Committee followed the mathematical solution in Foppl's *Technische Mechanik*, Vol. III, pp. 254–266, 1900 edition.[9]

[9] Report of the Special Committee for Study of Track Stresses, A. N. Talbot, Chairman, First Progress Report, *Proceedings of the A.R.E.A.*, Vol. 19, 1918.

Table 4-2. Modulus of Track Elasticity (u) [a]

Rail	Ties	Track and Ballast	u
85 lb	7 x 9 in. x 8 ft-6 in. spaced 22 in. c to c	6-in. fine cinder ballast, in poor condition, on loam subgrade.	530
85 lb	7 x 9 in. x 8 ft-6 in. spaced 22 in. c to c	6-in. cinder ballast, in fair condition, on loam and clay subgrade.	750
85 lb	6 x 8 in. x 8 ft-0 in. spaced 22 in. c to c	6-in. limestone on loam and clay roadbed. Good before tamping.	970
85 lb	6 x 8 in. x 8 ft-0 in. spaced 22 in. c to c	6-in. limestone on loam and clay roadbed. After tamping.	1080
85 lb	7 x 9 in. x 8 ft-0 in.	12-in. limestone on loam and clay roadbed. Good before tamping.	1065
85 lb	7 x 9 in. x 8 ft-0 in.	12-in. limestone on loam and clay roadbed. After tamping.	1090
85 lb	7 x 9 in. x 8 ft-6 in. spaced 22 in. c to c	24-in. crushed limestone on loam and clay.	1200
130 lb RE	7 x 9 in. x 8 ft-6 in. spaced 22 in. c to c	24-in. gravel ballast plus 8 in. of heavy limestone on well-compacted roadbed.	2900–3000
110 lb RE	7 x 9 in. x 8 ft-0 in. spaced 22 in. c to c G.E.O. fastenings	Flint gravel ballast on wide, stable roadbed.	2500, 2600, 3600 average 2900
110 lb RE	7 x 9 in. x 8 ft-0 in. spaced 22 in. c to c G.E.O. fastenings	Limestone ballast on wide, stable roadbed.	3700, 5500, 6200 average 5100
Concrete roadbed			6000–7000

[a] First and Sixth Progress Reports of the Special Committee on Stresses in Railroad Track, *Proceedings of the American Railway Engineering Association*, Vol. 19, 1918, and Vol. 35, 1934, A.R.E.A., Chicago, Ill.

The following development summarizes portions of the solution. The first, second, third, and fourth derivatives of the elastic curve for a continuously supported beam are respectively proportional to (1) the slope of the elastic curve, (2) the bending moment, (3) the shear, and (4) the load intensity. The differential equation of equilibrium, from the fundamental condition is

$$EI(d^4y/dx^4) = uy$$

This differential equation is satisfied by the following equation:

$$y = (-P/\sqrt[4]{64EIu^3})\exp(-x\sqrt[4]{u/4EI})$$

$$\times (\cos x\sqrt[4]{u/4EI} + \sin x\sqrt[4]{u/4EI})$$

Special values developed from the several derivatives of the foregoing are $x_1 = (\pi/4)\sqrt[4]{4EI/u}$, where x_1 = distance from the wheel load to the point of zero bending moment in the rail $(M = 0)$, $M_0 = P\sqrt[4]{EI/64u} = 0.318Px_1$, where M_0 = maximum bending moment (at the wheel load where $x = 0$), $Y_0 = -P/\sqrt[4]{64EIu^3}$, where Y_0 = maximum deflection (also at the wheel load where $x = 0$), $P_0 = P\sqrt[4]{u/64EI} = -uY_0$, where P_0 = the maximum intensity of upward pressure (at the wheel load, $x = 0$), and finally the distance $x_2 = 3x_1$, where x_2 = the distance from the wheel load to the point of zero upward pressure on the rail $(p = 0)$. E = modulus of elasticity of steel, 30,000,000 psi; I = moment of intertia of the rail.

Dr. Talbot and his committee developed a useful tool for determining the effects of a wheel load by means of a master diagram. See Figure 4-10. From this diagram, values of x, y, and M can be computed at any distance from the wheel in terms of percent of maximum value. The diagram clearly illustrates how the effects of a single wheel load are distributed over several ties, both behind and in front of the wheel (a simplifying rule of thumb has assumed that a wheel load is distributed equally over three ties, the one under the load and the two adjacent). The combined effect of two or more adjacent wheels is determined by superposition, that is, by taking the alegebraic sum of moments and/or deflections of each wheel at any one x position.

A stiff rail contributes to the stiffness and stability of the total track structure. From the properties of steel beams, rail weight varies with the cross-sectional area; stiffness varies with the area also and therefore with the square of the weight. Also from beam properties, stiffness varies with the cube of the height. This has

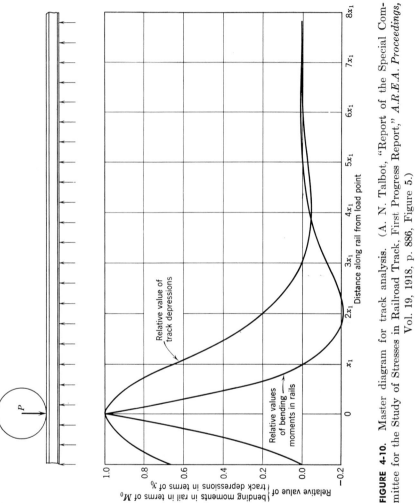

FIGURE 4-10. Master diagram for track analysis. (A. N. Talbot, "Report of the Special Committee for the Study of Stresses in Railroad Track, First Progress Report," *A.R.E.A. Proceedings,* Vol. 19, 1918, p. 886, Figure 5.)

tended to develop a high, girder type of rail for maximum stiffness with minimum steel. The measure of stiffness is the usual section modulus I/c, where I is the moment of inertia and c is the distance from the outer fiber (base of rail) to the neutral axis. The greater the value of I/c, the stiffer and stronger the rail. Dimensions and pertinent properties of the most frequently used rails are given in Table 4-3.

An initial step in rail design is to determine the allowable stress S in rail steel in pounds per square inch from the beam formula $S = M/(I/c)$, where M is the bending moment in inch-pounds, and c is in inches. The bending moment for the contemplated wheel load is computed on the basis of a design of rail and the stress is determined and compared with the allowable value. Allowable stress is based on the yield point of rail steel, usually taken as 60,000 psi. This initial allowable stress is generally reduced to 30,000 to 45,000 psi by allowing for such external factors as temperature stress in the rail, side-rod thrust (for steam locomotives), unbalanced superelevation, rail wear (especially on curves), and variations from the wheel-loading dia-

Table 4-3. Properties of Typical Rail Sections

Section	Weight per Yard (lb)	Moment of Inertia	Base to Neutral Axis (in.)	Section Modulus (base)	Area (sq in.)	Height (in.)	Base Width (in.)	Head Width (in.)
133 RE [a]	133.4	86.0	3.20	27.0	13.08	7 1/16	6	3
132 RE	132.1	88.2	3.20	27.6	12.95	7 1/8	6	3
131 RE	131.2	89.0	3.20	27.0	12.90	7 1/8	6	3
130 RE	130.0					6 3/4	6	2 15/16
120 RE [b]	120.9	67.6	2.92	23.1	11.85	6 1/2	5 3/4	2 7/8
115 RE	114.7	65.6	2.98	22.0	11.25	6 5/8	5 1/2	2 23/32
112 RE	112.3	65.5	3.00	21.8	11.01	6 5/8	5 1/2	2 23/32
110 RE [b]	110.4	57.0	2.83	20.1	10.82	6 1/4	5 1/2	2 25/32
100 RE	101.5	49.0	2.75	17.8	9.95	6	5 3/8	2 11/16
90 RA-A [c]	90.0	38.7	2.54	15.23	8.82	5 5/8	5 1/8	2 9/16
75 AS	75.2	23.0	2.36	10.0	7.38	4 13/16	4 13/16	2 15/32
119 CE&I [d]	118.8	71.4	3.12	22.9	11.65	6 13/16	5 1/2	2 21/32
106 CE&I	106.6	53.6	2.85	18.8	10.45	6 3/16	5 1/2	2 21/32
136 CE&I	136.2	94.9	3.35	28.3	13.35	7 9/16	6	2 15/16
155 PS [e]	155.0	129.0	3.38	36.7	15.20	8	6 3/4	3
152 PS	152.0	130.0	3.50	37.0	14.90	8	6 3/4	3
140 PS	140.6	97.0	3.37	29.0	13.80	7 9/16	6	3

[a] RE signifies American Railway Engineering Association design.
[b] Signifies not presently being rolled.
[c] RA signifies American Railway Association (forerunner of AAR) design.
[d] CE&I signifies Colorado Fuel & Iron design.
[e] PS signifies Pennsylvania Railroad design.

gram. The proposed wheel loading, rail design, and stiffness of ties and ballast are then considered with regard to the maximum allowable working stress. The final selection of rail and ballast is essentially an economic matter. Several conventional rail weights, for example, may be adequate for load support, but under conditions of dense, heavy traffic the heavier rail section, having a minimum of deflection, usually requires less track maintenance and affords a longer rail and tie life. The economies thus obtained often more than compensate for the cost of the greater quantity of steel in the heavier rail. However, there is no proven economy in substituting heavy rail for adequate rail support.

Safety and smooth riding require that rails be held to true alignment, gage, and surface. Irregularities in any of these factors produce shock, sway, and vibration which cause discomfort to passengers, damage to lading and equipment, and even derailment. Irregularities in any one of these three usually lead to irregularities in the others. Of the three, however, surface is the most important. Exact cross level must be maintained between the rails by good initial design and construction and by appropriately timed track-surfacing operations. The basic surfacing operation is tamping or packing ballast materials under the ties. This laborious task was once performed by hand with shovel, pick, or ballast fork. It is now largely carried out with powered mechanical tamping equipment.

Pavement. The term "pavement," as used in the first part of this chapter, refers to all of the superstructure between the subgrade proper and the wheel. Such a distinction is somewhat arbitrary, for the entire structure has the single purpose of bearing and distributing the load. The pavement, however, being in immediate support of the wheel, bears the greatest pressure intensities and must be designed for the purpose. The essential elements in the pavement are one or more bearing or subbase courses of broken stone or simply well-proportioned and compacted soils, with a wearing surface of soil, crushed stones with or without binder, or some form of concrete. Common usage frequently refers to the wearing surface alone as the "pavement." The wearing course gives a smooth-riding surface, waterproofs the subgrade and base courses, and protects the base courses from abrasion. See Figure 4-11. The heavier wearing surfaces, concrete for example, make a significant contribution to load distribution.

Pavements are often classified, according to the type of wearing

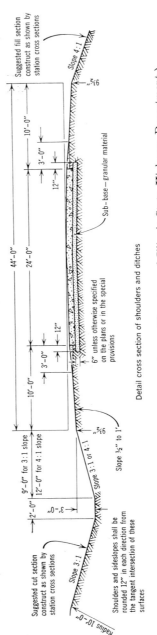

FIGURE 4-11a. Typical pavement cross sections. (Courtesy of Illinois State Highway Department.)

139

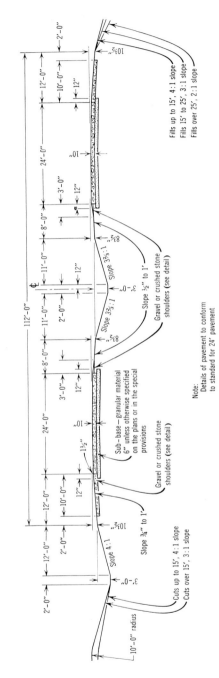

Standard design for dual portland cement concrete pavement with 40' depressed median
(Interstate highways)

FIGURE 4-11b. Typical pavement cross sections. (Courtesy of Illinois State Highway Department.)

surface, into two groups: *flexible,* including earth, gravel, macadam, and bituminous-surfaced roads, and *rigid,* composed principally of cement and asphaltic concretes, brick, and stone or wood block. The possible combinations of subgrade, base courses, and wearing surfaces are many, depending upon subgrade and pavement materials and bearing capacities, volume of traffic, wheel loadings, and climate. The final selection is usually that of the most economical grouping for the given conditions and materials available.

The section in this chapter entitled Action under Load has set forth principles that determine the thickness of flexible pavements. Lightly traveled roads, 50 vehicles or less per day, may have little or no pavement thickness but are merely given a high crown to facilitate drainage of the smoothed earth surface. Others have surfaces of untreated soil mixtures, gravel, or stone screenings and dust. Beyond 100 vehicles per day, dust nuisance and loss of wearing materials by abrasion and washboarding or corrugating of the surface, as well as the formation of ruts in wet weather, justify the use of some dust-laying and binder materials, such as calcium chloride, sodium, or bituminous oil.[10]   At traffic volumes of 200–300 vehicles per day, the addition of a base course, usually combined with some form of surface-bound treatment, is economically desirable. A road composed of soil materials mechanically blended together is referred to as mechanically or granularly stabilized. When the foregoing additives are present, the compound used often names the type of stabilization. Such roads must support the imposed loads without excessive deformation, resist wheel abrasion and corrugating, waterproof the subgrade and base course (if any), and yet have sufficient capillarity to maintain moisture for binding purposes. The quantities of sand, silt, and clay and other additives must be properly proportioned and controlled by tests for maximum stability.

Base courses, placed between the wearing surface and the subgrade, are strongly built to perform their function of bearing and distributing static and dynamic loads to the subgrade beneath. Such base courses may be one or more layers of sand, gravel, or crushed stone, varying in thickness, number, and combination. Treated base courses are formed by mixing the base-course materials with binder additives or preparing soil-cement mixtures by mechanical manipulation.

[10] American Road Builders' Association, Construction and Maintenance of Local Rural Roads, *Technical Bulletin No. 180,* Washington, D. C., 1951.

The *macadam* road is essentially one or more base layers of coarse, broken aggregates with a top dressing of finer particles, such as limestone screenings, formed into a hard-wearing surface by binding with water, limestone dust, or bitumens. These materials have been found suitable for traffic volumes up to 1000 vehicles per day.

Rigid-Surfaced Pavements. Heavy-duty rigid pavements include asphaltic concretes and Portland cement concretes. The asphaltic concretes consist of well-graded aggregates mixed either before, during, or after laying with bituminous oils. Strength is obtained by control of aggregate quality and number and thickness of base courses. Portland cement concrete may be laid directly on the rolled and compacted subgrade surface or placed as a wearing surface over one or more base courses. Asphaltic concrete may be similarly placed. Portland cement base courses are sometimes combined with asphaltic concrete wearing surfaces.

Portland cement concrete pavement is subject to a variety of stresses caused by the nature of concrete as a material. Concrete is high in compressive strength and low in tensile strength, with a resultant low beam or flexural strength. Concrete expands and contracts as it is wet or dry. Thus in curing or setting contraction occurs. It expands as temperature increases, contracts as temperature decreases. Often the stresses of temperature increases are offset by an opposite stress due to the drying effect.

Abrasive stress. Abrasive stress is caused by rolling wheels on the wearing surface. Although there is no reliable measure of abrasive stress, experience indicates a relation to compressive strength. Design usually calls for a compressive strength of 4000 to 4500 psi in 28 days, using a water-cement ratio of 6 gal. of water to 1 bag of cement. Abrasive stress is not considered a problem with modern pneumatic ties.

Direct compression and shear. These conditions result from wheel loads. Concrete pavement is resistive to relatively high compressive loads of 4000 to 8000 psi. Wheel loads are limited in many states to a maximum of 9000 lb, although a few states in the East permit as much as 11,200 lb. An average impact factor of 1.5 is commonly used in design, although the range is 1.25 to 2.00. Failures of highway slabs in direct shear and compression have been relatively few.

Compressive and tensile stresses. These stresses are caused by *flexure* of the pavement under wheel loads and are far more significant

than the foregoing. The term "rigid pavement" implies a resistance
to deflection or bending where subgrade support is inadequate.
Actually, bending and deflection do occur. In 1925 the late H. M.
Westergaard published the results of theoretical studies in which
he assumed that the slab acted as an elastic plate, elastically and
continuously supported by the subgrade.[11] He also assumed that
vertical subgrade reactions were directly proportional to the slab
deflections and were related to them by the modulus of subgrade reaction, k, expressed in pounds per square inch per inch of deflection.
(Note that Westergaard's k modulus differs from Talbot's modulus
of track elasticity u, in that u is expressed in pounds per inch
of track per inch of deflection, a linear rather than an area index.)
The subgrade modulus thus reflects both the stiffness of the subgrade
and stiffness of the slab.

Westergaard considered the effects of loads placed at three critical
positions on slabs of uniform thickness: the interior, the edge, and the
corner of the slab. For these slabs he found that the maximum unit
stress ocurred at the corners or edges rather than in the interior. He
established, empirically, a measure of the relative stiffness of the
slab in relation to that of the subgrade

$$l = \sqrt[4]{Et^3/[12(1 - u^2)k]} ,$$

where l = radius of relative stiffness in inches, t = slab thickness in
inches, E = modulus of elasticity of concrete in pounds per square
inch, usually taken as 5×10^6 psi, u = the Poisson ratio for concrete,
varying between 0.10 and 0.20 but usually taken in design as 0.15,
and k = subgrade modulus in pounds per square inch per inch of
deflection. The subgrade modulus can be determined by test-loading
a circular plate of 30-in. diameter. Values of k vary from 50 psi for
poor subgrades to 700 psi for very stiff subgrades. A value of 100 psi
for general use has been recommended by E. F. Kelley.[12]

Empirical formulas, modifying the Westergaard equations, have
been developed by the Bureau of Public Roads. Typical of these is
the following: $\sigma = (3P/t^3)[1 - (a\sqrt{2/l})^{1.2}]$, where σ = maximum
tensile stress in pounds per square inch produced by a load P at the
corner of the slab, P = load in pounds including an allowance for

[11] *Public Roads*, April 1926, and *Proceedings of the Highway Research Board*,
Part I, 1925.

[12] E. F. Kelley, Application of the Results of Research to the Structural Design
of Concrete Pavements, *Public Roads*, July and August 1939.

impact, t = slab thickness in inches, l = radius of relative stiffness in inches, and a = radius of area of load (tire deformation) in square inches. Westergaard's studies stand in the same relation to stresses in pavements and subgrades as Talbot's to stresses in railroad track.

An initial and overly simplified approach to the problem is found in the Older formula developed in 1920 by Clifford Older, then Chief Engineer of the Illinois State Highway Department. From observation of highway slab failures, Older observed that the corner of slab was the weakest point (an observation later confirmed by Westergaard's studies), as evidenced by corner cracks, usually on a 45-degree diagonal to the slab. See Figure 4-12. From the diagram we can see that M_e = the external bending moment caused by the wheel load W in pounds, x in. from the point of failure, and tends to produce cracking. M_e is resisted by the internal moment, $M_i = SI/c$, where, for the rectangular section along the face of the crack, I = moment of inertia = $bd^3/12$, $b = 2x$, and $d = t$, the slab thickness in inches. Thus $I = 2xt^3/12$. Equating M_e to M_i, $Wx = S(2xt^3)/t/2$, where S = the allowable flexural stress in concrete in pounds per square inch. Solving for the slab thickness, $t = \sqrt{3W/S}$. For static loading, S may have a value of 600 to 700 psi. Fatigue failure frequently occurs at a much lower stress because of repeated flexure under repetitively applied loads. A value of S not exceeding 350 psi is therefore recommended.

Slabs are not usually found in a free condition, that is, without additional support. Subgrade support and support from neighboring

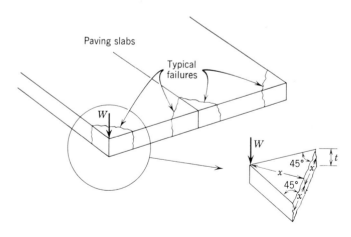

FIGURE 4-12. Older formula.

slabs can be expected. When slabs are connected end to end by reinforcing dowels, one third of the load is assumed to be carried by the adjoining slab so that $t = \sqrt{2W/S}$. When transverse reinforcing transfers some of the load laterally to adjacent slabs, the interior thickness is taken as $t_i = \sqrt{1.33W/S}$.

Because the foregoing does not take subgrade bearing capacity into account, the Older formulas are likely to give pavement too thick for the heavy wheel loads of trucks or airplanes. The Portland Cement Association has proposed empirical modifications that give results closely approximating those of Westergaard's more complicated equations. When the corner load is transferred by reinforcing dowels to the next slab, $t = \sqrt{1.92WC/S}$, and when there is no load transfer $t = \sqrt{2.4WC/S}$. The coefficient C relates the thickness to the bearing capacity of the soil in pounds per square inch. See Figure 4-13.*

Compressive stresses. Compressive stresses arise from contraction in the cooling and drying processes as concrete sets. Contraction in the slab is resisted by frictional contact with the subgrade, and cracks occur. Goldbeck equated these forces in the equation $L \times W_s \times b \times f = 12btS + S_aEs/E_c$ (see Figure 4-14), where W_s = weight of slab in pounds per square foot of slab area, S = allowable tensile stress in concrete in pounds per square inch, usually taken as 350 psi, f = coefficient of friction between slab and subgrade with an average value of 2.0, b = breadth of slab in feet, L = slab length in feet, E_s = modulus of elasticity of reinforcing steel = 30×10^6, E_c =

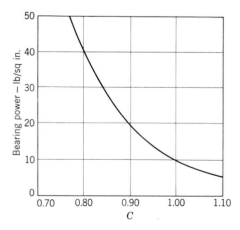

FIGURE 4-13. Relation between C and bearing capacity. (Courtesy of Portland Cement Association.)

*In the current edition of *Concrete Pavement Design,* published by the Portland Cement Association, the recommended design procedure utilizes Dr. Pickett's semi-empirical formulas for pavement stress.

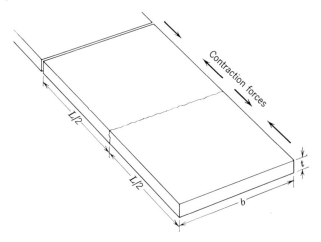

FIGURE 4-14. Resistance to contraction of a pavement slab.

modulus of elasticity of concrete $= 5 \times 10^6$, and $E_s/E_c = 6$ (approximately). Also, $a =$ cross-sectional area of reinforcing steel in square inches, and $S =$ working stress in reinforcing steel, 20,000 psi being an average value. Use of the Goldbeck formula indicates that cracks will occur on the average about every 30 ft of pavement length. Such cracks can be anticipated by introducing contraction joints at 20- to 35-ft intervals. Some designers permit the cracks to occur naturally, thus forming approximately 30-ft slabs and then filling the cracks as they open with asphaltic compounds. However, one body of opinion holds that contraction joints are necessary to prevent blow-ups caused by direct compressive stress.

Thermal, tensile, and compressive stresses. These stresses, due to changes in temperature, cause variations in slab length and longitudinal movement of the slab relative to the subgrade. Cracks will ensue unless provision is made for expansion and contraction joints. Such thermal joints are usually spaced every 90 to 100 ft, a multiple of contraction-joint spacing, replacing the contraction joints at those locations.

Studies made with continuous steel reinforcing have shown that only 500 to 1000 ft at each end of a long slab move over the subgrade with changes in temperature and with no movement of intervening slab. The end portions have thus developed enough frictional resistance with the subgrade to restrain the central portion. This is similar to the way continuous welded rail is restrained against temperature stresses by anchoring the rail through cross ties to the ballast.

More serious than longitudinal expansion and contraction is the warping or curling about a longitudinal axis as the upper and lower surfaces of the slab warm and cool. As the sun heats the upper surface, there is a tendency for the outer edges to curl downward because of the cooler shrinking effect of the underside of the slab working in conjunction with the warm and expanding upper surface. The opposite effect occurs at night when the base courses and underside may be warmer than the upper surface. Temperature differentials caused by changing seasons produce similar effects in which the underside of the slab changes its temperature more slowly than the upper. Thermal stresses may be as high as 200 psi. Compensation is afforded by thickened edges on the slab, which react less to temperature stresses, thus giving rise to 9-7½-9-, 10-7½-10-, 8-6½-8-in., etc., thickness of interiors and edges of slabs for various classes of highways. Longitudinal joints also aid in relieving thermal stresses. Westergaard developed empirical formulas, not reproduced here, setting forth temperature-warping stresses at edges and interiors of slabs.

Lanes. Two-lane pavements, 9 to 11 ft wide, were conventional good design a few years ago. Shoulders had minimum widths of 6 ft. Intersections with other highways were at grade and were protected by lights, signs, or the driver's own caution. Today's standards for safe, high-capacity, high-speed highways require separated roadways for movement in each direction, usually with two lanes per direction. Grade separations prevent cross interference of traffic at intersections and junctions. Lane widths should not exceed a maximum of 12 ft. Wider lanes give a false impression of three lanes where there are only two, with unfavorable effects upon safety. The roadways are separated by median strips high enough or wide enough to prevent a misdirected vehicle from entering the opposing lane.

WATERWAYS

Natural Waterways. Natural waterways—lakes, seas, and rivers— sometimes serve as established by nature. Usually, however, such natural waterways, especially rivers, cannot be used consistently without considerable development and maintenance effort. To provide and maintain navigable depths and widths, the engineer must resort to direct blasting and excavation, to dredging with bucket or suction dredges, or to confining and concentrating the flow to provide higher velocities, thereby making a channel self-flushing or self-scouring. Rivers young in geologic time have steep gradients and swift currents. Navigation depth is secured by means of dams impounding slack-water pools. The older, meandering streams flow slowly but are subject to silting and sandbar formation as well as change of channel.

Primary channel requirements for barge operations were set forth by Act of Congress, May 15, 1928, as 300 ft of width and 9 ft of depth. The Act of December 22, 1944, revised the depth to 12 ft for the Mississippi River. The characteristic profile of erosive, slow-flowing, nontidal rivers (the best for navigation purposes) is that of a series of pools and bars. The deep pools usually occur at bends where crossing bars have accumulated and act as small dams. See Figure 4-15.

In periods of high water flow across the bars of the open stream is usually sufficient for the required depth for navigation. At times of low water only the pools furnish the necessary depth. Channels can be dredged through the crossing bars, but the operation must be repeated frequently because the bars are soon reformed by silting. The practice of channel regulation in the United States is based on the theory of making the flow of the rivers accomplish as much of the regulation as possible. In this instance the design aims at confining most of the flow to a single, narrowed channel. This increases the flow velocity and the scour to a level that is sufficient to keep

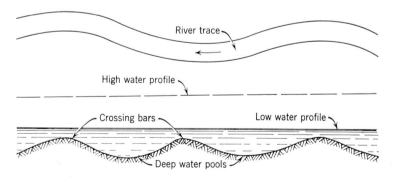

FIGURE 4-15. Profile and trace of a slow-moving river.

the channel open without disturbing the low-level, pool-crossing bar (which provides minimum low-water navigation depth) or the cross section of channel at high water. Within these limits, no more than 3 ft of additional depth are usually obtained at the bars. Contraction of the silted channel is usually accomplished with spur dikes. See Figure 4-16. The velocity increase must not be great enough to interfere with navigation. The current should not exceed 4 mph for uncanalized rivers, and the increase in flow velocity should stay within this range. Such rates of flow will possibly be exceeded for short periods in flood stages and require a suspension of river traffic.

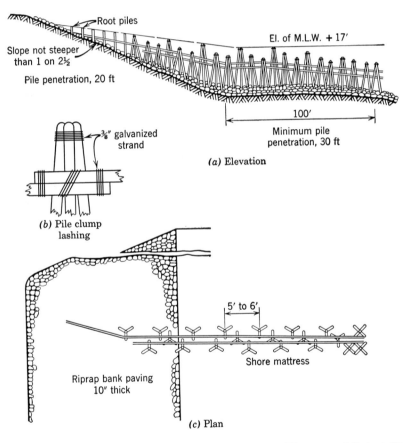

FIGURE 4-16. Spur dikes for self-regulation of rivers. (Courtesy of Robert W. Abbett, editor, *American Civil Engineering Practice*, Vol. II, John Wiley and Sons, 1956, p. 15-105, Figure 44.)

Another problem of regulation is the guiding of the current to provide a sinuous rather than a straight trace or alignment over long reaches. The straight alignment, in the absence of training works, may afford an unstable location. Stability of trace is obtained by the use of training dikes and jetties. Side channels and sloughs are closed by pike dikes that cause sedimentation and damming of the unwanted channels by silt carried in the river's flow. Channel widening may be required at bends of sharp curvature because of the difficulty of steering the rigid type of United States' tow around it. Such curvature must permit maximum discharge during flood conditions as well as navigation during normal and low-water periods. Both requirements are met by placing spirals at the ends of the circular curves that form the main trace of the curve. Spirals based on the cubic parabola (similar to railroad spirals) are used. These spirals are only approximately accurate from the standpoint of geometry. Design is frequently accomplished by drawing a curve section to scale and maneuvering scale models of tows on them in passing positions.

Other regulatory and maintenance works include revetments for bank protection, levees to protect shoreline communities in times of flood, dredging, and the removal of snags.

Canalized Rivers. When sufficient depth of flow is not otherwise obtainable throughout the year, resort can be made to storage reservoirs to provide artificial pools and slack-water navigation. Such canalization increases silting and a loss of valley storage, interferes with local land drainage, and causes increased and heavy evaporation from the larger surfaces of slack-water pools. The design of navigation dams is outside the scope of this book, but basic requirements and principal navigation features should be noted.

There are two significant requirements for a lock and dam design: (a) there must be provision for the passage of floods without increasing flood height by impounded back water, and (b) the ability to transport sediment delivered by tributaries must not be impaired; otherwise silting, dredging, or both will become excessive.[13]

The requirements for an economical warrant are rivers that are natural routes for water-borne commerce and that possess permanent

[13] James H. Stratton, Canalized Rivers and Lock Canals, Section 15, River Engineering, Abbett's *American Civil Engineering Practice*, Vol. II, John Wiley and Sons, New York, 1956, p. 15-148.

beds and banks. Rivers with a heavy bedload movement, as indicated by meandering, bank caving, and bar-building activity, and rivers with steep gradients are usually not suited physically or economically for conversion into canalized waterways.

The dams used in canalized waterways are the weir type that permits flow over crest or sill. These dams are further classified as navigable and non-navigable. In times of highwater the navigable dam can be lowered to permit movement over its crest or sills. See Figure 4-17. It is used where flow is of sufficient volume to permit open-river navigation for long periods each year. Non-navigable dams may have either a fixed crest or a movable crest of the taintor or roller type. See Figure 4-18. The non-navigable, movable-crest dam has gained preference in the United States because with it a nearly constant pool level can be maintained. This is advantageous to real estate, industrial, and other development along the shore. Taintor gates are simple and effective and are most frequently used today for non-navigable dams. The roller gate can discharge water either underneath or over the top. It is useful in skimming ice and debris with a minimum of water loss.

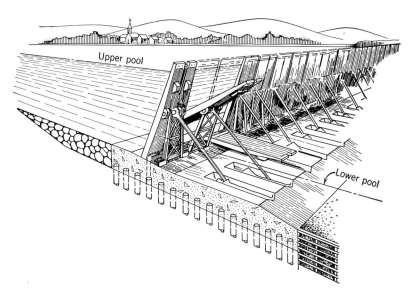

FIGURE 4-17. Navigable-type dam. (Courtesy of Robert W. Abbett, editor, *American Civil Engineering Practice*, Vol. II, John Wiley and Sons, 1956, p. 15-150, Figure 68.)

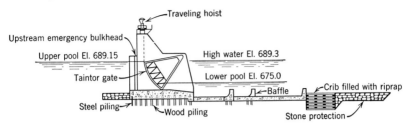

FIGURE 4-18. Movable-crest dam. (Courtesy of Robert W. Abbett, editor, *American Civil Engineering Practice*, Vol. II, John Wiley and Sons, 1956, p. 15-152, Figure 71.)

A necessary requisite of dams is a stable foundation. Protection against piping caused by erosion must be provided, and a cutoff wall or baffle is required to prevent seepage flow under the dam. Very extensive subsoil explorations are warranted.

Navigation Locks. Locks are used to overcome elevation, whether in artificial or man-made canals, around falls and rapids in open rivers, or to change from one pool to another in combination with non-navigable dams. Shipping is raised or lowered over the obstructing crest and elevation in a rectangular compartment having a movable gate at each end. For upstream locking, a vessel enters the chamber through the open downstream gates. The downstream gates are then closed behind it, and water from the upper pool is allowed to flow into the lock chamber. When the chamber water level has risen to the upper pool level, the upstream gates are opened, and the vessel proceeds on its way. A downstream movement occurs in reverse order of the upstream move.

Locks are constructed of concrete, bedrock, or steel sheet piling, with earth or rock backfill. Unless underlain with bedrock, a floor is necessary to prevent erosion from the turbulence of emptying and filling the chamber. The problem of chamber-wall design is similar to that of dams and retaining walls and is outside the scope of this book. Lock gates are of timber, steel, or concrete and of miter, rolling, sector, or vertical-lift design. See Figure 4-19.

The lock chambers are filled and emptied through culverts in the walls with valve control over the culvert flow. Ports must be placed both for upstream and downstream movement. Taintor, cylindrical, and butterfly valves are used for control.

Rapid emptying and filling of the lock chamber is desirable to

FIGURE 4-19. Features of a lock chamber, showing miter gates and flooding ports of lock culvert lateral system during construction of Markland Locks, Warsaw, Kentucky. (Courtesy of Dravo Corporation, Pittsburgh, Pennsylvania.)

speed movement through the locks. However, a flow that is too rapid, especially at the start of the operation, causes unfavorable turbulence both in chamber and pool. If the chamber is filled too rapidly for an upstream movement, it may cause sufficient drawdown of the upper pool level to allow shipping to touch bottom. Too heavy a downstream surge may seriously reduce vertical clearances under bridges and other overhead obstructions. Either situation may also contribute to bank erosion.

The chamber design must include means of securing the vessels by cables to minimize their movement in the swirling turbulence and reduce damage to vessel and chamber. The pull on river-barge mooring cables may vary between 2000 lb for small vessels and 5500 lb or more for large ones. Many variations in culvert design, location, and control have been devised to reduce chamber turbulence. Some designs place ports in the base of the walls, others in the floors, and still others use a combination. The 1200-ft Chain of Rocks locks in the Mississippi River above St. Louis can be filled safely in $7\frac{1}{2}$ minutes.

Lock-chamber dimensions are determined largely by the size of vessels to be locked but are also partly determined by the trace of the stream. The lock chamber and land-side guide wall should be in a straight line. (The river wall is extended only on the upstream side to prevent vessels from going over the dam or through the rough water being circumnavigated.) Long locks and land walls are difficult to place when the river has considerable sharp curvature.

The usual size of Mississippi River system locks has been 110 x 600 ft. These dimensions are no longer acceptable for modern design of floating equipment. Tows may consist of 6 to 20 barges, varying in size from 25 x 175 ft, with 10 ft of draft, to 48 x 280 ft, with 11 ft of draft. The 1200-ft lock is becoming the standard wherever conditions permit. On the Great Lakes the size of bulk-cargo freighters governs. These ships may be as long as 730 ft. At the Soo the MacArthur Lock, largest and most recently built (1949), is 800 ft long, 80 ft wide, 31 ft deep, and has a lift of 21 ft. Its cost was 14 million dollars. The Davis and Sabin locks are both 1350 ft long and 80 ft wide but have depths of only 23.1 ft.

Man-Made Canals. Man-made canals are two general types: (a) those connecting bodies of water at approximately the same elevation throughout and (b) those which must overcome elevation in their course and for which locks must be used as described above. Vessels move through canals under their own power or are pulled by a horse, mule, or electric locomotive on a towpath or track alongside the canal. Electric locomotives supplement ships' power in the Panama Canal. Ships use their own power exclusively at the Soo.

Embankment materials must not permit excessive leakage or percolation of water from the channel. Part of the slope may be the levee type, composed of soil excavated from the canal bed. The embankment or levee for a canal, as for a river, is built much as an earth dam with an impervious core of fine-grained soils topped on the slopes with coarser materials to resist wave wash.

A principal problem in canal design and location is that of obtaining and holding water to float the vessels. In a constant-level design water may flow in from both directions from the bodies of water being joined. Water may also be obtained for any type of canal by tapping parallel rivers or lakes with connecting channels (as has been done for the New York State Barge Canal), by drawing on streams flowing transversely to the canal, or, if sources of this kind are not available, by building storage reservoirs from which the canal can be supplied. Gatun Dam in the Panama Canal system fulfills this function. Pumping, except for very small channels, is usually an uneconomical method of supplying canals. Economy in initial construction and water supply can sometimes be obtained by using existing stream channels for part of the canal. This economy may prove illusory, for floods or low water may sometimes render the system unnavigable. Contact with adjacent streams might better be avoided except as water is drawn under control to fill the artificial channel. Natural watercourses may be bypassed by damming and diverting their flow, by crossing their courses on bridges, or, for small streams, by siphoning the flow under the canal bed.

QUESTIONS FOR STUDY

1. Using the cone theory of wheel-load distribution, determine the bearing capacity of a soil to support a wheel load of 6000 lb, transmitted by a 32 x 6 in. pneumatic tire through a 6-in. pavement.

2. Discuss the basic errors in the cone theory of wheel-load distribution and show how these errors have been compensated for in the equations developed for heavy truck and airplane wheel loadings.

3. What thickness of flexible pavement would be necessary for an airplane runway designed for a gross weight of 60,000 lb, using 17.00 x 18 in. tires, inflation pressure of 65 psi, laid on a subgrade with a bearing capacity of 45 psi?

4. Given an axle load of 60,000 lb and 21-in. spacing of 7 x 8 in. x 8 ft, 6 in. ties, what depth of ballast would be required to give a uniform distribution of pressure to the subgrade?

5. (a) Describe the characteristics of an ideal soil for subgrade purposes. (b) To what extent does such an ideal soil occur in nature?

6. What can be done to compensate for the deficiencies of a soil in using it for subgrade construction?

7. In what way are the problems of subgrade and canalway design and construction similar? Dissimilar?

8. What are the difficulties and possible sources of error in determining the size of drainage openings by use of the rational method? What are the advantages and the dangers of using an empirical equation for the same purpose?

9. Find the percent of maximum allowable bending stress developed at 50 and at 90 mph in a 115-lb RE rail, laid in track having a modulus of track elasticity of 2800. *Note:* a rule of thumb for dynamic loading is to increase static load one percent per mile per hour.

10. Given a subgrade with a bearing capacity of 40 psi, determine the required thickness of concrete pavement to support a wheel load of 9000 lb (a) without reinforcing dowels and (b) with reinforcing dowels.

SUGGESTED READINGS

1. Karl Terzaghi and R. B. Peck, *Soils Mechanics in Engineering Practice,* John Wiley and Sons, New York, 1948, pp. 372–406.

2. H. O. Sharp, G. R. Shaw, and J. A. Dunlop, *Airport Engineering,* John Wiley and Sons, New York, 1948, Chapters VIII and IX, pp. 63–110.

3. L. I. Hewes and C. H. Oglesby, *Highway Engineering,* John Wiley and Sons, New York, 1954, Chapters 12–18.

4. W. W. Hay, *Railroad Engineering,* Vol. I, Part Two, John Wiley and Sons, New York, 1953.

5. *Handbook of Drainage and Construction Products,* Armco Drainage and Metal Products, Middletown, Ohio, 1955, Sections VI, VII, and VIII, pp. 195–379.

6. *Concrete Pavement Design,* Portland Cement Association, Chicago, Illinois, 1951.

7. Eugene Y. Huang, *Manual of Current Practice for the Design, Construction, and Maintenance of Soil-Aggregate Roads,* Engineering Experiment Station, University of Illinois, Division of Highways, State of Illinois, and Bureau of Public Roads, U. S. Department of Commerce, Urbana.

8. N. M. Newmark, *Influence Charts for Computation of Stresses in Elastic*

Foundations, Engineering Experiment Station, Bulletin Series No. 338, University of Illinois, Urbana, May 1951.

9. Reports of the Special Committee for the Study of Track Stresses, *A.R.E.A. Proceedings, First Progress Report,* Vol. 19, 1918, *Second Progress Report,* Vol. 21, 1920.

10. H. M. Westergaard, Stresses in Concrete Pavements Computed by Theoretical Analysis, *Public Roads,* Vol. 7, No. 2, April 1926.

11. H. M. Westergaard, Analytical Tools for Judging Results of Structural Tests of Concrete Pavements, *Public Roads,* Vol. 14, No. 10, December 1933.

CHAPTER 5

TECHNOLOGICAL
CHARACTERISTICS

Inherent Advantages. Each carrier type has closely interrelated technological and economic characteristics which bring both advantages and disadvantages to its operation. The combination gives each carrier a particular field of usefulness. Outside that field, its usefulness may be marginal. The marginal carrier may remain in a particular kind of traffic because of the over-all demand for transportation (as in time of war, in a rapidly expanding economy, or when no other transport is available) or through special support from some form of government subsidy or regulatory restriction on competitors.

An efficient domestic or international system of transportation will permit and encourage the utilization of inherent advantages to the utmost. This is the declared policy of the United States Government, as stated in the Transportation Act of 1940. This amendment to the Interstate Commerce Act declares it to be the national transportation policy of the Congress:

To provide fair and impartial regulation of all modes of transportation so administered as to preserve the inherent advantages of each; to promote safe, adequate, economical and efficient service and foster sound economic conditions in transportation and among the several carriers; and to encourage the establishment of reasonable charges without unjust discrimination or unfair or destructive competitive practices.

Often the advantages of each carrier type are best realized in combination with those of other types. The full advantages of waterborne bulk-cargo carriers can be realized, for example, only in combination with a coordinated system of land transportation. Problems of adequate coordination and integration among transport agencies and facilities are considered later. This chapter, and those that follow, presents technological characteristics common to all or nearly all types of transport. These include units of carriage, buoyancy and stability, guidability and maneuverability, propulsive resistance, propulsive force, and the effects of curvature, grades, and elevation. Certain technological characteristics are reflected in carrier capacity and in the operational and economic aspects of transport. All are combined and interrelated in the planning and location of systems of transport.

Technological Classification. In Chapter 3 transportation agencies were classified in the conventional way as railroads, highways, airways, waterways, and pipelines. A different classification, which indicates something of the transportation potential of the carrier, is the unit of carriage. In Chapter 12 a relation is pointed out between the following groupings and the costs each type incurs.

Single units. This type of transport combines motive power (propulsion) and cargo space in one unit. The single-unit group includes automobiles, trucks, buses, aircraft, ships, rail cars (both double- and monorail), street cars, interurban cars, and rail-diesel cars when operated as separate units. Single-carriage cable cars might also be included.

Assembled or multiple units. The assembled or multiple unit system of transport has a separate motive-power unit which propels two or more cargo-carrying units. Railroads best exemplify this group. One locomotive hauls a few or a number of cars, as the volume of traffic requires. Towboat operation on inland rivers of the United States is similar. A tow may consist of 1 to 20 barges which are set out and picked up by the towboat (usually a pusher or ram type) at various points along the route. Aerial tramways, whose cars may be added or taken off at will, have some of the characteristics of assembled or multiple units. Multiple-unit trains, composed of conventional multiple-unit (MU) cars, of the more recent rail-diesel cars (RDC), or of other types of cars in commuting, rapid-transit, or branch-line service, combine elements of the single- and multiple-unit systems. Usually, with multiple-unit operation, one car is motored and pulls an unmotored trailer, but cars may be combined into trains of as many units as traffic requires. A highway tractor-trailer combination also combines elements of both groups. Normally there is only one trailer, but it is separate from the motive-power unit (the tractor) and can be set out and picked up at will. Thus one tractor can keep several trailers in short-haul operation. Also, tests are being conducted in the operation of so-called double bottoms, that is, two trailers hauled by one tractor.

Continuous-flow or stationary-propulsion systems. A third category includes those systems in which the transport "roadway" channels and guides the traffic as the propulsive force is supplied by one or several intermediate and stationary power sources. In pipeline operation the cargo moves, but the pumping units and pipelines remain fixed. In conveyors and moving sidewalks the belt moves, but again the prime mover is stationary. The propulsive unit for an aerial tramway is also fixed. Freight moved by a continuous-flow system requires no packaging or stowing (as presently operated) but may require positioning (the cargo must be centered on the conveyor belt) or processing (coal must be pulverized and placed in suspension for pipeline transport). The loading and unloading of the system is usually done without manual labor, that is, by means of a valve or a tripper and chute.

From the foregoing it is evident that the single-unit carriers have characteristics especially adaptable to moving small quantities of packaged goods, that multiple-unit systems can move either packaged or bulk products, and that continuous-flow carriers are especially suited to raw products in bulk quantities. All of these systems, except pipelines, find some adaptation to the transportation of human beings.

GUIDANCE AND MANEUVERABILITY

A technological characteristic that vitally affects the safety, reliability, and flexibility of a carrier is the way in which it is guided and the degree of maneuverability it permits.

Closed-System Guidance. Pipelines, conveyors, and moving sidewalks offer a confining roadway that prevents departure from the intended route or interference with other traffic. The adherence to route is independent of weather, and complete guidance is inherent in the system. The system offers, however, a minimum of flexibility. Special and often expensive installations are necessary to effect the discharge, loading, or transfer of traffic for pipelines and conveyors.

Rail-Flange Guidance. Railroad trains and rail cars of all types are guided by a flanged wheel bearing against a steel rail. The flange may project no more than an inch beyond the tread of the wheel, but, combined with vehicle weight and a smooth track, it gives complete safety in guidance with no dependence upon human effort. The vehicle cannot be blown or drift off course or become lost regardless of weather. Inclined planes, skips, elevators, monorail systems, and some types of cableways use similar guidance, usually with a double flange on the wheel. In a few situations the flange is on the rail and a flangeless wheel runs in a groove or channel. Rail-flange guidance definitely limits flexibility. The vehicle can go only where a track has been laid in advance. Switches, often in complicated systems, are necessary to divert trains from one track to another. However, the ubiquity of tracks and turnouts makes rail flexibility relatively good.

Roadway-Driver Guidance. Highways and airport runways (airplanes in the air are in a different category) offer a smooth, regular surface which indicates the route to follow and on which the vehicles travel. However, the driver or pilot must steer the vehicle continuously to keep it on that route and to avoid contact with other vehicles. There is little possibility of losing the way unless heavy storms reduce visibility to zero or the way becomes obliterated by drifting snow or sand. This does not mean that the driver cannot make a wrong turn at times! Guidance of highway vehicles by electronics, in which the vehicle would be held to a proper position on the roadway by inductive coupling to a cable laid down the center of the highway lane, has been proposed. Guidance would be similar to that given by the automatic pilot and radio beam of an airplane in flight. The possibilities of such a device are intriguing, and experimental installations have already been made.

Great flexibility is obtained with roadway-driver guidance because of the many highways, roads, lanes, streets, and alleys on which highway vehicles can be operated. Almost every community and building in each community can be reached by highway vehicles. Trucks can drive directly into a farmer's fields or to a contractor's job. Flexibility which enables vehicles to pass and go around each other at will also exists on the highways.

The hazards of this type of guidance are obvious. Any lack of skill or a moment's inattention on the part of the driver can spell disaster. In passing or overtaking, the drivers of both vehicles must be fully alert to prevent vehicle conflict. The human element bears the full responsibility.

Limiting Waterways. Narrow, confining waterways are found in canals and rivers of limited width. There is little possibility of losing

FIGURE 5-1. A river tow. (Towboat *Humphrey* with 11-barge coal tow; 1600-hp, 132-ft towboat built by Dravo Corporation, Pittsburgh, Pennsylvania, for Consolidated Coal Co.)

the way, but pilotage, a human element, is nevertheless required to prevent straying from the channel, running into sandbars or embankments, or colliding with other vessels. Canals operated by canalside or towpath haulage are restricted in direction without human aid.

In a river tow barges and towboats are lashed together in a single, more or less rigid unit (see Figure 5-1), in which the towboat actually pushes the barges instead of "towing." (Towboats are, in fact, sometimes referred to as "rams" or "pushers.") The towboat's rudder and manipulation of its propellers steers the entire combination. An attempt to pull a string of barges against variable river currents and around sharp bends in rivers and channels would end in disaster, possibly with the barges piled on the outer bank of the curve. By securing all the units in a single mass, the pilot has complete control over the entire combination. True towing, with the barges strung out behind, is usually attempted in the United States only in open water or in sea-level intracoastal waterways where currents are less dangerous. Considerable true towing is performed on European rivers but without the many barge units that are combined into the rigid type of "tow" employed in the United States.

Open Waterways. Lakes, oceans, and wide rivers offer no guidance to vessels. Constant pilotage must be observed to keep vessels on course and to avoid contact with obstacles and other vessels. Flexibility of direction is unlimited, but adequate harbors must be available for vessels to reach shore in safety.

Guidance of vessels during storms, when changing course, or when in harbor and in other restricted areas is provided by a helmsman in the wheelhouse. In very small vessels and in older sailing ships the rudder may be controlled directly by hand or by ropes or cables running from the wheel to the rudder post. In most ships of commercial size a small wheel is used to control a powered device that actually moves the rudder. When on course in calm water, the responsibility for guidance can be delegated to an automatic pilot, which guides the ship automatically, once a course is set, by control of a gyroscopic compass. Large ships have sufficient flexibility of guidance for open water. In harbors and narrow channels their extreme bulk and mass make guidance difficult, especially when the unfavorable tides and currents found in many harbors are encountered. Tugs are usually necessary to effect a safe berthing or putting out. In storms or foggy weather radar plus traffic regulations aid the helmsman to direct the ship.

Airways. Airways offer the same problems as open waterways with the additional requirement of guidance in three dimensions. (This requirement is also present for submarines in open waterways.) Aircraft are maneuvered or guided by movable surfaces—the ailerons, rudder, and elevators. Retractable flaps are also used to increase wing area at the slower speeds of take-off and landing. Airplanes can be flown and guided, like ships, with an automatic pilot, but human guidance is usually required in take-off and landing and under adverse weather conditions. An aid in guiding the plane is the radio beam (in various types) which establishes both a sonic and visual (on the instrument panel) indication of proximity to the established route.

Aircraft offer considerable flexibility in direction (although restrained by air traffic regulations), but adequate, smooth landing fields are mandatory. Helicopters overcome this difficulty to a considerable degree, as do experimental models of more conventional types of planes, which rise or land vertically on their tails but level off in full flight.

The guidance of aircraft, rockets, and other missile types by remote control through radio is a familiar event today. The reader should realize that the possibility therefore exists of extending that type of control to all other carriers—to trains, ships, trucks, and automobiles. One railroad already has a radio-controlled locomotive for trimming purposes in one of its large yards. The need has only to become sufficiently pressing for such operations to become commonplace.

BUOYANCY AND STABILITY

Buoyancy and stability are problems that primarily affect waterway and airway carriers. Early monorail designs introduced problems of stability by trying to balance the car on one rail with the aid of a gyroscope. More recent types have used a suspended-car design with enough over-all rigidity to prevent excessive side sway. The problem has not been entirely solved. Cableways may be forced to halt operations when high winds cause excessive swaying of the cables and cars. Stability also enters into questions of riding comfort and safety for railroad cars and highway vehicles on curves at high speeds (and also on tangents) and is a factor to be considered in designing the correct superelevation for the outside of a highway curve or railroad track. However, these are refinements compared to the importance of stability in ship and aircraft design.

Ship's Buoyance. Trains and automotive vehicles are supported by a substantial pavement or track and subgrade. Airplanes and ships must find support in fluid and unsubstantial media. Ships stay afloat through their buoyancy. Archimedes' principle states that a body immersed in a liquid is buoyed up by the weight of the volume of liquid displaced. Fresh water weighs 62.4 lb per cu ft, salt water, 64.0 lb. The weight of a ship in tons is equal to the weight of water its submerged portion displaces. A rectangular block H ft deep having a wetted length L, breadth B, and draft or submerged depth D would, in salt water, weigh $L \times B \times D/2240/64$ long tons; in fresh water the displacement becomes $L \times B \times D/2240/62.4$ tons. The displacement space equivalent of one ton of salt water is $2240/64 = 35$ cu ft; of fresh water, $2240/62.4 = 35.9$ cu ft. Both measurements are based on long tons.

Ship hulls, however, are not rectangular. They are more or less streamlined for easier movement against the resistance of water and waves. The ratio between the actual underwater volume and the corresponding LBD block is known as the block coefficient β. For

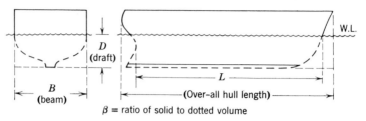

FIGURE 5-2. Block ratio.

a yacht, β may be as low as 0.50; for a barge, it may be as high as 0.95. It varies with the draft (and therefore with the weight of ballast, fuel, and cargo at any given time) and must be obtained from the designer's table or chart for the draft at any particular loading. The actual displacement (weight in long tons) of a vessel for salt water is $(LBD/35)\beta$. For fresh water, the displacement is $(LBD/35.9)\beta$. See Figure 5-2.

The safe depth of submersion is a function of the load, draft, and size of wave to be encountered. As allowed by law, it is indicated by the load line or *Plimsoll line*, so-named in Britain after its advocate of 1890, Samuel Plimsoll, who brought about legislative enactment in Britain that ships could not be filled with cargo to the point of dangerous overloading. A typical load line takes the form shown in Figure 5-3 and is located exactly amidship. The horizontal arms indicate the point to which a vessel may be legally and safely submerged, depending on its route and season. The Plimsoll mark on United States vessels is inspected regularly by the Coast Guard.

FIGURE 5-3. Load lines.

TF— tropical fresh water
F— fresh water
T— tropical water
S— summer
W— winter
WNA— winter, North Atlantic

Because the total actual weight of a vessel depends on the weight of what is in it, there are three displacement tonnages.

Light—vessel with crew and supplies but no cargo, fuel, or passengers.
Loaded—weight when loaded to maximum draft, to the deep load line.
Actual—weight of vessel and tonnage at any time during the voyage, varying with fuel, cargo, and passengers aboard.

Vessels have displacement curves showing the displacement tonnage (hence β) at any draft. The displacement of a warship is always given as actual weight displacement tons.

Four other tonnages are here noted as used in maritime circles.

1. *Dead-weight tonnage*, the maximum weight of fuel, passengers, and cargo a vessel can carry when loaded to the deep load line. It is the difference between displacement tonnage light and loaded and is the basis on which payment is made for vessels in charter.

2. *Vessel gross tonnage*, expressed in units of space, is based on an old assumption that 100 cu ft of space accommodates one ton of cargo. It is equal to the closed-in capacity in cubic feet divided by 100 (or the closed-in space in cubic meters divided by 2.83).

3. *Net tonnage* is the actual gross tonnage minus the space devoted to the operation of the vessel, that is, with space occupied by machinery and fuel, crew accommodations, stores, and galley deducted. Usually about 30 percent of closed-in space is so deducted.

4. *Cargo tonnage* may be expressed either in actual tons or measure (100 cu ft) tons. The long or 2240-lb ton is used in England, the short or 2000-lb ton in the United States, and the metric or 2204.6-lb ton in France. For bulky lightweight cargos, a measurement ton of 40 cu ft is used.

Aircraft. Only balloons and dirigibles have buoyancy in the same sense that a ship has. Archimedes' principle and Boyle's law both find application here. Nevertheless, heavier-than-air craft (omitting rockets) are sustained in flight by pressure from the medium in which they operate, that is, air. Bernoulli's law states that the pressure of any fluid stream is least when velocity is greatest, greatest when velocity is least. If we apply this law to an airfoil (wing), as shown

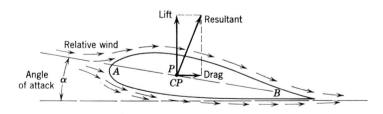

FIGURE 5-4. Forces acting on an airfoil.

in Figure 5-4, we cen see that the air stream has a greater distance to flow across the upper surface and flows faster, exerting less pressure, than it does on the under surface. The results are a difference in pressure beneath the upper and undersides of the airfoil and an upward lift or sustaining force.

Empirical expressions for forces acting on a plane's wing, based on Bernoulli's theorem, are

$$L = C_L(\rho/2)Sv^2 = \text{lift or sustaining force in pounds perpendicular to the selective wind}$$

$$D = C_D(\rho/2)Sv^2 = \text{drag or resistive force in pounds perpendicular to relative wind}$$

$$R = C_R(\rho/2)Sv^2 = \text{resultant of the foregoing forces in pounds}$$

In these equations $C_L =$ lift coefficient = the ratio between the lift of the airfoil and impact pressure of air on a flat plate of the same area. It varies from 0.0 to 3.0 (with flaps), as the angle of attack increases (it is three times greater at 6 degrees than at 2). Figure 5-5 shows C_L, C_D, and other characteristics varying with the angle of attack for an airfoil in frequent use (the N.A.C.A. with an infinite ratio). $\rho =$ air density, which varies with the altitude and temperature but which is usually taken as 0.002378 slugs per cubic foot at sea level; $v =$ relative velocity in feet per second (equal to 1.47 V, where V is the velocity in miles per hour); $S =$ wing area in square feet, including flaps for landing and take-off. The force supporting a plane can be seen in the following problem example.

Problem Example. A light transport plane on the ground is subject to an air pressure of 14.7 psi on both sides of the wings. When in motion at take-off, the air pressure above the wing is 14.523 psi. There is thus an upward difference in pressure of 0.177 psi or 25.5 psf of wing area. With an effective wing area of 987 sq ft, the total lift becomes 987 × 25.5 = 25,169 lb.

The resultant force R produces a moment about the leading edge of the wing. The supporting pressures under an airfoil may be considered concentrated at one point known as the center of pressure or center of lift. It is located by the percentage of chord length where it is applied behind the leading edge, whereby $CP =$ center of pressure $= AP/BP$. If the moment formed by the lift or resultant tends to raise the leading edge (thereby increasing the angle of at-

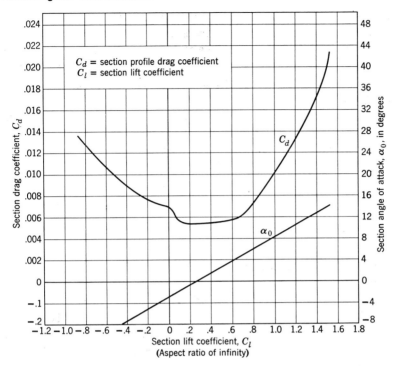

FIGURE 5-5. Characteristics of N.A.C.A. 63_1-412 airfoil. (National Advisory Committee for Aeronautics, Report No. 824, p. 165, by Ira H. Abbott, Albert E. von Doenhoff, and Louis S. Stivers, Jr., Langley Memorial Aeronautical Laboratory, Langley Field, Va., U. S. Govt. Printing Office, Washington, D. C.)

tack), there is a tendency toward stalling. If the moment tends to lower the leading edge, decreasing the angle of attack, there is a diving tendency. Values for the lift coefficient C_L and also the drag coefficient C_D, for various angles of attack, are shown in Figure 5-5 for the N.A.C.A. airfoil. Further explanation of these terms and factors is given later in this chapter.

The decreased pressure on the upper surface of the wing is based on a smooth flow of air over the surface, which occurs when the angle of attack α is small. Air will continue to flow smoothly as α is increased, until the "burble" angle is reached where the air flow breaks away from the upper surface near the trailing edge and burbles and eddies. Since the support at the trailing edge is decreased, the center

of pressure shifts forward and tends to depress the trailing edge still
further with an inclination toward stalling. The burble or stalling
angle varies with the shape of the airfoil (and with the speed) but has
a value of 16 to 20 degrees for most airfoils. Slots in the leading
edge of the wing reduce the stalling angle and the chance of falling
in a spiral.

Lift increases as the square of the speed, but the critical point
occurs at the slow speeds of take-off and landing. The C.A.B. sets
the minimum stalling speed in "approach" for various classes of airplanes. For larger craft, the long runways of modern airports are
required. Increased lift at slower speeds is obtained by the use of
retractable flaps which increase the wing area at take-off and landing
but which can be retracted to decrease resistance or drag when the
plane is in full flight. Jets and jet-assisted propeller planes develop
more initial speed and can take off in shorter distances. In landing
the propeller pitch may be reversed to act as a brake (thereby shortening runway requirements once the plane is on the ground).

The lifting power of a plane varies with wing and power loading.
Wing loading is the gross weight of the airplane in pounds divided
by its total wing area in square feet. Power loading is the gross
weight divided by total horsepower. The product of wing and power
loading gives a commonly used index for plane classification and runway design.

Ship Stability. Stability is the ability of a ship to remain in an
upright position about its axis or to return to that position if moved
from it by an outside force, such as a wave. When a ship is in trim,
the deck is level and the center of gravity G and center of buoyancy B
are on the same vertical axial line. See Figure 5-6a. If disturbed
from that position, a stable ship will tend to return to its original
position of equilibrium. Consider the transverse section in Figure
5-6b. The vessel is shown in a heeled position with the center of
buoyancy shifted to B' and acting vertically upward to intersect the
extension of BG at M. A righting couple is produced to overcome the
heeling couple whereby

$$W \times GT = W \times GM \sin \theta$$

where $W =$ the weight of the vessel in displacement tons and
$GT = GM \sin \theta$ is the righting lever in feet. The point M is the
transverse metacenter and for small angles of heel (up to 15 degrees)

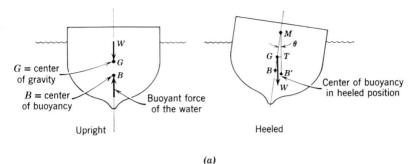

(a)

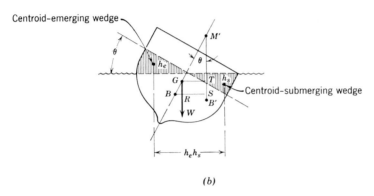

(b)

FIGURE 5-6. Ship's stability: (a) angles of heel < 15 degrees; (b) angles of heel > 15 degrees.

is approximately fixed in position. GM is the metacentric height. The height of the metacenter above the center of buoyancy is $BM = I/V$, where V is the volume of displacement in cubic feet and I is the moment of inertia of the water plane about the axis of rotation.

The position of centers of gravity and buoyancy can be calculated by knowing the position and weight of the elements that comprise the ship. These will vary with the distribution and weight of cargo, fuel, and ballast. Typical metacentric heights vary from 1 to 2 ft for tugs and liners to 2 ft for cargo vessels and up to 5 ft for battleships.

For heeling angles greater than 15 degrees, M does not remain fixed but varies its position to M'. There is no simple formula for determining the value of BM', but a method frequently followed makes use of the Atwood formula developed about 1795.

V is the total immersed volume, and v is the volume of the emerging or submerging wedge in cubic feet; $h_e h_s$ is the horizontal distance in feet between the centroids g_e and g_s of the emerged and submerged wedges. A moment of $W \times GT$ ft-tons tends to right the vessel. $GT = BS - BR = BG \sin \theta$. The horizontal shift in the center of buoyancy to $B' = BS$. The increase in the submerged wedge volume is opposed by the buoyancy acting through B', so that, by taking moments, $BS \times V = v \times h_e h_s$ and $BS = v \times h_e h_s / V$; therefore, $W \times GT = W(v \times h_e h_s / V - BG \sin \theta)$. From this, GT and GM' are computed.

The statical stability of a ship is the moment in foot-tons that tends to right the ship when inclined to the corresponding angle of heel. Curves of statical stability are computed for various actual displacements and corresponding center-of-gravity positions. The dynamical stability is measured by the amount of work necessary to bring the ship from an upright to a heeled position, such as might be caused by a wave.

When G and M' coincide, the ship is in neutral equilibrium and will stay in that position until acted upon by an outside force. When G is above M', the ship is in a capsizing position. Changes in the metacentric height result from an alteration in displacement and in the corresponding position of the center of gravity. For various water-line displacements, the position of G and GM' are calculated from a metacentric diagram. Unstable loading, including both overloading and improper placement of the cargo in the holds and decks, may cause a dangerous shift in the center of gravity; for example, when unloading cargo from the lower portions of a hold while allowing heavy cargo to remain on upper decks. Ballast tanks help to keep a vessel stable by adding or discharging water from tanklike compartments to compensate for cargo changes. Care must be taken while loading and unloading a vessel that it does not get too far out of trim. The cargo is uniformly distributed or removed as the loading or unloading proceeds. Great Lakes bulk-cargo ships usually have trimming lights that indicate when the vessel is in proper trim during port operations. The conflicting requirements of maintaining trim during loading and cruising and during the taking on and discharging of cargo en route and of combining heavy with light cargo items makes the loading of any vessel, especially a general cargo ship, a problem for which a loading plan must be carefully prepared in advance by one skilled in the art. Those items to be off-loaded at the first port of call must be readily accessible. On the other hand, the center of gravity must be kept as low as possible by placing the heavier cargo items near the bottom of the hold, regardless of order of unloading.

The longitudinal metacenter is not so critical in most ships as is the transverse. Its determination and solution are, however, similar to that of the transverse.

Aircraft Stability. The forces that sustain an airplane in air are roughly analogous to those that affect the stability of a ship. Stability in an aircraft is the ability to fly in a straight line and to remain in or return to the same attitude with respect to the relative wind. The distribution of individual pressure and vacuum forces acting on an airfoil varies with the angle of attack. See Figure 5-4. The center of lift or pressure in an aircraft, where these forces are assumed to be concentrated, corresponds to the center of buoyancy in a ship. As the angle of attack increases, the center of pressure moves forward; as it decreases, the center of pressure moves backward. Consequently, the location of the resultant forces also varies with the angle of attack. Lift is always perpendicular to the direction of the relative wind.

An airplane possesses stability only when the forces acting on it are in equilibrium, that is, when the sum of the vertical forces, the horizontal forces, and the moments about any point are zero; when $\Sigma V = 0$, $\Sigma H = 0$, and $\Sigma M = 0$. The active forces in level flight are the propeller thrust (forward), the drag (backward), the lift (upward), and the tail load, which may act either upward or downward.

An airplane must have stability about three axes of movement.

Longitudinal stability involves the pitching of a plane about the lateral axis and the relations between the center of pressure and the

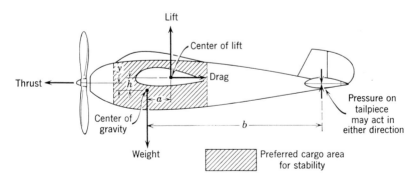

FIGURE 5-7. Stability of a plane in horizontal flight.

center of gravity. There is no change in the axial position of the center of gravity (where the mass of the plane is considered as being centered), but the position of the center of lift varies with the speed and angle of attack.

As the center of pressure moves forward, the resultant force on the wings exerts a turning effect about the tail as a pivot. See Figure 5-7. The leading wing edge tends to rise, thereby increasing the angle of attack still more and increasing a tendency to stall. Airplane stability is dependent upon the location of the center of gravity with relation to the center of lift. The center of gravity must set in front of the center of pressure or lift for the corresponding flight speed to provide a restoring moment to offset the lift at the center of pressure and its tendency to rotate about the tail. Horizontal tail surfaces or stabilizers aid in reducing pitch and in keeping the center of pressure back of the center of gravity.

A summation of moments counterclockwise about the center of gravity (see Figure 5-7) would be

$$\text{thrust} \times (y) - \text{drag} \times (h) + \text{lift} \times (a) \pm \text{tail load} \times (b) = 0$$

For a high-wing monoplane, the forces normally acting on the tail will be positive (downward) because of downwash from the wing. If the angle of attack is lessened by a gust of wind when the airplane is flying in a stable position, the lift will be decreased and the center of lift moved backward (reducing the angle of attack still more). However, the downward pressure on the elevators will be increased to form a moment that will tend to rotate the plane to stability. For a low-wing plane, the normally acting forces will be upward (negative). The forces acting normally on the tail may also be reinforced upward or downward by raising or lowering the elevators at the trailing edge of the tail.

In designing an airplane for cargo service, the relation between positions of the center of lift and the center of gravity must be carefully considered. A minimum shifting of the center of lift is desirable. Every unit of weight acts with a moment arm, depending on its position, to oppose or reinforce the moment of lift. Weight in the tail has the greatest adverse effect because of the long moment arms involved. The area adjacent to the center of pressure requires minimum weight-distribution planning because of the shorter moment

arms. The problems of correct weight distribution in loading and unloading a cargo plane are similar to those for a ship.

With changes in *lateral stability*, the center of gravity does not
remain in the same vertical plane. Unstable lateral motions include
rolling and side slipping. Yaw and roll are mutually causal, and side
slipping produces both. Yaw should turn the plane in the direction
in which it is slipping. The fixed vertical fin to which the rudder is
attached in the tail assembly or empennage aids in reducing lateral
instability. Owing to lateral symmetry along the longitudinal axis,
lateral balance is obtained by a symmetrical distribution of weight on
each side of a vertical plane through the longitudinal axis. This
factor must be kept in mind in loading cargo planes. Setting wings
at a dihedral angle also increases lateral stability.

EFFECTS OF RESISTANCE ON TRANSPORT

Introduction. If there were no friction or gravitation, a vehicle and
its load, once set in motion, would continue in that state, according to
Newton's laws, until acted upon by an outside force. Actually, there
are a great many resistive forces acting to retard the movement of a
train, truck, ship, or aircraft. These are caused principally by the
friction of moving parts, by air, wind, or wave pressures, and by
turbulence, shock, sway, and concussion. Gravity, or the effects of
overcoming elevation, is also a form of resistance. Because additional
tractive force is required to overcome these resistive forces, as the
speed increases, acceleration may also be considered a kind of resistance. The total of such forces varies with the weight of vehicle and
cargo and with the speed of the vehicle. In one way or another, the
total propulsive force of the motive power unit is expended in overcoming resistance.

There is much similarity in the cause and effect of resistive forces,
whatever the name and units applied. In railroading the term is
"tractive" or "train" resistance and is expressed as pounds of resistance, in total, per car or per ton. Unit resistance, pounds per ton,
decreases as the weight of the vehicle increases. The same terms and
units apply to highway vehicles, and the opposing force is sometimes
referred to as "road" or "tire-rim" resistance. In water transport
skin friction and residual resistance are also expressed in pounds,
as is drag or the summation of resistive forces acting on an airplane

in flight. Pipeline operation encounters flow resistance, usually expressed in pounds per square inch or in feet of head—but the total resistance is expressed in pounds. The frictional and grade resistance for conveyors can be similarly expressed. All resistances can also be expressed in terms of resistive or elevation head and also in terms of equivalent distance of level tangent movement.

A definite series of relations exists between transportation capacities, propulsive or motive power, and the resistance to movement of the several forms of transport. In all cases the principal effects of resistance are to reduce the speed or the amount of tractive or propulsive force available for moving the vehicle and the pay or revenue load. The effort expended in overcoming resistive forces, which act upon the dead weight of power unit and cargo container, is wasted from a transportation standpoint. Nevertheless, it is a loss inherent in each system, although not to the same extent. Measures of transport efficiency are the pounds of resistance per gross ton and per revenue or net ton and the ratio between the two. A second criterion is directly related, that is, horsepower per gross and per net or revenue ton. These are discussed in later pages.

Tractive and Road Resistance. A vehicle moving upon tangent track or roadway, in still air, and at constant speed encounters resistance that must be overcome by the tractive effort of the locomotive, truck, or automobile engine. These resistances include (a) rolling friction between wheel and rail or tire and pavement, which is probably fixed in quantity for a given type of surface but may vary with the condition of the surface, especially highway surfaces; (b) axle-bearing friction that varies with vehicle weight and load and with the type of bearing; (c) losses that vary with the speed, principally flange friction in the case of railroads but also sway, buff, and concussion, including the effects of bumps on rough roads; and (d) air resistance that varies directly with the cross-sectional area, with the length and shape (streamlining) of the vehicle, and with the square of the speed.

The Davis formula for train resistance is generally used by railroad engineers.[1] It combines the foregoing terms into a single empirical formula, whereby

$$R_t = (1.3 + 29/w + bV + CAV^2/wn)wn$$

[1] W. J. Davis, Tractive Resistance of Electric Locomotive and Cars, *General Electric Review*, Vol. 29, October 1926, pp. 685–708.

where R_t = train or tractive resistance in pounds for car or locomotive on tangent level track in still air

w = weight in tons per axle of car or locomotive

n = number of axles

b = coefficient of flange friction, swaying, and concussion (0.045 for freight cars and motor cars in trains, 0.03 for locomotives and passenger cars, and 0.09 for single-rail cars)

C = drag coefficient of air (0.0017 for streamlined locomotives and single- or head-end-rail cars, 0.0025 for other locomotives, 0.0005 for freight cars, and 0.00034 for trailing passenger cars)

A = cross-sectional area of locomotives and cars (usually 105 to 120 sq ft for locomotives, 85 to 90 sq ft for freight cars, 110–120 sq ft for multiple-unit and passenger cars, and 70 to 110 sq ft for single- or head-end-rail cars)

V = speed in miles per hour

For speeds greater than 50 mph, the experimental values prepared from the field tests of Tuthill, which extended the Schmidt tests on which the Davis equation is based into the higher speed ranges, should be used.[2] See Figure 5-8. More exact studies take into account track flexibility, wind resistance, streamlining, losses due to car axle generators, and condition of the rails.

Monorail, rack, and cable systems are subject to similar types of tractive resistance. In the case of rack railways, the friction between gear and rack has to be added. This, however, would be small compared to the total grade resistance of a slope steep enough to require the use of a rack system. Monorail equipment encounters different resistance values, depending on the design of truck and method of suspension. Tests and published data for this type of equipment are lacking. Recognition may be given the resistive losses for a monorail with the Davis formula, using Davis's values for the single-rail car where steel wheels are used and tire-on-pavement rolling resistance values where rubber tires and concrete rails are used.

Propulsive resistance for highway vehicles is directly analogous

[2] John K. Tuthill, High Speed Freight Train Resistance, *University of Illinois Engineering Experiment Station Bulletin 376*, Urbana, 1948, and Edward C. Schmidt, Freight Train Resistance, *University of Illinois Engineering Department Station Bulletin 43*, Urbana, 1934.

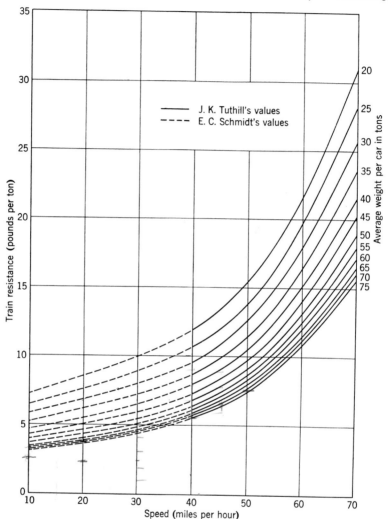

FIGURE 5-8. Schmidt-Tuthill train resistance curves. (Courtesy of *University of Illinois Engineering Experiment Station Bulletin 376*, 1948, p. 29.)

to tractive resistance for trains. The propulsive resistance (tire-rim or road resistance) is again taken at constant speed on tangent roadway in still air. The variety of factors that affect resistance includes the friction of main and shaft bearings, gears and differential, design and state of tire tread, wheel bearings, condition of roadway surface, impact and concussion, air resistance, and gross weight of vehicle.

1. The friction losses in main and shaft bearings and in transmission and differential gears are usually accounted for in the mechanical efficiency of the engine as a part of a 10 to 15 percent internal-loss factor.

2. The condition of the roadway reflects its material, degree of crowning, and state of maintenance. A constant unit resistance in pounds per ton is often combined with a surface condition factor to give a total value for rolling resistance. Based on an average speed of 40 mph, concrete in good condition is usually assigned a resistive effect of 20 lb per ton, 30 lb per ton, when in fair condition, and 40 lb per ton, if the paving is in poor condition. Corresponding values for macadam pavements are 30, 45, and 70 lb per ton, respectively, and for earth roads, 70, 90, and 150 lb per ton.

These simplifications do not take into account variations with gross vehicle weight (corresponding to car weight for railroads). Using a series of total road resistance tests made for the Bureau of Public Roads, Starr determined rolling resistance by deducting air resistance from the total resistance for speeds of 4 to 40 mph.[3] To these results, Mr. Starr fitted a straight-line equation having the form [4]

$$R_r = 17.9 + (1.39V - 10.2)/W_v$$

where R_r = unit rolling resistance in pounds per ton
V = speed in miles per hour
W_v = gross vehicle weight in tons

Total unit tire-rim or road resistance can be obtained by adding the conventional value for air resistance, $R_a = CAV^2/W_v$, whence

$$R = 17.9 + (1.39V - 10.2 + 0.0024AV^2)/W_v$$

Here 0.0024 represents the drag coefficient (sometimes taken simply as 0.002) and A is the cross-sectional area of the vehicle.

In both rail and highway resistive expressions one finds an equation of the form $A + (B/W) + CB + DV^2$ that contains a fixed factor

[3] C. C. Saal, Hill Climbing Ability of Motor Trucks, *Public Roads*, Vol. 23, No. 23, U. S. Bureau of Public Roads, May 1942, pp. 33–54.

[4] Millard O. Starr, A Comparative Analysis of Resistance to Motion in Commercial Transportation, unpublished Master of Science thesis, Department of Mechanical Engineering, University of Illinois, Urbana, 1945.

for rolling resistance, one that varies with the weight, another varying with the speed, and a fourth term that varies as the square of the speed. Air resistance, being greater at high speeds, is more important to passenger vehicles, but trucks and buses, running 50 and 60 mph or better, are likely to find propulsive resistance and especially air resistance of marked significance.

Since the tests were conducted on good concrete roads, the effect of other types and qualities of road surfaces can be applied to the value computed for rolling resistance (air resistance excluded) by modifying that part of the total equation by the ratio of good concrete road to the road surface under consideration.

Ships. The most important resistances to be overcome by a ship's propulsive units are (a) skin friction, that is, friction of quiet water on the wetted surface of the hull, (b) streamline resistance, (c) eddy-current resistance, and (d) wave resistance. These resistances are taken at constant speed in still air. In addition, there is air resistance of $R_a = CAV^2$ on that part of the ship that is out of the water. The slow speed and streamlining of most ships keep this from being excessive.

Skin friction, which constitutes 50 to 85 percent of the total, depends upon the speed and the design of the hull. Durand's commonly used empirical formula for skin resistance is $R_s = fA_wV^{1.83}$, where R_s is the total skin friction in pounds and f is the friction factor varying from 0.01 for hull lengths of 20 ft to 0.0085 for 600 ft (longer hulls produce better streamline effects) and increasing 25 to 50 percent for dirty hull bottoms and up to 100 percent for fouled and barnacled hulls. V is the speed in knots (1 knot = 1 nautical mile or 6080 ft per hr). A_w is the wetted surface of the hull in square feet and is equal very approximately to $15.6\sqrt{D_s \times L}$, where D_s is the displacement in tons and L is the length in feet. Note the similarity of this expression to that for air resistance. The exclusion of eddy resistance from the expression accounts for the exponent of 1.83 instead of 2.00. The remaining resistances (known appropriately as residual resistance), include streamline resistance caused by eddy-current effects, but principally by wave action, and are included in the Taylor empirical equation [5]

$$R_r = 12.5 \times \beta \times D_s \times (V/\sqrt{L})^4$$

[5] D. W. Taylor, *The Speed and Power of Ships*, John Wiley and Sons, New York, 1910.

where R_r = resistance in pounds
  β = block ratio
  D_s = displacement in tons
  V = speed in knots
  L = wetted length of hull in feet

The expression $(V/\sqrt{L})^4$ is the ratio of speed to the square root of the length and relates the effect of stern and bow waves on one another.

The total resistance is $R = R_s + R_r + R_a$. R_a is the air resistance of the portion of the ship out of water, A = cross-sectional area, C = drag coefficient = 0.002, and V = speed in knots. Unit resistance would be R/D_s, in which D_s = gross loaded displacement. Giving each term its detailed components,

$$R = (f15.6\sqrt{D_s L}\ V^{1.83} + CAV^2)/D_s + 12.5\beta V^4/L^2$$

In a narrow canal or channel water is crowded against the confining walls or slopes, increasing the resistance so that $R_c = 8.5R/(2 + a/15.6\sqrt{D_s \times L})$, where R_c = resistance in a confining channel, R = resistance in a large body of water, a = cross-sectional area of the channel in square feet, and D_s and L have the same meaning as before.

Aircraft. The subject of airplane resistance is rather complicated. The following discussion is greatly simplified for inclusion in the scope of this book. It illustrates the principles and demonstrates the similarity of airplane resistance to other types of propulsive resistance.

Airplane resistance, more commonly called "drag," is the resistance of air to the forward motion of the plane. Rolling and bearing friction resistances are absent. Nevertheless, weight, as represented by the required wing area for a given weight of plane, enters the evaluation. From fluid mechanics, the resistance of a fluid to the passage of a body is $D = C_D(\rho/2)Sv^2$, where C_D is a coefficient depending on the shape of the body with skin friction and eddy components, ρ is the fluid (air) density in slugs per cubic foot at the altitude of flight, S is the wing area in square feet, and v is the velocity in feet per second. This expression is similar to that for lift except for the coefficient; the two expressions for drag and lift are sine and cosine components, respectively, of the total force acting on the wing or airfoil.

Drag is composed of two elements: (a) parasitic drag caused by the frontal pressure and side friction on the parts of the plane and (b) induced drag inherent in the production of lift, due principally to the downdraft at the ends of the wings. Resistance = drag = D = $(C_{Dp} + C_{Di})(\rho/2)Sv^2$, where C_{Dp} and C_{Di} are parasitic and induced-drag coefficients, respectively. The values of these coefficients vary with the type of airfoil and are usually determined by wind-tunnel tests. These values are presented graphically in Figure 5-5. Values can also be computed.

C_{Dp} is determined as the sum of the component drags on the several parts of the plane structure. The drag-coefficient values in Figure 5-5 are for the wing alone. Parasitic drag also arises from the tail assembly, the fuselage, engine nacelles, and other elements offering frontal areas. These component drags are expressed as the combined equivalent drag of a flat plate perpendicular to the relative wind and having a coefficient of unity. Thus the total C_{Dp} equals the C_{Dp} for the wings (in Figure 5-5 or equivalent) plus an assumed C_{Dp} for the tail area and other elements. The tail area is often taken as 30 percent of the wing area with a C_{Dp} of 0.01; a value of 0.10 is used for the remaining elements.

The ratio of wing span to average wing chord or width is the aspect ratio $AR = b/c = b^2/S$, where b is the span, c is the chord, and S is again the area. Values of AR may be as low as 2 to 3 for missiles and supersonic craft, 6 to 8 for small planes, and 8 to 15 for long-range commercial transports. Data in Figure 5-5, following the current practice, are based on airfoils of infinite length. Obviously such an airfoil has no induced drag but only the parasitic drag. With airfoils of finite length, air moves under the wing tips to the area of lower pressure above the tip, thereby introducing down-wash velocities along the wing span that reduce the lift and the angle of attack. To maintain the same lifting force, the angle of attack of a finite airfoil must thereby be increased by a small induced angle, α_1 creating in turn an additional or induced drag. The induced or additional angle of attack for the finite length of airfoil can be determined, from principles of fluid flow, as $\alpha_1 = C_L/\pi AR$ and C_{Di} as $C_L\alpha_1$, whereby $C_{Di} = C_L^2/\pi AR$.

It should be noted that for level flight there is only one speed for each angle of attack, hence only one lift and one C_L for that speed and angle.

Induced drag is dependent only on wing span. An increase in wing span decreases the induced drag. A longer wing creates a greater bending moment. Wing strength, and usually weight, must be increased. Proper design calls for an economic balance between wing span and induced drag.

Drag increases as the square of the speed but decreases with altitude because of lower atmospheric densities at high altitudes. A decrease in wing span decreases parasitic drag but also reduces lift. The designer must determine whether he requires speed or load-carrying capacity for a given thrust and horsepower. In summary, the gross load that an airplane can support in level flight in still air at constant speed at a given altitude depends on speed, a factor of power plant, on air density, a factor of altitude, and on drag, a factor of wing span and angle of attack. Drag divided by gross weight gives unit resistance.

Problem Example. Given a light transport airplane with two 48-in. diameter, 1600-hp engines (1300 hp at 8000 ft), fuselage diameter of approximately 8 ft, wing area of 980 sq ft (N.A.C.A. 63_1-412 section, aspect ratio of infinity), and lift of 25,000 lb. Determine (a) the adequacy of the wing area for landing and take-off speeds of 80 mph and (b) the drag when flying at an elevation of 8000 ft at 180 mph.

1. Lift = L = gross weight = 25,000 lb = $C_L(\rho/2)v^2S$. Assume maximum lift; C_L (from Figure 5-5) = 1.56.

$$\rho = 0.0024 \text{ slugs/cu ft at sea level}$$
$$v = 80 \times 5280/3600 = 118 \text{ ft/sec}$$
$$S = \text{required wing area in square feet}$$
$$25,000 = 1.56 \times 0.0024 \times 118 \times 118 \times S/2$$

S = 959 sq ft; this is less than 980 sq ft; therefore, the given wing area is adequate.

2. Drag = $C_D\rho v^2S/2$ where $C_D = C_{Dp} + C_{Di}$. At an altitude of 8000 ft and speed of 180 mph,

$$C_L = \text{weight}/\rho v^2S/2 = 25,000/0.0019 \times 264 \times 264 \times 980/2$$
$$C_L = 0.385$$

From Figure 5-5, C_{Dp} for the airfoil = 0.0055. Assume C_{Dp} = 0.01 for tail drag and 0.10 for frontal areas; also assume the tail area as approximately 30 per cent of wing area and aspect ratio (AR) = 8.

$$A_e = \text{equivalent area} = (0.30 \times 980 \times 0.01) + (8 \times 8 \times \pi/4 \times 0.10)$$
$$+ (2 \times 4 \times 4 \times \pi/4 \times 0.01) + 1.0$$

A_e = 9.21 sq ft = $C_{Dp}S$; C_{Dp} (excluding wing) = A_e/S
Total C_{Dp} = C_{Dp} (for wing) + A_e/S = 0.0055 + 9.21/980 = 0.015
$C_{Di} = C_L^2/\pi AR = C_L^2/(3.14 \times 8) = 0.385 \times 0.385/25.12$
C_{D1} = 0.0059
$C_D = C_{Di} + C_{Dp}$ = 0.0059 + 0.015 = 0.0209
Drag = $D = C_D\rho v^2S/2$ = 0.0209 × 0.0019 × 264 × 264 × 980/2
D = 1356 lb
Unit drag = D/W = 1356/25,000/2000 = 108.5 lb/ton

Pipeline Resistance. Pumping pressures and flow resistance in pipelines are analogous to tractive effort and tractive resistance for railroads and highways. Flow resistance consists principally of (a) the frictional resistance between the liquid and the inside walls of the pipe, which depends in turn on the roughness factor of the pipe's interior, the pipe diameter, and the number and type of joints and fittings (increasing the diameter of the pipe reduces the percentage of total flow in contact with the walls of the pipe); (b) internal resistance within the liquid itself—its viscosity and the temperature which affects the viscosity; (c) condition or type of flow, that is, whether streamline (laminar) or turbulent.

These factors are reflected in the basic Fanning equation for flow resistance, $h = f\rho Lv^2/2gd$, where h = flow resistance in feet of head, L = length of line in feet, v = flow velocity in feet per second, d = diameter of pipe in feet, g = acceleration due to gravity = 32.2 ft/sec², f = pipe friction coefficient, and ρ = density in lb/ft³ = specific gravity $\times$ 62.4.

The value of f was determined by Reynolds as a function of the ratio between dv and the viscosity. This dimensionless ratio, called the Reynolds number, is $N = dv\rho/u$, where d, v, and ρ have the meanings given above and u is the viscosity of the fluid. Reynolds found the flow to be laminar or streamlined when $N < 2000$. When $N = 3000$, the flow is likely to be turbulent. See Figure 5-9. Between $N = 3000$ and $N = 2000$ flow may be laminar or turbulent, but conservatively it is considered turbulent. For every value of N there is a corresponding value of f. Further experiments indicated that for streamlined flow $f = 64/N$. If this value for f is substituted in the Fanning equation and head is converted to pounds per square inch of pressure, the resulting equation is the same as Poiseuille's expression for flow in small tubes,

$$P = P_i - P_f = 2uvL/9gd^2$$

where P = pressure loss in pounds per square inch over the pipe length, L, in feet, and d, g, L, v, and u have the same meaning as in

Streamlined flow   Turbulent flow

FIGURE 5-9. Streamlined and turbulent flow.

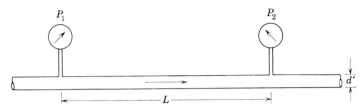

FIGURE 5-10. Pressure loss in a pipeline.

the Fanning equation. P_i and P_f are the initial and final pressures over length L. See Figure 5-10.

A more usable expression for pressure loss in streamlined flow is expressed in pipeline units.[6]

$$P = 1500 \ Bu/D^4 \quad \text{and} \quad P = 962,000 \ Qu/D^4$$

where P = pressure loss per mile of line in pounds per square inch
B = flow in barrels per hour (1 bbl = 42 gal)
Q = flow in cubic feet per second
D = diameter of pipe in inches
u = absolute viscosity in feet-pounds-seconds

The Fanning formula for turbulent flow is properly used for N values greater than 2000. The value of f must be obtained experimentally or from experimental values reduced to tables and charts, as in Table 5-1.

Reduced to practical pipeline units, the Fanning formula becomes

$$P = 0.55830 \ fB^2\rho/D^5 \quad \text{and} \quad P = 229,610 \ fQ\rho/D^5$$

where P = flow resistance per mile in psi
f = pipe friction coefficient—experimental values
B,Q,D,ρ = the same as in the preceding equations

Petroleum is usually described by giving the specific gravity in degrees American Petroleum Institute (° API) based on an arbitrary scale in which water has a specific gravity of 10° API. Standard specific gravity is related to API gravity by the equation spec grav 60° F/60° F = 141.5/(131.5 + ° API).

Viscosity, u, is determined in the petroleum industry by the Saybolt Universal Viscometer and is the time in seconds for 60 cc (⅛ pint)

[6] W. G. Helzel, Flow and Friction in Pipelines, Pipeline Section, *Oil and Gas Journal,* Tulsa, Oklahoma, June 5, 1930, pp. T-203–T-224.

Table 5-1. Pipe Friction Coefficient (f) [a]

$N = dv\rho/u$	f	$N = dv\rho/u$	f
2,500	0.0475	30,000	0.0230
3,000	0.0450	35,000	0.0225
4,000	0.0415	40,000	0.0220
4,500	0.0400	50,000	0.0210
6,000	0.0375	60,000	0.0200
8,000	0.0335	80,000	0.0180
10,000	0.0315	100,000	0.0175
20,000	0.0265		

[a] Based on Figure 13, Pipeline Section Flow and Friction in Pipelines, W. G. Helzel, *Oil and Gas Journal*, Tulsa, Oklahoma, June 5, 1930, p. T-223.

to flow through a capillary tube 0.1765 cm ($\frac{1}{16}$ in.) inside diameter and 1.225 cm ($\frac{1}{2}$ in.) long at a specified temperature. Viscosity decreases rapidly as the temperature rises. *Kinematic viscosity* is the ratio of absolute viscosity to density. In English units kinematic viscosity $= u/\rho = 0.00000237t - 0.00194/t$, where u again is absolute viscosity in feet-pounds-seconds, ρ is the density in pounds per cubic foot, and $t =$ time in Saybolt seconds.

This discussion of viscosity is necessary to determine u values for the equation $N = dv\rho/u$.

A convenient expression for the foregoing in pipeline units is $dv\rho/u = N = 0.02381 (B/D) (\rho/u)$, where B is in barrels per hour, and D is the inside diameter in inches.[7] The relation between gravity and viscosity is not clearly defined. Figure 5-11 has been prepared as an aid to students in solving problems and represents only an averaging of relations from data contained in the U. S. Bureau of Mines Bulletin No. 291. A problem example will make the use and significance of these relations more easily understood.

Problem Example. Given 900 bbl of crude oil per hour to be pumped through a 10-in. line (specific gravity of the oil is 30° API), what is the loss in pressure in a level line 30 miles in length?

1. From Figure 5-11, the viscosity of 30° API crude oil is 95 Saybolt seconds.

[7] W. G. Helzel, Pipeline Section Flow and Friction in Pipelines, *Oil and Gas Journal*, Tulsa, Oklahoma, June 5, 1930.

2. $N = dv\rho/u = 0.02381\ B\rho/Du$ in pipeline units
$\rho/u = 1/(u/\rho) = 1(0.00000237 \times 95 - 0.00194/95)$
$\rho/u = 4902$
$N = (0.02381 \times 900/10) \times 4902$
$N = 10{,}490$
3. Since $N = 10{,}490 > 2000$, flow is turbulent and the Fanning formula in pipeline units $P = 0.55830\,fB^2\rho/D^5$ should be used. D is given, but f and $\rho =$ 62.4 $\times$ spec grav must be determined.
$\rho = 62.4 \times 141.5/(131.5 + 30°\ \text{API}) = 62.4 \times 0.87$
$\rho = 54.3$
$f = 0.0312$ by interpolating in Table 5-1
4. $P = 0.55830\,fB^2\rho/D^5 = 0.55830 \times 0.0312 \times 900^2 \times 54.3/10^5$
$P = 7.81$ psi per mile
5. For a 30-mile line, $P_{30} = 30 \times 7.81 = 234.30$ psi

Belt Conveyors. Conveyor systems are subject to two principal types of resistance—roller resistance and a form of grade resistance, as the load may be raised or lowered through a difference in elevation opposed or aided by the forces of gravity. The elevation phases of the problem are considered in a later chapter. An empty horizontal belt encounters resistance in its frictional contact with the rollers and idler pulleys. The amount of frictional resistance will vary with the materials of belt and rollers, the lubrication of the idler pulleys, their spacing, the arc and area of contact, and whether or not the rollers are wet or dry, clean or dirty. An important factor is the amount of tension imposed on the belt by idler pulleys or counterweight or other means to insure slack-side tension. There would be no effective or power-producing tension at the driving pulley without some slack-side tension because conveyors work by friction drive.

A considerable amount of resistance has to be overcome by the driving pulley even when the belt is empty. The addition of cargo

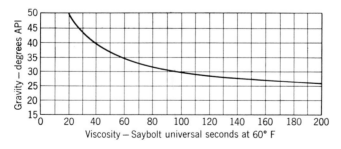

FIGURE 5-11.   Typical gravity-viscosity relations of crude oil. (An averaging of values from *Bureau of Mines Bulletin 291*.)

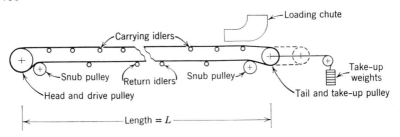

FIGURE 5-12. Typical horizontal conveyor. (Courtesy of *Goodyear Handbook of Belting: Conveyor and Elevator*, Goodyear Tire and Rubber Company, Akron, Ohio, p. 9.)

load to the belt imposes additional weight on the pulleys and increases the resistive forces. There is some air resistance, but because of negligible frontal area and low speed, air effects and the variations with speed that accompany air resistance are neglected. Few studies have been made for the resistive forces on belt conveyors in terms of pounds per ton.

In computing the propulsive resistance of belt conveyors, the usual practice is to consider first the resistance of the empty belt, then the additional resistance occasioned by the cargo load, and, finally, the effects of gradient.

Resistance varies with the length and width of the belt (or flight) and with the load imposed on the rollers over which the belt moves. For a horizontal belt, the length of belt L is taken as the center-to-center distance between the head or driving pulley and the tail and take-up pulley. See Figure 5-12. For inclined belts at the usual angles of inclination, little error is had in using the horizontal projection of the center-to-center contour distances. The greatest error (for a maximum inclination of approximately 23 degrees for the full belt length), is approximately 8.7 percent.[8] It is generally much less because the maximum inclination is usually not involved and the inclination seldom extends over the entire flight. It is significant principally in computing friction loads of empty belts. Even in extreme cases of maximum inclination, it is a much lower percentage with loaded belts, when total effective friction is considered. With empty inclined belts, the actual contour distance should be used when other than approximate solutions are required.

[8] *Handbook of Belting—Conveyor and Elevator*, Section 6, The Goodyear Tire and Rubber Company, Akron, Ohio, 1953, pp. 67–107.

The propulsive resistance or friction force for an empty belt is, therefore, equal to the length of belt $\times$ weight of moving parts (belt and rollers) $\times$ the coefficient of frictional resistance. The Goodyear equation expresses this in the form $R_e = CQ(L + L_0)$, where $R_e = $ total resistance of empty belt in pounds and $C = $ frictional factor or the average coefficient of friction.[9] Propulsive resistance is comprised of approximately 20 to 30 percent bearing resistance of the idlers, 30 percent friction between belt and roller, and 50 to 60 percent internal-load friction, that is, shifting and reshaping of the load as it passes over the rollers. The following is the Goodyear evaluation of C:

1. $C = 0.03$ for antifriction installations on temporary, portable, or imperfectly aligned structures.
2. $C = 0.022$ for conveyors with high-grade antifriction idlers on permanent or other well-aligned structures.
3. $C = 0.012$ for conveyors in group 2 but with grades requiring restraint of the belt when loaded to prevent running backward due to gravity.

$Q = $ weight of moving parts per foot, center-to-center distance (of head and tail pulleys), including weight of belt and an average per-belt-foot allocation of the supporting idlers. The value for Q may be computed accurately by the equation

$$Q = 2B + W_1/l_1 + W_2/l_2$$

where $B = $ belt weight in pounds per lineal foot, W_1 and $W_2 = $ weight of revolving parts carrying idlers and return rolls, respectively, and l_1 and $l_2 = $ respective spacing in feet of conveyor idlers and return rollers. For quick computation, the values of Table 5-2 may be used. These data are based on 5-in. rollers (except for 42- to 60-in. belts, on which 6-in. rollers are used), return-roller spacing of 10 ft, and 3- to 4-ft spacing for idlers. $L = $ length of horizontal belt in feet, equivalent to the center-to-center spacing of the head and tail pulleys; L also is the horizontal projection of the contour distance for inclined and declined flights. $L_0 = $ a length constant in feet; it is an added distance to include constant frictional losses, independent of belt length, and is usually referred to as terminal friction. Corresponding to the three values given for C are L_0 values of 150 to 250, 200 to 1000, and 475. The higher values are used only in empty-belt calculations of tension, where, as in a slightly regenerative decline belt, empty-belt calculations of tension determine the belt design.

[9] *Ibid.*

Table 5-2. Average Values of Q for Ply-Type Belts [a]

Belt Width (in.)	Q (lb)	Belt Width (in.)	Q (lb)
14	13	36	39
16	14	42	52
18	16	48	61
20	18	54	71
24	21	60	85
30	31		

[a] *Handbook of Belting—Conveyor and Elevator*, Section 6, The Goodyear Tire and Rubber Co., Akron, Ohio, 1953, p. 68.

The added weight of cargo per foot of belt is $2000T/(60S)$, where T = tons per hour, and S = feet of travel per minute. This equation reduces to $100T/3S$. Total loaded-belt resistance then becomes

$$R_L = C(Q + 100T/3S)(L + L_0)$$

It should be noted that the only variables in this equation are weight and length of belt. Width and speed are assumed constant for any given installation. For a given quantity of load per hour, R_L will decrease as speed increases. This is because the variation in speed affects the load per foot of belt length. If the load per foot of belt length remained fixed, that is, total T became variable, R_L would increase as speed increased.

Problem Example. Given a horizontal 42-in. conveyor belt 1200 ft long, running at a speed of 700 ft per minute and moving 1200 tons per hour. What total and what unit resistances are being overcome for (a) the empty belt and (b) the loaded belt?

1. From Table 5-2, for the 42-in. belt, $Q = 52$ lb. The Goodyear frictional constant is $C = 0.022$ (for a permanent structure), and the length equivalent for terminal resistance is $L_0 = 200$.

2. For the empty belt, total resistance = R_e.

$$R_e = CQ(L + L_0) = 0.022 \times 52(1200 + 200)$$
$$R_e = 1601.6 \text{ lb}$$

3. Unit resistance = R_e/weight of empty belt and rollers. Unit resistance = $1601.6/(52 \times 1200/2000) = 51.3$ lb/ton.

4. For the loaded belt, total resistance = R_L. The load per foot of center-to-center distance = $100\ T/3S$.

$$R_L = C(Q + 100T/3S)(L + L_0)$$
$$R_L = 0.022(52 + 100 \times 1200/(3 \times 700))(1200 + 200)$$
$$R_L = 3361.6 \, \text{lb}$$

5. Unit resistance $= 3361.6/(1200/2000)(52 + 100 \times 1200/3 \times 700)$. Unit resistance $= 51.3 \, \text{lb/ton}$—the unit resistance has not varied with the load.

Aerial Tramways. The commonest type of long-distance aerial tramway, ropeway, or cableway consists of a small monorail trolley truck with grooved wheels or sheaves running on a fixed cable, from which the cars or buckets are suspended. Propulsion comes from a parallel, moving cable with a lever or self-locking friction grip that clutches the moving cable. A similar pair of cables is used for the bucket return. See Figure 5-13.

Tractive resistances encountered are the frictional resistance of the grooved wheels on the fixed cable, bearing friction of the grooved wheels in the trolley assembly, air resistance, and the frictional resistance of the traction cable passing over the sheaves at intermediate towers and angle stations and over the driving sheave. The resistance between the trolley wheels and the cable is a function of the coefficient of friction and the weight. It is usually neglected. Resistance of the trolley-wheel bearings is also a function of the weight and the bearing-friction coefficient, usually taken as 0.02 for plain bearings and

FIGURE 5-13. Aerial tramway, two-wire system. (Wilbur G. Hudson, *Conveyors and Related Equipment*, Third Edition, John Wiley and Sons, 1954, p. 279, Figure 11-7.)

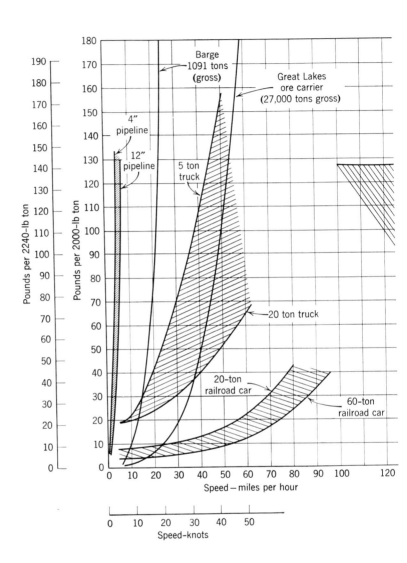

Pounds per 2240-lb ton

Pounds per 2000-lb ton

Barge
1091 tons
(gross)

Great Lakes
ore carrier
(27,000 tons gross)

4"
pipeline

12"
pipeline

5 ton
truck

20 ton truck

20-ton
railroad car

60-ton
railroad car

Speed — miles per hour

Speed-knots

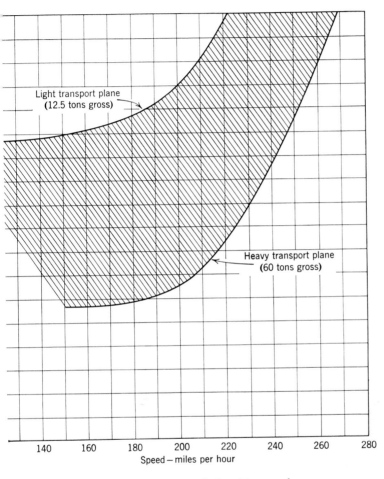

FIGURE 5-14. Typical resistance-value ranges.

0.01 for roller bearings. Some resistance arises from side sway when winds are blowing. Air resistance is present but because of the slow speed and small car area it is neglected. The total force to overcome is $T - S$, where T and S are tensions on taut and slack sides, respectively. The cable assumes the form of a catenary, so that the cars are always running more or less on an incline. Grade resistance is therefore usually present in quantities to warrant deferment of further discussion on cableways to a later section on effects of grade and elevation.

In Summary. From the foregoing it is clear that each mode of transport experiences a more or less wide range of resistance values that usually vary with speed and load. The ranges of typical values for the foregoing types of transport are shown in Figure 5-14. Because load and speed of conveyors are mutually variable, conveyor systems do not lend themselves to this type of presentation. The variations would appear with changes in belt length or in tons per hour being moved.

QUESTIONS FOR STUDY

1. A Great Lakes ore carrier has a length of 600 ft, a beam of 65 ft, and a draft with maximum load of 24 ft. The ship with fuel and crew weighs 7000 tons and carries 18,000 tons of cargo. What is its block coefficient?

2. A Great Lakes bulk-cargo carrier is 620 ft long and has a 70-ft beam and a draft of 25 ft when loaded with a cargo of 19,700 tons. If the block coefficient is 0.891, what is the weight of the ship with equipment and fuel but without cargo?

3. What wing area is required to support an airplane flying 200 mph with an angle of attack of 8 degrees at an altitude of 10,000 ft (air density = 0.001756)? Will this same wing area be adequate when landing at a speed of 80 mph, assuming maximum safe angle of attack?

4. Using the Davis equation, compute and plot the unit and total resistance at speeds of 10 to 40 mph of (a) an 8-wheeled empty car weighing 20 tons and (b) an 8-wheeled loaded car weighing 60 tons.

5. Compute and plot comparative curves of resistance for a 10-ton truck with cross-sectional area of 96 sq ft and a 1500-lb passenger automobile with cross-sectional area of 30 sq ft at speeds of 10 to 60 mph. At what speed does streamlining become significant for each?

6. What is the unit resistance for a 200-ft towboat (pusher type), 45 ft wide and 12 ft deep, with a draft of 9 ft and block coefficient of 0.87 at speeds of 10 to 40 mph? Assume that the total height of vessel above water line is 30 ft.

7. What is the total resistance of a 16-barge tow when each barge is 230 ft long, 45 ft wide, has a block coefficient of 0.95, weighs 472 tons empty, and has a loaded draft (corresponding to the foregoing block coefficient) of 9 ft?

8. A crude-oil pipeline 8 in. in diameter is to carry 800 bbl per hr. The oil has a specific gravity of 32° API. If the pumping pressure of a pump station is 600 psi, how many stations will be required in a level line 200 miles long?

9. Compare the unit resistance of a 42-in. conveyor belt 1600 ft long, fed at a varying rate so that the belt always contains 60 lb of load per foot of length when running at speeds of (a) 600 ft per min and (b) 800 ft per min. What would be the comparison if the belt carried a fixed load per hour of 1080 tons regardless of belt speed?

10. Compute for each of the preceding railroad cars, automobiles, trucks, ships, and towboats (Questions 2, 4, 5, 6, and 7) the resistance at 60 mph and show graphically in a bar or similar type of graph.

SUGGESTED READINGS

1. W. J. Davis, Jr., Tractive Resistance of Electric Locomotive and Cars, *General Electric Review,* Vol. 29, October 1926, pp. 685–708.

2. E. C. Schmidt, Freight Train Resistance, Its Relation to Average Car Weight, *University of Illinois Engineering Experiment Station Bulletin 43,* Urbana, 1910.

3. A. I. Totten, Resistance of Lightweight Passenger Trains, *Railway Age,* July 17, 1937.

4. E. C. Schmidt and F. W. Marquis, The Effects of Cold Weather upon Train Resistance and Tonnage Ratings, *University of Illinois Engineering Experiment Station Bulletin 59,* Urbana, 1912.

5. M. O. Starr, *A Comparative Analysis of Resistance to Motion in Commercial Transportation,* thesis submitted in partial fulfillment of the requirements for the Degree of Master of Science in Mechanical Engineering, University of Illinois, 1945.

6. Train Resistance of Freight Trains Under Various Conditions of Loading and Speed, Report of Committee 16, *Proceedings of the A.R.E.A.,* American Railway Engineering Association, Vol. 43, 1942, pp. 51–71.

7. R. G. Paustian, Tractive Resistance as Related to Roadway Surfaces and Motor Vehicle Operation, *Iowa Engineering Experiment Station Bulletin 119,* Ames, 1934.

8. E. G. McKibben and J. B. Davidson, Effect of Inflation Pressure on the Rolling Resistance of Pneumatic Implement Tires, *Agricultural Engineering,* Vol. 21, No. 1, 1940, pp. 25–26.

9. A. M. Wolf, Practical Tractive Ability Methods, *S.A.E. Journal,* Vol. 27, No. 6, December 1930, pp. 655–664.

10. D. W. Taylor, *The Speed and Power of Ships,* John Wiley and Sons, New York, 1910.

11. C. D. Perkins and R. E. Hage, *Airplane Performance, Stability, and Control,* John Wiley and Sons, New York, 1949.

12. *Handbook of Belting—Conveyor and Elevator,* the Goodyear Tire and Rubber Co., Akron, Ohio, 1953, Chapters 2, 4, 5.

13. *Oil Pipe Line Transportation Practices,* E. L. Davis and Charles Cyrus, editors, issued by the University of Texas Division of Extension and the State Board for Vocational Education, Trade, and Industrial Division, 1944, Chapter XIII.

14. W. G. Helzel, Pipeline Section Flow and Friction in Pipelines, *Oil and Gas Journal,* Tulsa, Oklahoma, June 5, 1930, p. T-223.

6

PROPULSIVE FORCE, HORSEPOWER, AND ELEVATION

PROPULSIVE FORCE AND HORSEPOWER

Horsepower. The objective of transportation is movement. It follows that a prime characteristic or attribute of the means of transportation is propulsive force and power. Propulsive force must be available to overcome resistance—train or tractive resistance, road or tire-rim resistance, drag, skin, wave, and residual resistance of ships and aircraft, roller and belt resistance of conveyors, and flow resistance of pipelines.

Grade resistance or elevation, that is, the effects of gravity on an incline or vertical rise, must also be overcome by the propulsive effort of the power unit. The close relation between effects of elevation and propulsive requirements permits, and indeed often necessitates, considering both together. The detailed effects may vary with the carrier, but elevation poses the common problem of how much propulsive force and horsepower and how much retarding effort must be available to raise or lower a vehicle and its contents a given number of feet.

The propulsive force exerted must be delivered at a certain rate so that all propulsion-resistance eventually resolves into problems of horsepower. Horsepower is the rate of doing work, or, more specifically, it is force times the distance through which the force is exerted in unit time divided by the unit work equivalent per horsepower for the unit of time under consideration. From this, $hp = F \times v/550$, where $v =$ speed in feet per second, that is, the distance moved in one second, and 550 represents the foot-pounds per second equivalent of one horsepower. Similarly,

$\text{hp} = F \times v'/33{,}000$ where v' = speed in feet per minute
$\text{hp} = F \times V/375$ where V = speed in miles per hour
$\text{hp} = F \times V'/325.6$ where V' = speed in knots

In each of the foregoing equations, hp = horsepower, and F = propulsive force, tractive effort, torque, thrust, or pumping force; F may also equal resistive force, tractive resistance, train resistance, road or tire-rim resistance, ship resistance, drag, flow resistance, etc., when the horsepower to overcome any of these is under consideration.

Propulsive force and resistive force are functions of the speed for a given horsepower and vice versa. A prime mover or propulsive unit must be able to exert enough force and horsepower at a given speed to overcome the resistive forces. At a minimum, the two must be equal if a desired operating speed is to be maintained. In most instances, for acceleration and as a reserve, there should be an excess of tractive force beyond that required to overcome resistance.

Prime Movers. A prime mover is a device that transforms the potential energy of fuel into mechanical energy capable of performing work. Coal has been a common source of fuel and energy for many years by producing steam to drive reciprocating engines and rotative turbines. More recently, gasoline and other petroleum distillates burned in internal-combustion engines and in jet chambers have supplemented or supplanted coal entirely as a source of energy. Water power, usually for driving turbo-generator conbinations, has also played an active role. Nuclear energy, solar energy, and exotic fuels are entering the scene, some already providing a source of power for rocket propulsion in a magnitude undreamed of a decade ago.

Until recent years, steam has been a universal source of energy for most transport systems—for ships, railroads, and pumping stations. The steam engine offers advantages in simplicity of design, construction, and maintenance. Because of conservative ratings, most steam engines permit a 10 to 25 percent operating overload capacity. They may be overloaded, even to the point of stalling, without injury to equipment. The steam engine has several disadvantages as well. The engine itself is usually heavy and bulky, at least for high horsepowers. It is often dirty and noisy, and the problems of water supply and ash disposal for the steam boilers are frequently acute. The horsepower curve rises slowly from zero at a standstill to a maximum (but holds that maximum rather well), thereby limiting the rate of acceleration at low speeds. There is little flexibility in control, and the transmission of power to the driving wheels or propellers sets up undesirable vibrations and dynamic impacts from the reciprocating motions of cumbersome shafting and rod arrangements. When turbines are used, complicated speed-reduction gears may be required.

Steam turbines on ships, in pumping stations, and in a few experimental locomotives offer freedom from reciprocating motion and dynamic impact. Their disadvantages for transport use lie in the high initial shaft rpm and the complex reduction gearing necessary to bring that speed to practical propeller, side-rod, or axle speed. Maintenance costs have been high, especially for locomotives.

Internal-combustion engines in either the gasoline-burning, spark-ignited or oil-burning compression type are constant-speed devices requiring some form of speed control through reduction gearing, transmission, or torque converter. Such devices have been bulky, complicated, and not always dependable for large installations (in road locomotives, for example) but have proved more practicable in fixed installations such as ships, pumping stations, or small power plants on automobiles, trucks, and buses. In pumping stations a fixed optimum speed can be used with a minimum of reduction gearing. The gasoline engine has found a wide field of usefulness in the airplane, in which reduction gearing is not necessary.

Maximum flexibility from an operating and design standpoint comes only with electric drive. The power plant may be miles away, as it is with electric locomotives, rapid transit cars, and trolley buses, or it may be self-contained, as in diesel-electric locomotives and turbo-electric ships. Electric coupling of the prime mover to the tractive element does away with the transmission or torque conversion and permits the full horsepower of the prime mover to be available over the entire speed range. The system usually consists of a steam, gasoline, or oil-burning engine driving an electric generator, which in turn provides energy for electric motors to move the driving wheels, propellers, pumps, or pulleys. The electric drive is especially useful in ships; the driving motors can be set in the stern of the vessel to permit very short propeller shafts and the generating equipment can be set midway in the vessel for better trim and stability. When smooth, rapid acceleration and deceleration for frequent starting and stopping are required, as in suburban and rapid-transit lines or in railroad-yard and switching operations, the series-wound d-c motor is usually the standard. The overload capacity of electric motors is of value, especially in starting heavy loads or negotiating steep grades. The motors may be operated well above continuous rated capacity for a short time—until they begin to overheat. When direct current is not available, a-c motors provide similar characteristics. Direct-current motors are seldom used when electric current is transmitted more than a few miles because of the heavy line losses; these losses are not present in a-c transmission. If the carrier must or can be run at constant speed, as with conveyors, pumps, compressors, cableways, and "drag" freight trains, the constant-speed induction motor finds a use.

Jet and atomic-energy principles should not be overlooked in connection with transportation. In airplanes the expulsion of fuel gases from the exhaust of the jet engine moves the aircraft by simple recoil. In gas-turbine locomotives jet gases are used to drive a turbine, which in turn drives a generator to furnish electric energy for the propulsion motors. Even with atomic energy, the anticipated system for most types of transport is that of an atomic-powered prime mover driving electric generators and motors. The prime mover will usually be located in a central power station but may find eventual application in ships, locomotives, and even airplanes and automobiles.

Thermal Efficiency. A pound of coal or a gallon of fuel oil contains a certain number of heating units from which energy capable of performing work is obtained. The potential heat or energy is expressed in British thermal units (Btu). One Btu is the amount of heat or energy necessary to perform 778 ft-lb of work or to raise the temperature of one pound of water $\frac{1}{180}$ of 32° F to 212° F, that is, a rise of 1° F at atmospheric pressure. A pound of coal will contain approximately 8500 to 14,500 Btu's. One gallon of fuel oil contains approximately 130,000 or about 18,000 to 20,000 Btu per lb. The equivalent of one kilowatt hour may be taken as 3412 Btu. Thus one pound of coal has the potential for doing 6,613,000 to 10,892,000 ft-lb of work.

Actually, only a small part of this potential energy is realized as power and propulsive force by transportation motive power. Thermal efficiency represents the percent of energy in the fuel that is available at the rim of the driving wheel or blade of the propeller. A modern stationary steam power plant can convert 18 to 32 percent of the heat in coal into energy in the steam. When a steam plant is crowded into the frame of a locomotive and given a fire-tube boiler and radiation and internal friction losses are included, the net available energy for pulling loads drops to less than 10 percent of that originally present in the coal and to little more than 5 percent after the locomotive has overcome its own inertia and tractive resistance.

Losses in the steam generator of fixed or moving plants include those due to incomplete combustion (losses in ashes and fines), to moisture in fuel and atmosphere, and to heat in sparks and gases, about 28 percent of the initial heat. There are additional losses from radiation through tube, boiler, piping, and cylinder walls and from incomplete utilization of the energy in the steam by piston or turbine blade. To these must be added frictional and inertial losses of moving parts of the prime mover and the energy cost of moving its own weight and that of its housing.

If the more efficient fixed steam plant is used to drive an electric generator and the current is fed via a power transmission line to the motors of an electric locomotive, a somewhat better efficiency results. If there is steam plant efficiency of 30 percent, electric-generator efficiency of 95 percent, power transmission efficiency of 90 percent, and traction-motor and gearing efficiencies of 85 percent, an over-all efficiency of 22 percent (22 percent of the energy in the initial pound of coal) is available in propulsive force at the driving wheel of the locomotive. If a screw-propellered ship is being driven, that efficiency is further reduced about 50 percent by losses in the propeller shaft and propeller. If a water-power plant is in question, the initial potential will depend on the hydraulic and velocity heads of the water, which are reduced immediately by internal flow losses of the water, conduit friction, etc. (see section on flow resistance, p. 182), and on the mechanical losses and utilization factor of the turbine wheels.

An internal-combustion engine can convert about 28 to 30 percent of the potential heat in a pound of liqud fuel into useful energy. Again there are incomplete combustion, moisture in fuel and atmosphere, and radiation losses to deduct. A diesel-electric locomotive, assuming 92 percent generator and 85 percent motor-gear efficiencies, would possess an over-all thermal efficiency of 23.5 percent. If the engine is used to drive a truck with 15 percent mechanical losses, the final recovery at the tire rim is 25.5 percent; if the engine is driving an airplane propeller with an efficiency of 75 percent, the recovery drops to 18.1 percent; and if the engine is on a ship with 50 percent shaft and propeller losses, the efficiency is only 12.8 percent.

Because diesel fuels contain approximately 6000 more Btu per pound than coal, there is a fuel saving in the internal-combustion engine. There is also a Btu difference between gasoline, kerosene,

and other petroleum distillates. Questions then arise about the relative abundance of various types of fuel and the effect on the economy
and the conservation policies of a country, as well as on the individual
carriers, of using one fuel in preference to another. A directly related
problem is the corresponding effect on the economy and conservation
of resources of using one type of carrier as opposed to another. These
are questions to which more research (and utilization of knowledge
already available) could profitably be devoted. This subject is given
further discussion in a section on performance criteria in a later
chapter.

Tractive Effort. Tractive force or effort is the term for propulsive
force usually found in railroad engineering. Tractive effort curves
for locomotives are prepared by the manufacturer or by the railroad's

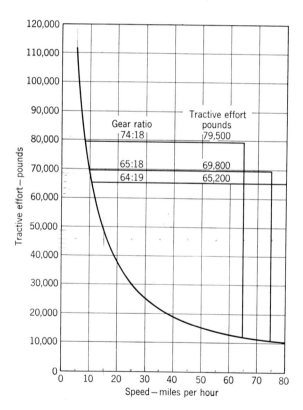

FIGURE 6-1. Tractive-effort curve—ALCO 2400-hp diesel-electric locomotive.
(Courtesy of ALCO Products, Inc., New York.)

own test department to show the tractive or propulsive force available at different speeds. Such a curve for a modern 2400-hp, general-purpose diesel-electric locomotive appears in Figure 6-1. Note that various gear ratios between the driving motors and axles give several different speed-pull ranges.

An approximate tractive effort curve for diesel-electric locomotives follows from the horsepower equation; it takes into account mechanical and electrical losses and losses to auxiliary units:

$$TE = (\text{hp}_r - \text{hp}_a) \times 375 \times e/V$$

where hp_r = rated output of the diesel engine

hp_a = horsepower used by auxiliaries

e = efficiency factor, mechanical-electrical, taken as 82.2 percent

V = velocity in miles per hour

When these factors are given numerical values from conventional design and operation, the equation reduces to

$$TE = 308 \times \text{hp}_r/V$$

The tractive effort range established by gearing is obtained by multiplying the foregoing expressions by the gear ratio.

Rated tractive effort for a steam locomotive is assumed constant to about 15 mph and is therefore used in most ruling grade studies in which the train speed is reduced by elevation effects to within that range. By equating work performed in the cylinders to work at the rim of the drivers during one revolution of the driving wheel, the rated or starting tractive effort is found to be

$$TE = 0.85Pd^2s/D$$

where TE = tractive effort in pounds

P = boiler (gage) pressure in pounds per square inch

d = cylinder diameter in inches

s = length of stroke in inches

D = diameter of driving wheel in inches

0.85 = factor to account for pressure drop between boiler and cylinder

Also, by work equations, the tractive effort of an electric locomotive is found to be

$$TE = T \times 24 \times G \times e \times N/(D \times g)$$

where T = torque in pound-feet

G and g = number of teeth in gear and pinion, respectively; the gear ratio

N = number of motors, each having torque T

e = mechanical efficiency of gears, 95 to 97 percent

D = driving wheel diameter in inches

Similar expressions can be determined for gas-turbine locomotives or other types having self-contained power plants generating electric energy for the driving motors.

There must be sufficient weight to give adhesion to the rails to prevent slippage. This limits effective tractive effort regardless of engine capacity. Diesel and electric locomotives, with steady rotative instead of reciprocating power delivery to the drivers, operate on an average coefficient of friction of 0.30 to 0.33. Experience indicates 25 percent of weight on drivers as the proper ratio between tractive effort and adhesive weight for steam locomotives. A locomotive with 240,000-lb weight on drivers might be designed for a maximum of 72,000-lb or 60,000-lb tractive effort, depending on whether it is steam or diesel-electric design. In locomotive design the reciprocal of the coefficient of friction is more often used. It is called the factor of adhesion. For a ratio of 0.25, the factor of adhesion is 4.0; for 0.30 it is 3.33.

Problem Example. A 400-ton locomotive with tractive effort of 38,000 lb at 30 mph has a unit tractive resistance of 4.4 lb per ton (by the Davis equation) and a total resistance of 1760 lb. The unit resistance of a 40-ton car at 30 mph (Davis equation) is 6.5 lb per ton. The locomotive can haul a trailing load, on tangent level track, of $(38,000 - 1760)/6.5 = 5575$ tons or a train of 139 40-ton cars.

Note in the foregoing example that 36,240 represents the gross tractive effort minus resistance of the locomotive by itself. The net tractive effort, called drawbar pull (DBP), is the force actually available for moving the cars and contents.

The tractive effort for a highway vehicle is usually expressed as torque, the force in pound-feet exerted at the rim of a flywheel of unit (1 ft) radius. Brake horsepower, also frequently used in rating high-way-vehicle motors, follows from the general horsepower equation: hp $= 2\pi RTN/33,000 = 0.00019TN$, where R = radius of flywheel = 1 ft, T = torque in pound-feet, and N = number of revolutions per minute.

Torque and horsepower curves are prepared by the manufacturer or obtained by purchaser's tests. See Figure 6-2. Torque curves of gasoline, spark-ignition engines show low values at low engine

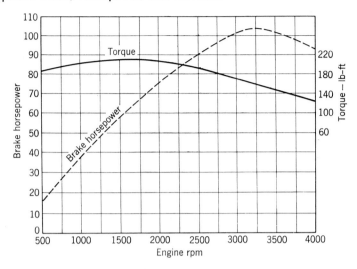

FIGURE 6-2. Torque-rpm curve (for a high-compression truck engine).

speeds, rise to a peak as engine speed increases, and then fall off rapidly. Diesel, compression-ignited engines show a flat curve with good torque at low speeds and little falling off at high engine speeds, making these particularly suitable for truck service. The most economical fuel operation comes within that speed range in which maximum torque is developed. For passenger vehicles in direct drive, this speed is about 45 mph.

Tractive effort curves can be computed from torque-hp-rpm curves by taking into account the effective gear ratio between engine shaft and rear wheels (or front, as the case may be) due to the transmission and differential gear ratios. The several possible gear combinations give a series of tire-rim torque curves. Tractive effort at the rear wheel tire rim is

$$TE = TG_tG_de/r$$

where TE = tractive effort in pounds
T = engine flywheel torque in pound-feet at a given rpm
G_t = transmission gear ratio
G_d = differential gear ratio
e = factor to cover mechanical transmission losses between engine shaft and tire rim; taken to be 0.85 to 0.90
r = loaded radius in feet of rear tires, varying with load on the vehicle and the degree of inflation

Problem Example. Assume a truck of 3 tons weight that delivers a torque of 300 lb-ft at 1400 rpm. The horsepower developed at this speed is $0.00019 \times 300 \times 1400 = 79.8$. Gear ratios are low, 6.10 to 1; second, 2.90 to 1; third, 1.60 to 1; fourth, direct (1 to 1); and differential ratio, 5.80 to 1. The truck is further assumed to have 32 x 6 in. tires, a frontal area of 50 sq ft and to be running on tangent level concrete road, offering a road resistance of approximately 20 lb per ton. In low gear the truck will produce a tractive effort at the tire rim of $300 \times 6.10 \times 5.80 \times 0.85 \times 12/15.8 = 6852$ lb. (*Note*: the 15.8 supposes a 0.2-in. radial deformation of the loaded tire.) From the horsepower formula, speed V is $79.8 \times 375/6852 = 4.4$ mph. In high gear, $TE = 300 \times 1.0 \times 5.80 \times 0.85 \times 12/15.8 = 1123$ lb. The speed is now $V = 79.8 \times 375/1123 = 26.6$ mph. Tractive resistance is found to be 131 lb. The available net tractive effort for hauling pay load is $1123 - 131$ lb $= 992$ lb at 26.6 mph on level concrete highway. In addition to moving its own weight, the truck can haul a load in tons equal to its net tractive effort of 992 lb divided by unit road resistance of 20 lb, or a pay load of 49.6 tons. Lower speed will permit a heavier load; higher speed requires a lighter load. Grades offer additional resistance, decreasing the allowable load or the speed or both. Heavier grades may be negotiated by shifting gears and decreasing the speed.

Thrust. The propulsive power of a ship or aircraft is made effective by the propeller thrust. Thrust is expressed in pounds. The total horsepower that must be delivered by the propeller against ship's resistance or airplane drag is termed effective horsepower. In the case of a ship the forward motion is imparted by frictional contact or thrust between propeller blade and water. The wake or tendency of water to follow behind a ship contributes to the thrust. There are, however, numerous losses. The blades do not bear at right angles to the water in comparison with the direction of the ship's motion. The formation of air pockets, called cavitation, around the propeller blades reduces the thrust. Shape of blade, diameter of screw and hub, number of blades, amount of screw out of water, position of propeller with relation to the ship's hull—these and other factors have a determining effect on the actual horsepower delivered by the propeller and its design and efficiency. The determination of these losses and comparative design effects involves procedures too complex and extended to be presented here. No great error will result for purposes of this text in assuming that 50 percent of the indicated horsepower of the ship's engines is lost in bearing and thrust-collar friction and in propeller inefficiency. Since the speed of a vessel is usually expressed in knots, the horsepower-thrust equation becomes $hp_i =$ thrust $\times$ velocity $\times 2 \times e/326$, where $hp_i =$ indicated horsepower of the ship's engines, velocity is in knots, 2 is a factor to cover the 50 percent loss of indicated horsepower in the propeller and shafting, and e is the mechanical efficiency of the engine, representing a 6 to 8 percent frictional loss therein. For diesel engines the frictional loss would be no more than 5 percent. When more than one propeller is used, horsepower requirements for each is the total horsepower divided by the number of propellers.

Marine power and thrust in earlier days were provided by steam-powered multiple-expansion engines driving directly on the propeller shaft. The marine power plant of today may be one or more steam (sometimes coal- but more often oil-fired) turbines driving electric generators, which in turn provide power for electric motors geared to the shaft. Diesel-electric drives are a modern development in which the diesel engine replaces the steam turbine to furnish power for the generators and motors. A diesel engine may be geared directly to the shaft through reduction gearing. The diesel-electric and the turbo-electric couplings are similar to the arrangement used in corresponding types of railroad locomotives.

Screw propellers found their initial field of usefulness in deep-draft shipping. Early river boats were propelled by paddle wheels mounted on the sides, but in later designs they were mounted at the stern. During the last 20 years towboats in increasing numbers have been built with stern propellers. The propellers are mounted in grooves or tunnels in the hull of the vessel, thereby permitting the shallow draft required for river boats and protecting the propellers from excessive damage when the draft is too great for the water's depth. See Figure 6-3.

The conventional solution of propulsive-force problems for aircraft derives from the thrust-horsepower equation

$$\text{hp}_t = \text{thrust} \times \text{speed}/33{,}000$$

where thrust is in pounds and speed is in feet per minute. Similarly $\text{hp}_d = \text{drag} \times \text{speed}/33{,}000$, where the drag in pounds establishes the necessary thrust required to overcome it. In uniform level flight the two must be at least equal to maintain a given constant speed; $T - D = 0$, where $T = $ thrust in pounds and $D = $ drag in pounds.

An airplane engine may be nominally rated in brake horsepower (Bhp) at a given number of revolutions per minute, but the effective or thrust horsepower is that which can be delivered by the propeller at a given altitude. Thp $= $ Bhp $\times n$, where Thp $= $ thrust horsepower and $n = $ propeller efficiency. Both engine efficiency and propeller efficiency vary with speed and with the air density at different altitudes. Engine efficiency, as in diesel-electric locomotives,

FIGURE 6-3. Screw propeller on a river boat. Undersize view of the towboat *A. D. HAYNES II*, showing propellers, rudders, and Kort nozzles. (Courtesy of the Dravo Corporation, Pittsburgh, Pennsylvania.)

can be improved at high altitudes with supercharging (forcing air to the fuel mixture under pressure). Curves prepared for each manufacturer's model show the brake horsepower at different revolutions per minute for various altitudes. See Figure 6-4.

In climbing, an airplane must lift its total weight upward at a certain rate. The rate of climb V_c = change in altitude in feet per minute = $da/dt = V \sin \theta$, where θ = the angle made by the path of a steady climb with the horizontal. From the horsepower equation,

$$V_c = \mathrm{hp}_e \times 33,000/W$$

where V_c = rate of climb in feet per minute

hp_e = excess thrust horsepower available at a given altitude (excess over that necessary to maintain horizontal flight)

W = weight in pounds of the plane and its contents

At any given altitude, the maximum speed is determined by the maximum horsepower available. At any speed less than the maximum, there is an excess of horsepower available for climb at any given altitude. See Figure 6-5. By inserting the value of excess horsepower in the equation for V_c, the rate of climb at a given altitude is obtained. Figure 6-6 shows a series of such points plotted for various altitudes.

The point at which the maximum thrust horsepower available equals the maximum thrust horsepower required establishes the ceiling of the airplane. The point at which rate of climb becomes less than 100 ft per min usually sets the service or cruising ceiling of the craft.

When the airplane is on the ground in take-off or landing, the more familiar rules of tractive resistance apply. The total ground resistance

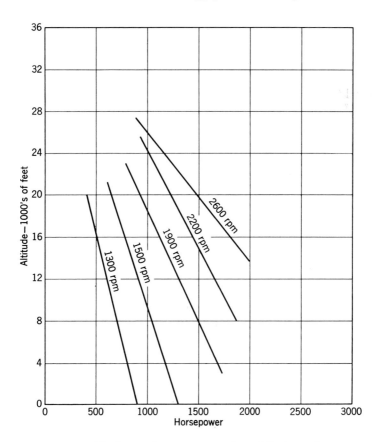

FIGURE 6-4. Engine performance at various altitudes and rpm.

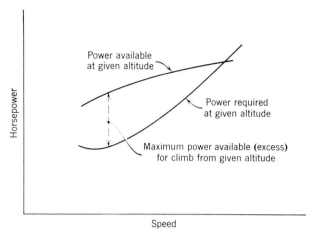

FIGURE 6-5. Excess horsepower available for climb.

is equal to the sum of air resistance and rolling resistance as for a land vehicle, or $R_g = D + R_r$. For an airplane, the air resistance is the drag, or $D = CD_p\rho v^2S/2$ and $R_r = f(W - L)$, where f varies from 0.02 for concrete runways to 0.10 for an average unpaved field with long grass, depending on the smoothness, and $L = $ lift $= C_L v^2S/2$. As the run starts, the effective angle of attack is minimal, giving a maximum L/D ratio. The accelerating force available to give the plane sufficient

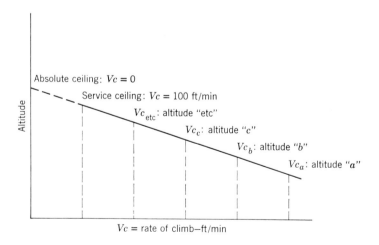

FIGURE 6-6. Ceiling of an airplane.

speed for take-off is the excess thrust $T_e = T_v - (D + R_r)$, where T_v = ground speed thrust and D and R_r are as given above. As the speed increases, the drag becomes greater because of the higher speed, tending thereby to reduce T_e. At the same time, however, the lift increases with speed and lessens the load on the wheels as more and more of the load is borne by the wings. As the angle of attack is changed abruptly to make the craft air-borne, the wing drag becomes much greater thereby reducing the speed. Take-off speed must accordingly be greater than the stalling speed to counteract the sudden drop in velocity. A take-off speed corresponding to 70 to 90 percent of the maximum C_L is used, whereby (using 90 percent) v (at take-off) $= v_{\text{stall}}.W/(C_{L\text{ max.}})S/2 = 1.054v_{\text{stall.}}$.

Problem Example. Referring to the problem example of Chapter 5, the propulsive force available for acceleration at the beginning of the take-off run (when, for example, the airplane has attained a speed of 20 mph) is $T_e = T_{v20} - (D + R_r)$. Assuming an 85-percent propeller efficiency, $T_{v20} = 2 \times 1600 \times 0.85 \times 375/20 = 51,000$ lb. $T_e = 51,000 - [C_{Dp}v^2S\rho/2 + 0.02(25,000 - C_{L\text{ min.}}v^2S\rho/2)]$. From Figure 5-5, $C_L = 0.43$, for an effective angle of attack of 2 degrees, and $C_{Dp} = 0.0056$. Inserting these and values for the wing area, speed of 20 mph, and ground-level density of 0.0024 in the foregoing equation, $T_e = 50,503$ at 20 mph.

As the plane is about to be air-borne, practically all the wheel load is taken by the wing so that R_r = zero and $T_e = T_v - D$. Assuming a stalling speed of 80 mph, v (at take-off) $= T_{84.32} - 0.013 \times 0.0024 \times (84.32 \times 1.47)^2 \times 980/2 = 102$ lb. ($T_v = 2 \times 1600 \times 0.85 \times 375/84.32 = 12,000$). $T_e = 12,000 - 102 = 11,898$ lb. This is a somewhat simplified approach to the problem.

Pumping Pressures. Oil is forced through a pipeline by a pumping pressure P, expressed either in pounds per square inch or in feet of head, which overcomes the flow resistance expressed in the same units. The total force to move the liquid and the corresponding horsepower required by the pumping equipment is the power actually delivered to the liquid, that is, the weight of the liquid $\times$ the head:

$$\text{hp}_f = W_f \times h/33,000$$

where hp_f = horsepower delivered to the fluid
W_f = weight in pounds of the fluid flow per minute
h = total head of liquid in feet and is equal to pumping pressure$/62.4 \times$ specific gravity of the fluid

Pumping pressure is provided by pumps in initial and booster stations along the line of flow. Reciprocating pumps were commonly used in early stations and have been installed in some more recent, but the multistage centrifugal pump is more widely used today. Steam and internal-combustion engines (usually diesels) and electric motors drive the pumps. The diesel engine has an advantage in pumping some oils in that the fuel can be drawn from the cargo being pumped.

The horsepower delivered by a reciprocating pump is the product of the force (pumping pressure P in pounds per square inch $\times$ area of the piston in square inches) and the distance in feet through which that force is applied in unit time:

$$\text{hp} = P(\pi d^2 s/4) \times n \times N/33,000$$

where d is the piston diameter in square inches, s is the stroke in feet, n is the number of strokes per minute, and N is the number of pump barrels or pistons.

In practical units the flow B is usually stated in barrels per hour. The volume of oil in barrels displaced per hour by the pump is $A \times s \times n \times 12 \times 60/9702$, where A is the piston area in square inches, s and n are as before, and 9702 is the number of cubic inches in a 42-gal barrel. The horsepower, then, is $\text{hp} = 0.0004PB$, where P is again the pumping pressure in pounds per square inch and B is the volume pumped in barrels per hour. For a multicylindered pump, the foregoing is multiplied by N, the number of pistons, and, for a double-acting pump, the number of strokes must be multiplied by two. The actual volume and therefore the horsepower delivered to the liquid may be 3 to 20 percent less than that computed from pump dimensions due to slip. Mechanical efficiency is the ratio of the horsepower delivered to the fluid hp_f to that delivered to the pump shaft ph_s by the prime mover, or $e = \text{hp}_f/\text{hp}_s$. Working pressures for piston pumps may be as much as 1400 psi.

Centrifugal pumps have different characteristics. The quantity of discharge varies directly as the speed, so that horsepower characteristics are usually expressed at a certain rpm and curves are prepared to show the relation between that speed and head, capacity, horsepower, and efficiency. The head or pumping pressure varies as the square of the speed and the horsepower as the cube of the speed. At a given speed, the capacity decreases as the pressure increases. Pressures of 1200 to 1400 psi are possible with these pumps. Two or more may be connected in series to develop the combined pressure of each. When combined in parallel, the capacities are correspondingly increased.

Aerial Tramways. Aerial tramways (also cableways or ropeways) are examples of band drive. Aerial tramways are in most frequent

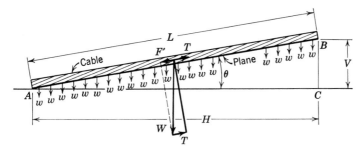

FIGURE 6-7. Forces in aerial-tramway traction cable.

use over rugged terrain and inclines where no other type of transport can penetrate economically. There is a similarity between the gradient analysis for cableways and that for railroads and other land vehicles, except that the angle of ascent (or descent) may be much greater than for railroads and highways. See Figure 6-7. The following derivations are based on an analysis by Edward B. Dunham.[1] Consider first a body on an inclined plane AB. To keep the body from sliding down the incline, a force T, equal in magnitude to the component of the total force acting down the plane, must be exerted up and parallel to the plane. W = weight acting at the center of gravity of the body = wL, where w = unit weight per foot of length of the body along plane AB having length L. Then $T = F' = wL \sin \theta$, which tends to move the cable down the plane. If the body is moved up the incline, an additional force F must be exerted to overcome the friction between the plane AB and the component of W perpendicular to the plane or $F = f'wL \cos \theta$, where f' is the coefficient of friction between the body and the plane.

In applying these relations to aerial tramways, the foregoing body may be considered as the traction cable having a unit weight per foot w, which includes a prorated share of the weight of the cars, so that for the loaded side of the system $w_l = (C_l/d) + w_r$, where w_l = weight per foot of cable of car and cable in pounds, C_l = weight of cars and contents in pounds, d = car spacing on the cable in feet, and w_r = weight per foot of the traction cable alone. See Figure 6-8. On the empty or return side, $w_e = (C_e/d) + w_r$, where w_e = weight per foot of cable and empty car (or loaded car if the cars are carrying a return

[1] Edward B. Dunham, Aerial Tramways and Cableways, Peele's *Mining Engineer's Handbook*, Third Edition, Section 26, John Wiley and Sons, New York, 1941, pp. 06–07, 24–25.

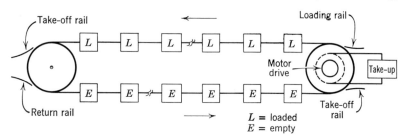

FIGURE 6-8. Aerial-tramway layout.

load), C_e = weight of empty car (or car plus return load) in pounds, and d and w_r have the same significance as before. The body or cable is moving on and supported by the plane AB, which in an actual installation becomes the rail cable. (*Note:* a similar analysis applies to tramways mounted on conventional steel rails but propelled by a traction cable.)

Let $L \sin \theta = BC = V$ and $L \cos \theta = AC = H$. The general expression for rope tension becomes $T = wV \pm f'wH$, where $f' = 0.02$ for sheaves and carriage wheels with plain bearings and 0.01 for roller bearings. The term $f'wH$ is additive when the rope is moving up the incline but negative when the rope moves down the incline.

Two possible situations must usually be considered in ropeway layouts: (*a*) loaded carriages descending and (*b*) loaded carriages ascending. In (*a*), with the loaded cars descending, T_l = tension on the loaded side = $w_lV - F'w_lH$, and T_e = tension on the ascending side with (usually) empty cars = $w_eV + f'w_eH$. The effective tension E or tractive effort = $T_l - T_e = T - S$, where $S = T_e$ = slack or empty side tension. In (*b*) with the empty side descending, $T_e = w_eV - f'w_eH$, and the loaded side ascending has $T_l = w_lV + F'wH$. Again $E = T_l - T_e = T - S$. See Figures 6-7 and 6-8.

The horsepower requirements are hp = $Ev/33,000 = (T - S)v/33,000$, where E and S have the foregoing values, and v is the traction rope and car speed in feet per minute. Frictional losses in the prime mover and operating mechanism have a horsepower equivalence = $0.000,001W_mv$. The total horsepower, then, is hp = $[(T - S)/33,000 \pm 0.000,001W_m]v$, where W_m = weight of moving terminal machinery in pounds.

It can be seen from the foregoing that when there is a significantly lower elevation at the discharge end of the system the power needs will be very small or may even permit regeneration and a gain in power for other uses.

From analytical mechanics, the band drive equation $T = Se^{\pi f n}$ indicates the relation between tight and slack side tensions needed to produce drive, where T = tension on the tight side in pounds, e = base of natural logarithms = 2.71828, f = coefficient of rope or sheave friction = 0.170, when rope and sheave are dry, and 0.085, when wet, and n = number of half- or 180-degree turns of laps on the driving drum or sheave. The usual form of the band-drive equation comes by subtracting S from both sides of equation or $T - S$ = tractive force = $S(e^{\pi f n} - 1)$. Computations have been simplified by using tables that evaluate the expression $e^{\pi f n}$. A summary of such evaluations is given in Table 6-1.

In designing a system, a trial selection of driving sheave is made, and the value of S is determined from $T - S = S(e^{\pi f m} - 1)$ by substituting therein the value for $T - S$. If S is less than tension T_e on the slack or empty side, no tension weight is required other than that needed to keep the tension rope taut at the drive sheave. If S is greater than tension T_e, $S - T_e = T_w$, a tension weight equal to twice the difference T_w, or $2T_w$, is placed at the lower or nonpower end. The minimum size of cable consistent with other requirements is desirable, since the cables constitute the major items in cableway construction and operating costs. It should be noted that power

Table 6-1. Values of $e^{\pi f m}$

f	n = Number of Half-laps about Sheave or Drum					
	1	2	3	4	5	6
0.070	1.246	1.552	1.934	2.410	3.033	3.741
0.100	1.369	1.875	2.566	3.514	4.810	6.586
0.150	1.602	2.566	4.111	6.586	10.551	16.902
0.200	1.875	3.514	6.856	12.346	23.140	43.376
0.300	2.566	6.586	16.902	43.376	111.318	285.680
0.500	4.810	23.140	111.318	535.448	2575.940	—

Condensed from William Hewitt, as reported by E. B. Dunham's Aerial Tramways and Cableways, Peele's *Mining Engineer's Handbook*, Third Edition, Section 26, John Wiley and Sons, 1941, pp. 26–27.

drives can also be placed on the lower rather than the upper end of a system, a variation not detailed here.

Conveyors. The conveyor is a variation of belt drive. The principles of design are similar to those for cableways. Resistance of rollers, load, and elevation are usually overcome by an electric motor, mounted on, coupled to, or geared to the drive-pulley shaft. There must be frictional adhesion (as with trucks, locomotives, and other wheeled vehicles) between the driving-pulley surface and the belt, in order for the belt to move. This again requires an effective or tractive tension equal to the difference in tight and slack side tensions, whereby $E = T - S$, where E = effective tension in pounds, and T and S are, respectively, the tight and slack side tensions in pounds. The horsepower to drive the belt is hp $= Ev/33,000$ or hp $= (T - S)v/33,000$, where v is the belt speed in feet per minute. There must be tractive (effective) force and horsepower to (a) move the empty belt on the incline, (b) move the load horizontally, and (c) raise the load vertically.

When a load is to be raised H feet above the horizontal on an inclined belt (see Figure 6-9), the length of belt on the incline is $L_i = H/\sin A$. The cargo load per foot of belt is from the earlier section, $= 100T/(3S)$ from which the total cargo W on the rollers is $W = (100T/3S)(H/\sin A)$. A component of gravity R tends to move the loaded belt downward. It must be restrained by an equal and opposite force $F = W \sin A = (100TH/3S)(S/33,000) = TH/990$. Using values from Chapter 5 for a level loaded belt, the horsepower to move the level empty belt $= CQ(L + L_0)(S/33,000) = C(L + L_0)(0.03QS)/990$, and to move the load alone on a level belt the horsepower $=$ hp$_l = CQ(L + L_0)(\text{speed}/33,000) = C(L + L_0)(100T/3S)(S/33,000) = C(L + L_0)T/990$. The total horsepower on an incline will be the sum of the horsepower for the empty belt plus horsepower to move the load horizontally plus horsepower to raise the load H feet: hp $=$ hp$_e +$ hp$_l +$ hp$_v = C(L + L_0) \times (0.03QS/990) + C(L + L_0)T/990 \pm TH/990$ or hp $= C(L + L_0) \times (T + 0.03QS)/990 \pm TH/990$ where $(TH/900)$ is added if the point of discharge is higher than the point of origin, subtracted if it is lower.[2]

Like cableways, the maximum or tight side tension is a function of the adhesion to the driving pulley. With conveyors, the value of n, the number of half-turns around the driving pulley, becomes the

[2] *Goodyear Handbook of Belting: Conveyor and Elevator,* the Goodyear Tire and Rubber Company, Akron, Ohio, 1953, pp. 70–71.

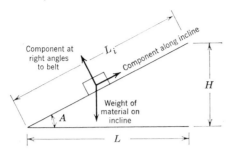

Component at right angles to belt

L_i

Component along incline

H

Weight of material on incline

A

L

FIGURE 6-9a. Conveyor belt on an incline—theory of vertical lift.

FIGURE 6-9b. Conveyor belt on an incline—world's highest conveyor-belt lift; raises 1200 tons of coal per hour a height of 868 ft, in a Southern Illinois coal mine. (Courtesy of the Goodyear Tire and Rubber Company, Akron, Ohio.)

arc of contact in half-turn or 180-degree multiples. Thus the previous expression, $T = Se^{\pi f m}$ may be converted to the logarithmic base 10, and, putting the equation in its more useful form, $T - S = S(10^{0.00758fa} - 1)$, where $a =$ arc of contact and f is the coefficient of friction. A lower value of S, and therefore of the maximum T, is obtained by increasing the coefficient of friction either by lagging the pulley or by snubbing the belt to increase the area of contact or both. The coefficient of friction between rubber (covered) belting and pulley steel is 0.25. If the pulley has a rubber lagging, f is increased to 0.35. Theoretically, $f = 0.55$ to 0.75 for clean rubber surfaces in contact. These ideal conditions do not exist in practice, where belt, pulley, or more likely both become greasy, dirty, wet, or dusty. The arc of contact can be further increased by using two drive pulleys interlocked or dual pulleys driven by separate motors.

In the design of the tractive requirements for a conveyor, the necessary horsepower is determined first, followed by the effective tension E, maximum tension T, and slack side tension S. The horsepower to move the empty belt is a function of its weight in pounds, the length of belt (per flight) in feet, and the belt speed in feet per minute. The weight of the belt is established by the belt materials, the number of plies, method of manufacture, and the width. Once a capacity in tons per hour has been determined, the belt width and speed to handle that tonnage are selected. These depend in turn on the weight per cubic foot of the materials being handled. The horsepower to move horizontally and raise the load is next determined by the methods earlier described or by use of manufacturer's or handbook values. An approximate 10 percent increase in speed requirements is desirable to compensate for belt slip.

The vertical rise in the load is a function of the length and gradient of the belt. The gradient on the belt is limited by the angle of repose of the materials being conveyed. The angle varies between 10 degrees for briquettes, 12 degrees for washed gravel, 15 degrees for grain and dry sand, 18 degrees for pit-run gravel and mine-run coal, and 20 degrees for bituminous slack coal, crushed ore, and damp sand.[3] The horsepower to overcome elevations usually exceeds that for moving the load and belt horizontally. A brake is needed to prevent the belt from running backward when stopped.

The conveyor belt is a constant-speed operation with an overload requirement at starting. A favorite type of conveyor drive is the double-wound rotor or slip-ring type of squirrel-cage induction motor with high torque but low starting current requirements.[4] Variation in the starting torque is desirable because of the higher

[3] Wilbur G. Hudson, *Conveyors and Related Equipment,* Third Edition, John Wiley and Sons, New York, 1954, p. 229.

[4] *Ibid.,* pp. 236–237.

torque required to put the belt in motion, especially when the bearings are cold. Other types of transport experience the same difficulty.

GRADES AND ELEVATION

Gradients. The effects of elevation on aircraft, conveyors, cableways, and, by implication, waterways have already been considered. There remains the effect of grades and elevation on land-based vehicles, especially railroads and highways. Gradient is defined as the rate of grade. In the United States gradient is usually defined as the vertical rise in feet per 100 ft of horizontal distance. Thus a 1 percent grade is a rise of 1 ft in 100 ft, a 2 percent grade is a rise of 2 ft in 100 ft, etc. The effects of gradients on construction and operating costs are often limiting. Grade resistance of 20 lb per ton of train or vehicle weight by percent of grade must be overcome by the tractive effort of locomotive or vehicle engine.

Assume a car of weight $W = 1$ ton (2000 lb) on a unit or 1 percent grade, AB. See Figure 6-10. The weight W, acting vertically downward, can be resolved into two components, V, acting perpendicularly into the plane of the road or rails, and F', which tends to roll the car downhill. To prevent downward rolling, that is, to overcome grade resistance, an equal and opposite force F must be exerted up the grade by the tractive force of the truck engine or locomotive. If we establish a proportion between force and distance triangles and assume $AB = AC$, approximately, we can see that $F/2000 = \frac{1}{100}$, from which $F = 20$ lb per ton by percent of grade. Note the similarity of this derivation to that involving aerial tramways and conveyors.

In the following problem examples, train and grade resistance are taken into account. The conditions of the earlier problem on train

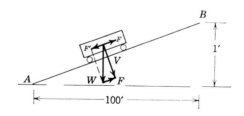

FIGURE 6-10. Derivation of unit grade resistance.

resistance are the same except that the train is operating on an 0.80 percent grade.

Problem Example. The total locomotive resistance becomes 400(4.4 + 0.8 × 20), or 8160 lb, leaving a drawbar pull of 29,860 lb. Unit resistance for the 40-ton cars at 30 mph is 6.5 + 0.8 × 20, or 22.5 lb per ton. The tonnage rating of the locomotive will be 29,860/22.5, or 1327 tons. The train will now consist of 1327/40, or 33 cars. Introducing the 0.80 percent grade has reduced the train load or tonnage rating from 5576 tons (139 cars) to 1327 tons (33 cars), a reduction of approximately 76 percent. If 60,000 tons are to be moved daily, 11 trains will be required on level track, and 45 trains will be required on the 0.80 percent grade (assuming no reduction in speed).

Problem Example. Using the earlier truck problem and assuming a 4 percent grade, the combined resistance to overcome by the engine tractive effort or tire-rim torque for the truck alone is $R = 3(20 + 4 \times 20) + 0.002 \times 50 \times 708 = 371$ lb of the available 1124-lb tractive effort (using a simplified version of the road-resistance formula to obtain that part of the resistance). Only 753 lb of tractive effort are now available to move net tonnage or pay load. The combined road and grade resistance of pay load per ton is $20 + 4 \times 20 = 100$ lb per ton. The total pay load the truck can carry on the 4 percent grade is 753/100 = 7.53 tons. This is a decrease of 42.1 tons or 85 percent. To haul a given quantity of freight at the same speed, 85 percent more truck units would be required, if the same speed and gear combination were maintained, than on a level highway.

The locating engineer must therefore keep his gradients as light as possible. In rugged difficult terrain light grades usually require expensive construction by heavy excavation, bridging, or tunneling. Development, the introduction of additional distance to reduce the rate of grade, lowers the gradient but may be hard to secure. The added distance and curvature increase construction and operating costs, especially for railroads.

The ruling grade of a railroad is that which establishes the maximum train load to be hauled at a given speed by one locomotive. Steeper grades may appear on the profile, but they must be operated with helper engines, by reducing train loads, or, for very short grades, by momentum. A ruling grade on the highway defines the maximum load a truck can haul at a given speed with a stated gear combination, usually low gear. The ruling grade concept is not widely used in highway design and operation because other factors are usually more restrictive.

Analogous to the ruling grade is the limiting grade, which is so steep that it reduces vehicle speed and thereby limits the number of vehicles that can negotiate that grade in a given time. Its effect is a function of the speed that can be maintained by the slowest-moving class of vehicles operating over it, and therefore it has a significant influence on highway capacity.

Other Effects of Gradients. In addition to limiting the size of load and therefore the speed and number of hauling units, gradients affect operating costs by (a) wear and tear on equipment, (b) fuel consumption, and (c) increased time on the road.

Wear and tear. The use of sand, drag of brakes, and wheel slippage introduce significant wear on railroad tracks and equipment and may affect other cost items, for example, signals. Every 26.4 ft of rise and fall (26.4 ft of rising grade followed by 26.4 ft of descending grade) on heavy grades will increase costs per 1000 gross ton-miles as much as 9 percent.[5] Grades also cause excess wear on truck motors, bodies, brakes, and tires and, to a lesser extent, on passenger vehicles. The amount is small in comparison with fuel costs occasioned by heavy grades and can usually be ignored except in the most rugged terrain.

Fuel. Gradients require increased fuel consumption. For railroads, the 7 to 9 percent increase in cost per 1000 gross ton-miles occasioned by grades is for fuel. Consumption for highway vehicles maintaining a constant speed increases as the percent of grade.

Ideally, the increased fuel consumption due to an ascending grade can be compensated for by the decreased consumption as the vehicle descends the opposite slope, where the force of gravity acts to overcome propulsive resistance. Three situations may exist that warrant examination.

1. When the force of gravity just equals propulsive resistance at the desired speed, no propulsive force or fuel (except that used by an idling engine or, in a steam locomotive, that used to maintain a potential reserve of steam) is required, and a constant speed is maintained. For an average train resistance of 6 lb per ton, this equilibrium grade would be 0.30 percent. For an average truck resistance of 40 lb per ton at 40 mph, the balancing grade would be 2 percent.

2. When gravity acts with less than the force of propulsive resistance (lighter grades than the "balancing grades" in the foregoing example), propulsive effort must be exerted by the truck or locomotive engine to maintain a constant speed rather than a deceleration.

3. If the grade is heavier than the foregoing examples and exerts a gravitational force greater than the average propulsive resistance,

---

[5] W. W. Hay, *Railroad Engineering,* Vol. I, John Wiley and Sons, New York, 1953, pp. 168–172.

the vehicle will accelerate. If acceleration is not unduly great so that no brakes are applied, the grade is termed "drifting" or "floating." If acceleration extends beyond safe or authorized maximum speeds, brakes must be applied to offset the effects of gravity. If no brakes are applied, the same fuel economy as in the first situation will exist, but long and continued brake application can be costly, and even a slight application will cause a theoretical loss in economy. For a train, delays as great as 20 to 30 minutes may ensue to permit cooling the wheels and brakeshoes. Electric trains descending long grades can, in some installations, reverse the leads on the motors and cause them to generate electric energy, which is fed back to the line as a credit to power consumption. The drag on the motors may reduce the need for conventional braking. Diesel-electrics may also enjoy the advantages of dynamic braking but not of power regeneration. The energy generated by the motors when "generating" has to be wasted in heat through grids on the locomotive roof.

For highway vehicles, the maximum ascending grade (6 to 7 percent), for greatest economy, should permit approximately the same speed as on the level with no change in gears. The economical descending grade is the floating grade, about 6 percent for passenger vehicles but less for trucks and buses.

Length of grade. Long ascending grades require increased fuel consumption over an extended distance. Use by trucks of lower gears increases fuel consumption and time. Over a long run, the accumulation of the time thus lost may be a critical factor in wage costs both for trucks and trains. Long grades dissipate in external losses the velocity head or momentum that comes from initial speed. Lowered speed on long grades contributes significantly to traffic congestion (note the limiting-grade concept), reduces highway and track capacity, and creates accident hazards on highways.

Long, descending, floating and drifting grades are economical and permit the recapture of energy expended in attaining the initial elevation (at a fuel saving) up to the limit of that necessary to overcome propulsive resistance in the descent.

Railroad grades for high-speed, main-line operation should not exceed 0.50 percent, although 1.0 percent is acceptable. Grades of 1.0 to 2.0 percent are considered difficult and are used only on secondary lines, industrial roads, or when extremely heavy terrain prohibits anything better. Grades over 2.0 percent are very difficult and occur only when no other grade can be located. Few grades anywhere exceed 3 percent. Adequate traction cannot be maintained on grades of 5 percent or more without some form of rack assistance.

Highway requirements are less exacting in these respects, owing partly to the lightness of the vehicles, partly to the ability to shift gears, and partly to the higher coefficient of friction between the tire and pavement. First-class roads should not exceed 3 to 5 percent for dense, high-speed passenger and heavy truck traffic. Secondary roads or those designed principally for passenger vehicles may go as high as 7 percent. Anything over 7 percent is excessive and should be used only for temporary or occasional hauling.

Momentum. The reader is probably aware that a hill can be negotiated with more ease, to a greater elevation, and at a faster speed if approached at a high rate of speed by "taking a run for it." The aid thus rendered by speed is called momentum. From mechanics, a body, by virtue of its elevation, possesses potential energy and the ability to acquire speed, due to the acceleration of gravity as it falls from that elevation. Expressed mathematically, $h = v^2/2g$, where h = the elevation or height of fall in feet, and v is the final speed in feet per second that the body has acquired. Conversely, a body moving at a velocity of v ft per sec can expend that kinetic energy in rising to an elevation of h ft. If the velocity is expressed in miles per hour and approximately 5 percent is added to include rotative energy stored in moving wheels, $h = 0.035V^2$. The energy of momentum is additive to the energy being exerted by the prime mover, engine, or locomotive.

Such additional energy might be used to overcome a grade at a high average speed or to cross a summit at a higher elevation in the same horizontal distance, that is, by a steeper grade. Thus, if by virtue of the motive power alone, a grade of G_t can be overcome in the distance L (in 100-ft engineering stations), the maximum grade G_m that can be attained by motive power and momentum together would be

$$G_m = G_t + 0.035(V_i{}^2 - V_f{}^2)/L$$

where V_i and V_f are the initial and final velocities, respectively.

For example, a train or truck can just maintain motion on a 2400-ft, 1.2 percent grade at a speed of 10 mph by virtue of motive power alone. If the grade is approached at an initial speed of 30 mph, the 10-mph minimum could be maintained over a steeper grade of the same length of $G_m = 1.2 + 0.035(30^2 - 10^2)$ or a 2.4 percent grade.

Momentum should never be considered, except as a factor of safety, in the design of ruling grades. A tonnage train stopped on the ruling grade would lose all its momentum and be unable to start. A truck could shift gears (unless already in low gear) but at a sacrifice of speed.

Short grades can be negotiated by momentum both on railroads and highways. The loss of speed on the ascending slope can be regained on the downward slope. On a rolling profile it is thus possible to operate with no throttle change. The demand on the engine is constant, as if the train or truck were on a level grade. There is some loss in time but a saving in fuel. This is, in a sense, a rewording of the floating- and drifting-grade concept.

Elevation in Pipelines. The problem of grades as such does not arise in pipeline location except as it affects the difficulties of actual

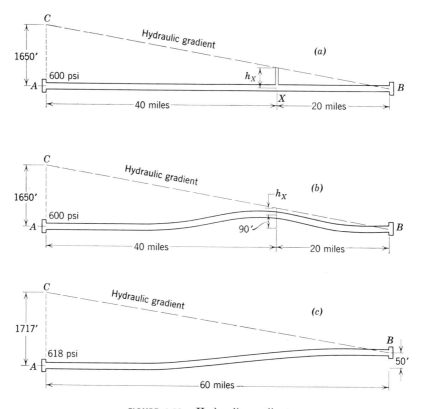

FIGURE 6-11. Hydraulic gradients.

construction. Differences in elevation between initial and final terminals or between any two pumping stations on the line are, however, important and add to or subtract from the pumping effort, depending on whether the initial point is higher or lower than the terminal point.

The high point between two stations is determined, and a hydraulic gradient is prepared. The hydraulic gradient is the loci of equivalent heights of columns of liquid if piezometer tubes were to be placed at intervals along the line. It shows the pressure change between any two points. In Figure 6-11a CB is the hydraulic gradient for the line AB. The only resistance to the 600 psi pumping pressure is flow resistance, which is sufficient to reduce the pressure to approximately zero at B. AC is the pressure in equivalent feet of head obtained as shown in the following problem example.

Problem Example. The unit pressure at the base of a 1-cu-ft column of water is $62.4/144 = 0.434$ psi. Oil with a specific gravity of 0.82 weighs 0.82×62.4, or 51.2 lb per cu ft density, and unit pressure is $51.2/144 = 0.360$ psi. The head AC corresponding to 600 psi is $h_a = 600/0.36$, or 1650 ft. At X, 40 miles from A, the head h_x by similar triangles is 550 ft and pressure is $550 \times 0.36 = 198$ psi. As a check, the average pressure loss of $600/60 = 10$ lb per mile. In 40 miles the pressure loss is 40×10, or 400 psi, leaving 200 psi pressure at X. A piezometer tube placed in the pipe would rise to the height $h_x = 550$ ft.

If elevation is introduced between A and B, as in Figure 6-11b, the head at X is no longer $h_x = 550$ ft.

Assume that the elevation of the line at X is 90 ft. The head required to overcome the 90 ft of rise would be 90 ft, leaving $h_x = 460$ ft and pressure at $X = 165.6$ psi. Since A and B are still at the same level, the loss of pressure in raising the oil over the crest of X is regained in going back to the lower elevation at B. If, however, B is at a higher elevation than A, sufficient initial head must be added at A to overcome the resistance of elevation. If the 800 psi is just enough to overcome flow resistance on an effective level grade, there must be additional pressure and head to lift the oil 50 ft higher to the elevation at B. Pressure at A must be $600 + (50 \times 0.36) = 618$ psi and $h_{AC} = 618/0.36 = 1717$ ft.

If B had been lower than A, gravity would have aided the flow. In general, the difference in heads between "upstream" and "downstream" ends of the line must be added to or subtracted from the pressure losses caused by resistance alone. If an intermediate elevation were higher than the hydraulic gradient, the line would not continue to flow unless there were suction (vacuum) applied at the downstream end. Thus the locating engineer's principal concern with intermediate grades and elevation is to stay below the hydraulic gradient and select the easiest route for construction. The over-all differences in elevation should be kept to a minimum to avoid the need for excess pumping pressures. Here again a balance must be secured between costs of building to a low elevation and costs of building and operating higher-pressured pumping units. This problem must be resolved at the time the hydraulic gradient is prepared. Abrupt changes in elevation, even within the hydraulic gradient, should be avoided, especially close to a pumping station. It is desirable to have the initial terminal at a lower level than the gathering lines so that gravity will aid in feeding oil to the point of concentration.

Canal Gradients. Canals have a problem somewhat similar to that of pipelines, although in its application it is far more exacting. Canal grades are almost level and are of little value in overcoming elevation. Elevation is overcome by locks which raise (or lower) the vessels vertically in one or more stages through the lock chambers. The water level in the lock chamber is then raised or lowered by gravity, as explained in an earlier chapter. The engineer must balance the costs of crossing a divide at a low level with few locks against the cheaper but higher cost in locks of locating over a higher elevation. He also must decide whether to make the lift in several short stages or at one time in one big stage.

Airplane Elevation. Aircraft ceilings and rate of climb have been discussed in an earlier section. Gradients for airport runways should be as level as conditions permit. Only enough gradient to produce adequate drainage should be allowed in a commercial airport. As long-distance flights are normally made in the stratosphere to benefit by prevailing winds (and traffic clearance), to reduce air drag, and to avoid traffic at lower altitudes, variations in terrain have no meaning except in the presence of very high mountain peaks or ridges. Navigation charts must indicate these points, and routes will follow passes through the barriers or circumvent the peaks as a ship sails around a reef or island. Planes may also go to still higher altitudes and pass over these obstructions. For lower-flying craft, the passes must be clearly charted. The design of radio beacons and markers for established routes is a matter of navigational control and is discussed in a later chapter.

In regard to airport location, altitude has an important effect in determining the lengths of runways and therefore the space requirements. At high altitudes longer runways are required than for the same plane and load at lower altitudes because the density of the atmosphere is less and a greater initial speed is required to secure the

FIGURE 6-12. Longview Station, Mid-Valley Pipe Line Company—2–800-hp diesel engines pumping crude oil. (Courtesy of R. B. Ward and *The Oil and Gas Journal,* Tulsa, Oklahoma.)

FIGURE 6-13. Clark centrifugal compressors, Texas Eastern gas-transmission line. (Courtesy of R. B. Ward and *The Oil and Gas Journal,* Tulsa, Oklahoma.)

necessary lift for take-off. (More is said on this subject in the later discussion of terminals and in Chapter 5). A runway requirement of 4700 ft at sea level becomes 5700 ft at a 4000-ft elevation and 6700 ft at 8000 ft.

As in other modes of transport, an airplane may descend from a high to a lower altitude aided by the force of gravity, with reduced fuel consumption during the time of descent. Corresponding degrees of economy are not realized in practice because the airplane does not rise to higher elevations by the aid of momentum. If an initial terminal is higher than the destination terminal, there will be some economy in the downward flight, as contrasted to one in the opposite direction. However, as a significant percent of the airplane's power and fuel are exerted in producing lift, the relations between thrust, gravity, and drag are not so important as for land-based vehicles.

QUESTIONS FOR STUDY

1. Using thermal and mechanical efficiency values as given in this chapter, develop the over-all thermal efficiencies of a pipeline, a conveyor, and a cableway.

2. An 2400-hp diesel-electric locomotive weighs 130 tons and has a unit tractive resistance of 5 lb per ton at 20 mph on tangent level track. How many 60-ton cars can this locomotive haul on tangent level track? Compare its level track performance with what it could do on an 0.80 percent grade.

3. Using the locomotive of Question 2, plot a curve showing the relation between horsepower per ton and gradient on ½, 1, 2, and 3 percent grades.

4. A motor truck, weighing 5 tons empty, develops a horsepower of 180 at 1440 rpm. Gear ratios are low, 6.00 to 1, second, 3.00 to 1, third, 1.70 to 1, fourth, 1 to 1, and the differential ratio is 5.90 to 1. Tires are 32 x 6 in., depressing an average of 0.40 in. Cross-sectional area of the truck is 80 sq ft. The truck is on smooth concrete roadway. Determine (a) the available net tractive effort for hauling pay load and the speed in high gear when empty, (b) the pay load at that speed, and (c) the effect on pay load of a 5 percent grade.

5. Refer to the ship in Question 2, Chapter 5. What propeller horsepower and what shaft horsepower will be required to drive the ship?

6. Refer to Question 8 of Chapter 5. What pump horsepower and what prime-mover horsepower will be required if the pump is a three-pistoned, double-acting reciprocating machine?

7. Refer to Question 9 of Chapter 5. What horsepower will be required for the two belt speeds if the belt is (a) level throughout, (b) on a 12-degree slope throughout?

8. Given the following data for an aerial tramway, empty car weight = 500 lb, cargo weight per car = 900 lb, cars spaced with 400 ft of headway, weight of

traction cable = 0.92 lb per ft, horizontal length of tramway = 7200 ft, elevation of the lower end = 380 ft, elevation of the upper end = 1900 ft, and cars are equipped with plain bearings, calculate (a) force developed when the loaded cars are descending, (b) horsepower when loaded cars are descending, (c) propulsive force required when loaded cars are ascending, and (d) horsepower required when loaded cars are ascending.

9. Refer to Question 3 of Chapter 5 and plot the shaft horsepower requirements for the airplane flying at 10,000 ft altitude at speeds of 200, 250, and 300 mph, assuming a propeller efficiency of 80 percent.

10. A train approaching a 1.0 percent grade 4000 ft long is able to surmount the summit at 10 mph if it first stops at the foot of the grade. At what speed can the train cross the summit if it is traveling 50 mph at the foot of the grade?

SUGGESTED READINGS

1. R. P. Johnson, *The Steam Locomotive*, Simmons-Boardman, New York, 1945.

2. Charles F. Foell and M. E. Thompson, *Diesel-Electric Locomotive*, Diesel Publications, New York, 1946.

3. W. W. Hay, *Railroad Engineering*, Vol. I, John Wiley and Sons, New York, 1953.

4. A. M. Wellington, *The Economic Theory of the Location of Railways*, Sixth Edition, John Wiley and Sons, New York, 1887, Chapters IX, X, XIV, XX.

5. Wilbur G. Hudson, *Conveyors and Related Equipment*, Third Edition, John Wiley and Sons, New York, 1954, Chapters 10 and 11.

6. F. V. Hetzel and Russel K. Albright, *Belt Conveyors and Belt Elevators*, Third Edition, Section I, Belt Conveyors, John Wiley and Sons, New York, 1941.

7. John Walker Barriger, *Super-Railroads*, Simmons-Boardman, New York, 1956, Chapter II.

III

Factors
in
Operation

CHAPTER 7

OPERATING CHARACTERISTICS

In Chapter 6 the technological characteristics of buoyancy, stability, guidability, resistance, propulsion, and the effects of elevation and gradients were briefly reviewed. In this and the following chapter certain characteristics more closely related to the way in which a carrier is used and operated are surveyed. Included here are flexibility, speed and acceleration, dependability, safety, utility, criteria of performance, and carrier capacity. These characteristics are not far removed from technological features. Technological considerations establish the absolute limits for this group of characteristics. It is only within these limits that other considerations, such as the economic, operate to determine the exact nature of these characteristics as known and used in practice.

FLEXIBILITY

Flexibility of transport is a characteristic with many meanings. There is flexibility of route and movement, flexibility of size, flexibility of interchange, and flexibility of types of traffic handled. Flexibility is a desirable characteristic, which contributes to utility and adaptability.

Railroads. Railroads possess great flexibility, partly because of the widespread network of tracks and routes, but more especially because they provide assembled unit transportation. Railroads can handle small-lot shipments of only a few pounds or mass movements involving many thousands of tons. In passenger service railroads provide both long-distance, overnight facilities and short-haul and commuting services. A few or many cars are placed in a train, depending on the volume of traffic and the locomotive capacity and speed. Diesel-electric and electric locomotives are especially flexible in permitting two or more units to be combined for heavy trains and operated from one control point. The overload capacity of electric motor drive permits easy starting and the addition of cars beyond the normal tonnage rating.

Although the rail network is composed of many railroads of independent ownership, the several companies function together almost as one system, to the convenience of the shipping public. A car loaded in New York and destined for Vancouver on the Pacific Coast may pass over the rails of half a dozen different companies and cross an international boundary without the doors of the car being opened. Many factors combine to make this possible.

1. The *widespread network of tracks* of *standard gage* (4 ft, 8½ in., measured ⅝ in. below the top of rail on the gage sides) makes it physically possible for any car to run on any track. (*Note:* the mileage of narrow-gage track remaining in the United States and Canada is negligible in amount.)

2. *Standardized equipment*—air brakes, couplers, car clearances, hand holds and steps, and car floor levels—permit cars of one railroad to operate safely in trains and facilities of another. Replacement parts are also standardized, so that a "foreign" car can be readily repaired when on the tracks of another owner. These features and the safe condition of the cars, inspected at the time of interchange, are in accordance with car-interchange rules promulgated by the Mechanical Section of the Association of American Railroads, under the general requirements of the Car Service Bureau of the Interstate Commerce Commission and subscribed to by most of the railroads of the United States and Canada.

3. A system of *car interchange and accounting*, required by the I.C.C. and supervised by the Car Service Division of the A.A.R., provides for the orderly return of cars to their "home" or owning road and for a user fee or per diem charge per car paid to the owning road by a carrier for each day a foreign car (one from another railroad) is on its tracks.

4. A further element of flexibility is the *varied types of equipment* available for the peculiar demands of particular commodities. Gondola cars carry coal, ore, gravel, and stone; box cars haul grains and serve as general-purpose cars. Tank cars, cement cars, stock cars, refrigerator cars, gas cars, acid cars, and well cars (for oversized loads) are typical examples.

Railroads lack flexibility in regard to size of plant required. Even a small or temporary operation requires a large initial investment in land, tracks, and equipment. The same basic facilities must be provided for a few trains as for many. Undertaking the establishment of a new railroad (or portion thereof) or ceasing to furnish rail service once it has been offered is thus a difficult and complex affair. This difficulty of entrance and exit to and from service introduces lack of flexibility into decisions to initiate or to abandon railroad operation.

The very fact that equipment interchangeability provides flexibility in one direction may also reduce it in another. In general, any innovation must be able to function in combination with the old established practices. Transitions from old to new devices and equipment are therefore often slow. Furthermore, there is little incentive for an individual railroad to provide improved rolling stock when the new cars are likely to be on the tracks of another railroad much of the time. The great strength and durability built into equipment for safety and economy prolong economic life beyond that desired from the standpoint of obsolescence. Railroads have continued outmoded cars in service because they were not yet "worn out." A railroad is not willing to sacrifice its large investment in an existing plant and equipment merely to adopt the latest designs or follow modern trends. The financial advantage in scrapping existing plant and methods must be obvious and clear cut.

Highways. Highway transportation exemplifies the single-unit mode of transport. The vehicle unit is a passenger car or a truck or tractor-trailer combination with load capacities varying from $\frac{1}{4}$ ton to 50 tons. Over-the-road trucks usually haul from 10 to 20 tons. Vehicle dimensions are limited by state law and vary considerably. Widths range from a minimum of 66 to a maximum of 96 in., lengths from 40 to 65 ft over-all; the maximum height is 12.5 ft. Flexibility of load size is limited to the capacity of the vehicle. If more traffic is to be moved, additional complete units—power plant, cargo space, and operator—must be provided.

Nevertheless, an especially favorable characteristic of highway vehicles is also their flexibility. The smaller capacity of trucks makes them more attractive to small-lot shippers, and the varied types of truck and trailer bodies, almost as many as railroad-car types, make the truck adaptable to a variety of commodities. No large plant is required for a small-scale or temporary operation. Only the needed number of trucks has to be obtained (now available by rental in many localities). The highways are already at hand for the use of all. Traffic increases can be met by adding more vehicles. If traffic declines, truck units are returned from rental or stored with a minimum of overhead expense.

A more important attribute of highway flexibility is the ability of the vehicle to go anywhere a fair roadway is available, even across fields and open country, if the going is not too rough. It was pointed out in Chapter 3 that the highway network is more far reaching and complex than is that of the railroads. A truck loaded at the shipper's door can go directly to the door of the consignee with no intermediate handling. Especially useful is the truck's ability to thread its way through the maze of city streets and alleys to move goods more readily within terminal areas with more convenience to the shipper and consignee. The farmer can drive his trucks into the fields or onto his barn floor for loading.

Road flexibility lies in the ability of vehicles to meet, overtake, and pass other vehicles on the same roadway strip (but with unfortunate effects on safety).

Because trucks are not operated in assembled units, they are subject to less shock and stress than are railroad cars or even tow barges. Construction can be lighter, so that economic life more nearly approaches obsolescent life. It is thus easier for the highway vehicle to represent the latest improved designs and technology.

Considerable flexibility also arises from the separation of tractor and trailer units. The tractor is free to move other trailers after one has been "spotted" for loading or unloading (stripping). There is some interchange of trailers between different lines. So far this practice has been limited in extent and is far from being as widespread as freight-car interchange on the railroads. There are no corresponding rules of interchange in effect.

The relatively small amount of shock in truck transit works as an advantage to the shipper. He can load and ship without extensive packing and crating. This is especially favorable when no intermediate handling is involved. An outstanding example of the truck's advantage in this respect is in hauling household goods, which can be loaded directly into the van with no prior crating or packing.

The foregoing characteristics commend truck operation to short-distance hauling of small quantities. The average intercity truck haul is under 300 miles (250 miles in 1950 for carriers reporting to the I.C.C.). The *Transport Inc. Research Manual of Highway Carriers,* Washington, D. C., 1954, gives the following percentages for various lengths of haul for Class I highway carriers:

Length of Haul (miles)	Percentage of Carriers
Less than 100	23.7
100–199	31.3
200–299	18.6
300–399	11.5
400–499	6.1
500–599	2.5
600 or more	6.3

There is little doubt concerning the efficiency of truck operation within a 150-mile radius of large population or traffic centers. For terminal movement of LCL freight, the truck is indispensable. Even the truck's strongest competitor, the railroads, admit the value of trucks on road hauls of 200 miles or less. The efficiency of truck operation on longer hauls is under debate. It is a fact that many trucks are operating successfully on hauls of 500 to 1000 miles and a few are even performing transcontinental service. Additional aspects of this situation are considered in the next chapters.

For passenger transportation, nothing approaches the convenience and flexibility of the private automobile. Automobiles are the chief carriers of passengers in the United States. The automobile is available whenever the traveler is ready to go and will take him almost anywhere he desires. Much of the automobile's flexibility is being lost, however, in traffic congestion and parking difficulties and in the high accident rates which they entail.

Buses possess flexibility similar to that of trucks and automobiles, although their use as long-distance carriers is limited from the standpoint of passenger comfort.

Waterways—Barge Tows. River transport is assembled unit carriage. Some of the flexibility of rail transport is found in modern barge operation. Most river and canal traffic is handled in tows, which may be large or small, depending on the available traffic at a given time or place. Barges are picked up and set out at various points along the route but with somewhat more time and effort than railroad cars. Modern steel barges hold 1000 to 3000 tons. Open-top barges are available for coal, aggregates, and ore. Covered barges carry grains, sulfur, and cement. Compartmentized barges move petroleum and its products. Individual barge units can be laid up when not needed at a low overhead cost and called back to service when traffic demands.

Tows meet and pass in normal width channels at the will of the pilot and according to the "rules of the road." There is no forced adherence to a fixed path. River and canal transport, however, lack the flexibility of route location. Their use can be realized only where waterways are available. Barge transport is most efficient when used for large-scale, bulk transport, where speed is not an object.

Waterways—Ships. Ships in coastal, intercoastal, and Great Lakes service are single-unit type carriers and offer a low degree of flexibility. The entire ship, a large expensive plant, must be moved whether it has a full cargo or none at all (return loading is often a problem). Laying up unnecessary units in a fleet is a costly alternative. There are two principal types of freighters—general-cargo and bulk-cargo. General-cargo ships carry any type of freight and have their cargo space compartmentized by decks and bulkheads. Bulk-cargo ships have long, open, and unobstructed holds to permit easy loading, trimming, and unloading of coal, ores, grains, aggregates, and other granular materials. The holds in tankers are compartmentized to permit the handling of several different grades of oil and other products at one time and to prevent excessive surging of the cargo with the ship's movements. A few types of special-purpose ships handle perishables, livestock, and automobiles and ferry railroad cars and motor-truck trailers. Ships that concentrate on Great Lakes–St. Lawrence Seaway trade during the summer must have a flexibility of design that will permit their withdrawal for service in other waters, such as the Caribbean, during the winter season when the lakes are frozen.

Deep-water shipping is limited by channel and harbor availability. As indicated above, weather imposes restrictions on the Great Lakes and upper St. Lawrence from early December until late March or April.

Airways. Aircraft offer a varied degree of flexibility. Like ships, they are single-unit carriers, and the high investment and operating costs (of larger craft) are incurred whether the plane flies loaded or empty. The pay load is only a few tons, and there is little variation in type for special purposes or commodities (except for the military tanker used for refueling in midair).

Airplanes have flexibility in direction of movement, but that flexibility is being rapidly curtailed by increasingly severe traffic restrictions made necessary by traffic densities and high speeds that require an excessive amount of air space for safe maneuvering. Airplanes must maintain flight to stay in the air and can land only at locations that must meet exacting requirements, at least for the larger planes, of length and wheel-load support. For smaller craft, suitable landing fields are usually adjacent to almost every community. In unsettled country landing strips can be built with relative ease for light airplanes and then developed for use by medium-sized craft. This permits transportation in undeveloped areas with no intermediate structures, that is, no expensive track, pavement, pipeline, or canal to construct across difficult intervening miles. Airplanes are therefore especially useful in opening up new territory. The initial means for building the Quebec, North Shore, and Labrador Railway were first flown into that rugged north country by airplane. Africa today is largely without railroads, highways, or river transportation in the interior, but it is criss-crossed with air routes.

The helicopter is an exception to the foregoing disadvantages. It can rise and descend almost vertically on any terrain or even on a broad roof; hence, in several areas, it performs a useful taxi service between airports or between airports and the center of town. Jets are under development with even more nearly vertical take-off capabilities.

Pipelines. Pipelines are a continuous-flow type of carrier and probably the least flexible of all forms of transportation. Traffic can only move one way through a line of pipe. Possible types of traffic are limited—crude and refined petroleum, natural and manufactured gas, water, sewage, and, less often and as a plant facility, chemicals, refrigerants, and heat. Coal and ore are being piped in suspension in at least two instances. Conventionally, pipeline transportation is limited to movements of oil, gasoline, and natural gas.

Portions of cargos cannot be readily picked up or discharged between terminals except at booster pumping stations. A further lack of flexibility is in size of cargo. By their very nature, pipelines must handle only large shipments. The I.C.C. has recognized this characteristic by permitting the lines to require a minimum tender for shipment, sometimes 10,000 but more often 100,000 bbl, in their tariffs. Smaller shipments may be accepted but will be held until a larger shipment of the same grade and specification is offered with which the smaller lot can be combined.

Delivery is continuous and may, within limits, be adjusted to the rate at which the consignee desires to receive it. A stoppage of pumping at or between any two stations will halt that much of the flow. Pumping may continue from the rear until the storage capacity of the nonpumping station has been filled; then the entire operation must stop until the forward station can resume. Pipelines can act in emergencies as huge underground storage reservoirs. They must, however, be kept filled, if only with water, when not in use to reduce the rate of pipe deterioration and the formation of air pockets when the line returns to operation.

Pipelines can be laid over almost any terrain and, being below ground, do not interfere excessively with land use. Rights of way are usually secured by easement.

Conveyor Systems. Like pipelines, conveyors are a continuous-flow type of carrier. There is little flexibility in discharging or taking on cargo at intermediate points or in the size and type of cargo. These factors must, within confining limits, be established at the time of initial design. Belt conveyors are usually limited to dry, granular products—coal, aggregates, ore, and grain. Other types of conveyors have not yet been adjusted to long-distance movement. Unlike pipelines, conveyors can be adapted to carry passengers through the medium of moving sidewalks and belt-conveyed cars. Freight carriers can handle small or large quantities of freight, but the high initial cost can only be justified when large cargos are involved. As with pipelines, a stoppage of one part of the system halts the entire operation, unless the line of flow is broken by occasional surge piles.

Cableways. Aerial tramways offer a special flexibility in regard to location. There is scarcely any terrain that cannot be overcome by rope rails and towers. Mountainous areas, desert land, and locations in which broad river crossings present problems to other land-based transport can be overcome with relative ease by cableways.

Aerial tramways usually offer restrictions of size of individual shipments (large machines and tanks, for example, could not be handled) but are suited to a great variety of small objects as well as granular bulks. When handling granular bulks, the cableway's performance is similar to that of a pipeline or conveyor. It delivers an almost continuous flow of the product, depending on the car spacing. Cableways could be designed to handle liquid bulk, but the economies, compared to pipelines, would probably be unfavorable.

Cableway flexibility is further seriously limited, usually to terminal points, in regard to origin and destination of traffic. There are no

Table 7-1. Flexibility Characteristics

Characteristics	Railroads	Highways	Waterways	Airways	Pipelines	Conveyors	Aerial Tramways
Adaptability to terrain	Good	Good	Poor	Good	Good	Fair	Excellent
Extent of available routes	Good	Excellent	Fair	Good	Fair	Poor	Poor
Facility of movement	Good	Excellent	Good	Excellent	Poor	Poor	Poor
Adaptability to size and type of load	Excellent	Poor	Good	Poor	Poor	Poor	Poor
Ease of interchange	Excellent	Fair	Fair	Poor	Fair	Poor	Poor
Ease of entrance to and exit from service	Poor	Excellent	Good	Fair	Poor	Poor	Poor
Adaptability to varying sizes and volumes of traffic	Excellent	Poor	Good	Poor	Poor	Fair	Poor
Adaptability to varying types of traffic	Excellent	Good	Excellent	Poor	Poor	Fair	Fair
Continuity of flow in spite of local stoppages	Excellent	Excellent	Excellent	Excellent	Poor	Poor	Poor
General or over-all flexibility	Good	Good	Fair	Poor	Poor	Poor	Poor

interconnected cableway systems. Each installation has been a single-purpose operation and serves one user. Exceptions are the few with common-carrier status in the Alpine countries. Cableways share with pipelines and conveyors the objection that operational difficulties at any one point halt the entire flow of traffic.

A comparative evaluation of the foregoing aspects of flexibility for the several carrier types is summarized in Table 7-1. These comparisons are based entirely on the technological possibilities for each type without regard to aid or restriction by agreement, competition, or government regulation.

SPEED AND ACCELERATION

Acceleration Principles. Earlier chapters have shown that horsepower and propulsive force vary with speed. For a prime mover of given horsepower, propulsive or tractive force varies inversely as the speed. Tractive force decreases as speed increases. Thus for a given horsepower one can have speed or haul a heavy load, but one cannot do both at once. This relation is commonplace. Hauling capacity is traded for speed, and vice versa, in transport design and operation. As a train or truck climbs a grade, the addition of grade resistance demands a lessening of speed. As a grade is descended, the force of gravity tends to accelerate the speed.

Acceleration may be thought of as a form of resistance because it requires additional horsepower and propulsive effort even though the grade is level and the weight constant. A common acceleration problem is to determine the maximum speed that a vehicle can attain in a given time and distance. The average rate of acceleration may then be computed.

Newton's Second Law of Motion states that the force necessary to impart uniform acceleration to a body is in proportion to its mass, or $F = ma$, where F is the force in pounds, m is the mass $= w/g$ (w being weight in pounds, g the acceleration due to gravity $= 32.2$ ft per sec per sec), and a is the acceleration in feet per second per second. Also, from physics, $t = v/a$, $S = vt$, and $S = at^2/2 = a(v/a)^2/2 = v^2/2a$, where $t =$ time in seconds to travel S ft at v ft per sec. If these values are substituted in the force equation, $F = wv^2/2gS$. If weight is expressed in tons W, $g = 32.2$; if velocity is expressed as $V =$ miles per hour, $F = 66.8WV^2/S$. The distance to accelerate from an initial speed V_i to a final speed V_f is $S = 66.8W(V_f^2 - V_i^2)/F$. By a similar process of development, the time t to accelerate from an initial to a final speed is $t = 91.1W(V_f - V_i)/F$. Unit acceleration (and deceleration) follow from the same equation by dividing both sides by the weight W. The accelerative force F then becomes the unit accelerative force F'. With wheeled land vehicles curvilinear motion is imparted to the wheels in addition to the motion of translation imparted to the vehicular body. The practice is to assume a 5 percent energy requirement for the rotating wheels. The foregoing equations then become, approximately, $S = 70W(V_f^2 - V_i^2)/F$ and $t = 95.6W(V_f - V_i)/F$, respectively.

But acceleration does not take place at a constant rate. Its graphical representation is curvilinear rather than a straight line. A practical solution to the equation lies in taking successively small increments of speed, 0 to 2, 2 to 4, 4 to 6 mph, etc., and computing the individual distances and times, using the average speed and accelerative force over each velocity range. Speed-distance, speed-time, and time-distance curves may thus be plotted from a solution of the two basic equations. By applying appropriate portions of these curves to a railroad, highway, or monorail profile, the entire speed, gradient, time, and distance relations and the performance of the motive power in making a run can be computed and plotted graphically. This is of considerable value in establishing schedules, predicting performance, and studying and designing profiles and motive-power units. Electronic computers may be used to speed the process of calculation.

The same equations may be used in the same way to determine time and distance for deceleration. Deceleration is indicated by negative values for time and distance if the initial and final velocity subscripts are adhered to as given. F becomes the decelerating force and, for unbraked deceleration, is equal to the retarding effects of propulsive and grade resistances. The same factors are additive to braking force when speed is reduced by brake application.

Dr. L. K. Sillcox points out that maximum braking force is obtained if the wheels continue to turn when the available coefficient of friction between wheel and rail or tire and pavement is 100 percent, that is, when the force resisting sliding is equal to the weight that the vehicle imposes on the roadway. Under most favorable conditions, seldom reached, a well-sanded rail provides an adhesion value of 40 percent of the car weight; 50 percent is a practical maximum under existing design. This limits deceleration to 6.4 ft per sec per sec, or 4.4 mph per sec. Automotive tires have gripped concrete highway surfaces with an adhesion approaching 100 percent, permitting a deceleration of 32.2 ft per sec per sec (equal to the acceleration of gravity).[1] Values of 40 to 80 percent are more often in effect. However, for all types of wheeled vehicles, the actual value is a function of the speed and materials of wheel and surface and whether the surface is wet, dry, oily, or glazed. Total braking distance is also a function of driver perception time and brake-application time. Perception time varies with the individual and circumstances from 0.50 to 3.0 sec. Brake-application time for highway drivers and vehicles varies from 0.20 to 1.7 sec. For railroad trains brake-application distance is usually taken as 1.47 $V_i t$, where V_i is the initial speed in miles per hour and t is the brake-application time per car. For modern high-speed, quick-acting airbrakes, it may be as low as 0.10 sec per car.

Practical Speed Factors. The resistances normally encountered by various types of carriers usually falls within fairly well-defined limits for each carrier type. Consequently, normal, *average*, and *maximum* operating speeds for the several types are well established and herewith briefly reviewed. Faster than normal speeds are possible with any type of transport (as evidenced by racing cars, speedboats, and supersonic aircraft) if one is willing to pay the price in increased operating and maintenance costs and decreased cargo capacity. The impact on railroad and highway pavements varies approximately as the square of the speed, requiring more exacting and costlier standards of maintenance for a relatively small increase in speed. The same impact must also be absorbed by the vehicle. Fuel, operating, and other maintenance costs would increase proportionately. Speed is therefore usually a matter of economics.

Trains. A few main-line passenger trains have authorized speeds of 100 mph, but a majority hold to a maximum speed of 75 to 85 mph. Less important trains and those on secondary lines seldom exceed 60 to 70 mph. On branch lines 30 to 50 mph usually prevails. Commuting, subway, and other types of rapid-transit lines seldom exceed speeds greater than 45 to 50 mph because of frequent station stops. The fastest speed ever made by a train was 205 mph, made by the *Mistral*, in 1955, an electric train, on the Région Sud (Paris-Lyon-Marseille) of the French National Railways (S.N.C.F.).[2] The aver-

[1] L. K. Sillcox, *Mastering Momentum*, Second Edition, Simmons-Boardman, New York, 1955, p. 33.

[2] *Les Chemins de fer en France,* Société Nationale des Chemins de Fer Français, March 1955, pp. 25–27.

age passenger-train speed in the United States is about 40 to 50 mph. Station stops increase the time of otherwise fast schedules. Mr. Donald R. Steffe, in the May 1955 issue of *Trains*, reported 3225 runs in 1954 with an average speed of a mile a minute or faster over 169,747 route miles.

Dispatch or expedited freight trains hauling merchandise and perishables are lightly loaded to permit running at passenger-train speeds of 50 to 60+ mph. More heavily loaded "regular" trains run 40 to 50 mph. "Drag" freights loaded with low-grade freight to full tonnage capacity seldom exceed 25 to 40 mph and may crawl up mountain grades at 10 to 20 mph. Way freights have a low terminal-to-terminal average because of frequent stops and station work. Eight hours or more may be spent in traversing a 50-mile run. The statistical average speed for all freight trains in the United States in 1958 was 19.12 mph and 40.2 mph for all passenger trains.[3] Speed of railroad-freight movement is more dependent on fast yard and terminal movements than on line-haul running time.

Highway vehicles. Highway vehicles offer a wide range of speeds. Modern sports cars are capable of 100 to 130 mph. Speeds over 300 mph have been reached in special speed-trial models. Most stock cars can reach 75 to 90 mph. Many states have imposed maximum open-road speed limits of 65 mph, and a few states enforce 50 mph. Conservative opinion holds that 55 to 60 mph should not be exceeded except in passing. Speeds of 45 to 50 mph are considered the most economical in regard to fuel, oil, and tire consumption. Because of the light loads and high power of modern passenger cars, only the steepest grades reduce their speed appreciably. The average speed today for passenger automobiles is approximately 50 mph.

Trucks, buses, and semitrailer combinations are able to run on level and gently rolling grades at speeds up to 60+ mph. Their over-the-road average is about 40 mph, but it is much less than this when steeper grades and city traffic reduce speeds to 20 to 30 mph. Heavily loaded trucks may crawl up steep grades at 7 to 20 mph. Average terminal-to-terminal speeds for trucks vary from 23.0 to 34.0 mph.

Waterways. Ocean and lake-going passenger vessels can offer cruising speeds of 20 to 35 knots, but most freight carriers are within the 10- to 20-knot category. Great Lakes carriers average about 10 knots. Quick turnarounds in port are considered more important than high cruising speed. Here, high speed is sacrificed for cargo capacity.

---

[3] *A Review of Railway Operations in 1958,* Tables 14 and 15, Bureau of Railway Economics, Association of American Railroads.

River and canal carriers also sacrifice speed for capacity. In addition, the narrowness of channel makes slow speed a safety requirement in some situations. River current has a marked effect on speed. Under normal water conditions, downstream shipping on the Lower Mississippi moves about 14.0 mph. Upstream, the speed is reduced to 7.5 mph. On the Upper Mississippi and on the Ohio, downstream speeds of 9.0 mph and upstream speeds of 7.0 mph usually prevail. However, upstream speed against a stiff flood current may drop to 2 to 4 mph. On the coastal canal waters speeds of 6 to 8 mph, depending on load in the vessel, are customary.

Aircraft. Airplanes are the reverse of water transport. They offer only high-speed, low-weight cargo and passenger movements. Small single- and twin-engined private planes fly as fast as 150 mph. Twin-engined private and commercial planes of the DC-3 and similar types have a maximum cruising speed of 150 to 200 mph; four-engined commercial transports are capable of 400 mph; the recently inaugurated jet transports cruise up to 600 mph. The 1954 average speed for scheduled domestic air carriers was 205.8 mph, and 242.1 mph for international air carriers.[4] Maximum cruising speeds are usually maintained in normal flight, but the aid or hindrance of tail or head winds and the size of the load carried can make significant changes in speed. Supersonic speeds of military and experimental aircraft have not yet entered commercial flying.

Pipelines. Pipelines do not provide rapid movement of freight, but the flow is continuous, so that the quantity moved per 24-hour period compares favorably with that of other modes of transport. The actual speed depends upon the size of pipe, viscosity, density, and temperature of the liquid and the pumping pressure. It ranges from 1 to 5 mph.

Conveyors. Belt conveyors, like pipelines, operate at slow speeds but produce a high tonnage per 24-hour period because of their continuous-flow characteristic. Conventional speeds for conveyors range between 300 and 800 ft per min (3.4 to 9.1 mph), depending upon size of lumps and width of belt.

Aerial tramways. Cable and car speeds for aerial tramways range from 4 to 6 mph, with 6 mph being a common approximation.

The foregoing normal speed ranges are summarized in Table 7-2

[4] *Statistical Handbook for Civil Aviation,* compiled by the Civil Aeronautics Administration, U. S. Department of Commerce, Washington, D. C., 1955, pp. 61, 75.

Table 7-2. Transport Speed Ranges

Carrier	Normal Range	Practical Maximum	Speed-Trial Maximum
Railroads			
Passenger, main line	75–100 mph	120 mph	205 mph
Passenger, secondary	60–70 mph		
Passenger, branch line	30–50 mph		
Statistical average	40.2 mph *~ Pass.*	75 mph	
Freight, dispatch	50–60 mph	75 mph	
Freight, "regular"	40–50 mph		
Freight, slow or "drag"	25–40 mph		
Freight, steep grades	10–20 mph		
Statistical average	19.2 mph *~Freight*		
Passenger automobiles	50–75 mph	100–120 mph	392.4 mph
Trucks	40–60 mph	65 mph	
On grades	20–30 mph		
Steep grades and city traffic	7–20 mph		
Average	23–34 mph		
Ships, deep water			
Passenger liners	20–40 knots	35.59 knots	
Freighters	10–25 knots	30 knots	
Great Lakes bulk cargo	8–12 knots	20 knots	
Tows			
Lower Mississippi			
Upstream	6–8 mph		
Downstream	10–14 mph		
Upper Mississippi and Ohio			
Upstream	5–7 mph		
Downstream	8–10 mph		
Upstream, flood stage	2–4 mph		
Intercoastal waterways	6–8 mph		
Aircraft			
Single and twin-engined private planes	125–150 mph		
Twin-engined commercial	150–250 mph		
Four-engined transports	300–400 mph		
Four-engined jet transports	400–600 mph		
Military and experimental	600– mph and up		1404.09 mph
Pipelines	1–5 mph		
Conveyors	300–800 fpm (3.4–9.1 mph)		
Aerial tramways	4–6 mph		

for the reader's convenience. The reader should never forget that it is not maximum speed nor even cruising speed that is most important but the over-all speed from the time a shipment leaves the consignor to the time it is received by the consignee. This speed reflects the efficiency not only of road movement but also of terminal operations.

DEPENDABILITY AND SAFETY

Importance. Dependability refers to the safe, on-schedule movement and delivery of goods and passengers and freedom from delays and from loss and damage en route. It is one of the most important characteristics a carrier can offer. The nice interrelation of industrial-commercial elements requires that all coordinate perfectly. Parts and raw materials must arrive on schedule to insure continuity in manufacturing processes. The assembly line shuts down if short-term inventories are depleted by transport delays. Speed of individual movement is usually not so essential as maintaining a steady flow of raw materials, parts, fuels, and lubricants. Transport delays are costly both to the public and to the carriers. Delayed perishables spoil. Delays to livestock cause loss of weight and may require additional feeding and watering en route by the carrier. Opportunities in critical markets may be lost. Delayed newspapers, magazines, and newsreels lose their timeliness. Delays to persons mean lost opportunities, contracts unsigned, appointments missed, deathbeds reached too late. A carrier with a poor record for dependability stands in a difficult competitive position with its contemporaries. Many shippers place dependability first in selecting a carrier.

Safe operation is a principal factor in dependability. Accidents leading to damaged equipment and lading and to injuries and fatalities among passengers and workmen cannot be a part of a dependable transport system. Most of the elaborate and expensive systems of operational control are installed to provide increased safety. Dependable, efficient operation and safe operation are complementary factors. No effort of man has yet been carried out entirely free of accidents and disaster. All transport operators, urged on by government inspection and regulation, are desirous of and strive for safety. Nevertheless, it is self-evident that some types of transport are inherently less susceptible to accidents than others. These differences are reflected in the accidents-to-passenger statistics given in Table 7-3.

Table 7-3. Comparative Transportation Safety Record [a]

(Passenger Fatality Rate per 100,000,000 Passenger Miles)

	1956		1957	
Carrier	Actual Fatalities	Rate	Actual Fatalities	Rate
Airlines				
Domestic scheduled	143	0.64	30	0.12
International	9	0.17	40	0.67
Motor buses	80	0.16	70	0.13
Railroad passenger trains	57	0.20	17	0.07
Passenger autos and taxis	26,100	0.27	25,700	0.26

[a] Based on similar table, *Air Transport Facts and Figures*, Twentieth Edition, Air Transport Association of America, Washington, D. C., 1959, p. 30.

Individual Carriers. The characteristics of dependability and safety may be briefly summarized for each transport type.

Railroads. The flanged-wheel-on-a-steel-rail principle of guidance enables trains to operate safely and with amazing consistency in almost any weather or conditions. Elaborate systems of signaling and established operating practices prevent traffic conflicts. Short of a major track or wheel failure, a train cannot leave its established path. A well-organized system of trained personnel, mechanized work equipment, and beforehand preparations keep the tracks open and trains running regardless of weather, fire, flood, landslide, or other disaster and minimizes the delays that do occur. It is traditional and, on busy lines, a practical necessity to keep tracks open and trains running regardless of cost and effort. A system of detour arrangements with other railroads helps to move the trains when tracks are completely blocked.

Railroads fail chiefly in terminal movements due in part to outmoded facilities and practices in some terminals, to congestion, and to the multiple handling of cars and LCL items. Traffic frequently experiences delays because of awaiting classification in yards. Delay in carrier make-up for the road is a characteristic problem of mass-produced, assembled-unit transport. Modern programs are being carried out to improve these conditions. Shock from impact and concussion gives rise to considerable damage in transit. Employee campaigns, improved methods of stowage (including movable bulkheads for part loads), better car trucks and springs, and a precise control of car speeds in classifications yards are aimed at overcoming these handicaps.

Highway transport. Human guidance is necessary with highway vehicles. Each year sees an increasingly high toll in death, injuries, and property damage. Private vehicles are the worst but by no means the only offenders. The intermingling, meeting, and passing of vehicles on the same roadway places full responsibility for safety on the driver. Lack of skill, inattention, or recklessness, even in trivial amounts, may culminate in a major highway disaster. All the skill and experience of a well-trained truck or bus operator may be set at naught by the carelessness of an untrained, irresponsible driver in a private car. Happily, the divided-lane design of the most recent highways isolates cars going in opposing directions. Passing still remains a significant hazard.

Bad weather, especially ice, snow, and fog, reduces highway speeds or halts traffic entirely. Private automobiles and light trucks are especially dangerous to operate in rain, snow, and ice. Since they are light, they lose adhesion and face skidding hazards. Even the heavier semitrailers may skid and jackknife on slippery roads or steep hills. Like the railroads, highway departments organize men and machines to keep the highways open, but, all too frequently, highways are reported as closed or unsafe.

Few highways are without time-consuming detours at one or more points or one-way traffic situations during a part of the year. Congestion due to rush hours, athletic events, holiday travel, and the shoe-string extension of urban areas tends to make schedules an uncertain quantity. Nevertheless, common and contract carriers make an effort to maintain good on-time records. In terminals and metropolitan areas dependability is as good or better than over-the-road operation. Here the flexibility of motor-truck operation is especially advantageous in providing prompt service.

Highway vehicles are subject to less shock and impact than railroad equipment, whereby a low rate of loss and damage is realized with much less packing and crating. Since there is not much trailer interchange, long-distance shipments usually have to be transshipped at several intermediate points if moving LCL. Offsetting delays, losses, and damage may then arise from the excess handling.

Waterways. When weather is good, waterways offer as dependable service with as few inherent dangers as any other agency. Damage from shock and rough handling is at a minimum, although this is not an important factor in the handling of bulk cargos. The dangers of instability due to improper stowage and discharge of cargo or of poor initial design have been noted in Chapter 5. Fires at sea have accounted for numerous disasters over the years. Ships and tows are dependent on human guidance, and collisions between vessels or with other obstructions, bridge piers for example, sometimes occur. Weather can have a severely adverse effect on all shipping. Even with the aid of modern radar, collisions have occurred in fog, and ships have gone off course and become lost. Fog can also halt traffic in harbors, rivers, and locks. High winds and storms may cause coastal shipping to put into port, and heavy seas can spring plates and cause leaks or shift the cargo to a less stable position. Nevertheless, the great bulk of shipping, especially on the lakes and rivers, goes about its task with little interruption or untoward incident.

Aircraft. One principal characteristic of airplanes works against their safety and dependability; that is, the plane must remain in motion, its engines must function, to sustain flight and avoid a disastrous crash. Planes do have a margin of safety in that a multi-engined craft can usually make a safe landing with one or more engines idle. It is a measure of the excellence of engine design and ground-crew maintenance that relatively few accidents occur from engine failure; there was only one for scheduled domestic airlines in 1954 and none for international scheduled flights in that year. Non-air-carrier (private) flights, however, had a total of five power-plant failures. Accidents attributable to power plants other than outright failures numbered seven for domestic scheduled carriers, none for international and 442 for non-air-carriers.[5]

Airplanes are susceptible to weather conditions. Commercial airliners are able to rise above most bad weather to maintain schedules, but even these planes must delay take-off when conditions are exceptionally severe. Smaller craft cannot fly at all when high winds or fog prevail. Weather creates uncertainties in route and landings. Fogbound and heavily congested airports may force a plane to fly off route and perhaps land at some point far from its scheduled destination before fuel runs out. Bad weather may also force a plane to miss a way stop. High winds alter scheduled times and may cause

[5] *Statistical Handbook of Civil Aviation,* compiled by the Civil Aeronautics Administration, U. S. Department of Commerce, Washington, D. C., 1955, p. 110.

unscheduled stops for fuel at intermediate points. In spite of modern electronic navigational aids, airplanes occasionally become lost, crash, or even collide.

Additional flying hazards include fire, lightning, and metal fatigue failure. The combination of increasing air congestion and high speeds is introducing collision hazards to an alarming extent. Each year, however, sees definite improvement in safety devices and methods and the airlines' safety record, over all, is excellent and continues to improve.

Pipelines. Pipelines probably offer the most dependable type of transport available today. Buried beneath the ground, the flow continues regardless of weather or traffic conditions. Nothing short of a major leak or complete pumping-station breakdown will halt or delay the movement, and these disruptions are relatively infrequent. Delay at one point, however, will halt all pumping in the section affected and may stop all upstream pumping if the delay is not ended before the emergency storage capacity at the station controlling the leaking section has been filled. Few accidents of a transport nature occur in pipelines. Passenger safety is not a factor. A leaking line may catch fire and cause local damage and loss of lading, but traffic accidents are not a part of pipeline operation.

Conveyors. A properly protected and enclosed conveyor can be fully as dependable as a pipeline. If it is exposed to severe weather, it can become completely immobilized. Cross-country conveyors of the future, in regions of ice, snow, rain, and high winds, will probably be fully enclosed. Passenger safety is not a factor with belt-type conveyors except when used as moving sidewalks—and accidents thus far have been infrequent. There are no inherent hazards in freight operation except for possible dust explosions when fine-grained, flammable materials are handled. However, a breakdown at any point in the system will halt the entire operation unless costly surge piling is performed.

Aerial tramways. The aerial tramway offers a dependable mode of transport generally free from accidents. Cars are attached to the cable loop and cannot become lost or, as long as the cable is operating, even delayed. Bad weather causes delays, and high winds will halt all operation for the storm's duration. Excessive icing can also halt operations and may even cause cable breakage when the increased weight and tension of the ice-coated cable is not properly included in the design. When passengers are carried, several supporting cables are used, each one alone being capable of holding the

Table 7-4. Transport Dependability

Carrier	Movement	Freedom from Loss and Damage	Combined Effect
Railway	Good to excellent [a]	Fair	Good
Highway—freight	Fair to good	Good	Good [b]
Highway—passenger	Poor	Poor	Poor
Waterways	Fair	Good	Fair to good
Airways	Poor	Good	Fair
Pipelines	Excellent	Excellent	Excellent
Conveyors	Excellent	Excellent	Excellent
Aerial tramways	Good	Excellent	Good to excellent

[a] Primarily line movement; as pointed out earlier in the section, railroads are subject to terminal delay problems.

[b] For motor freight; poor to fair for private automobile traffic.

car in case the others break. Cableways have the disadvantage, shared with pinelines and conveyors, that a delay, break, or obstruction at one point halts the entire system.

In Table 7-4 the several transport modes have been classed according to their dependability—safe, trouble-free, on-time movement of persons and goods—in light of the foregoing comments and the operating methods and technology in use today.

LAND USE

Problem of Land Use. The scarcity of land, especially in and near urban areas, and the high value attached thereto raises the question of the relative land use of the several carriers. When the carrier's route is provided by the state, as is the case with highways and waterways, the problem of withdrawal of large amounts of land from the tax rolls is a matter of serious concern for local communities and taxing authorities.

The basic land requirement of most transport systems is for right of way. Railroads, aerial tramways, highways, and others need a strip of land varying from 30 to 200+ ft in width, extending from terminal to terminal. Where there are deep cuts or fills, an even wider strip must accommodate the necessary cut or fill width and attendant drainage. On level ground the minimum width is $w = b + 2sd$, where b is the width of subgrade, s = rate of side slope, and d is the depth of cut or fill. Sufficient additional width is desirable for side and intercepting ditches. For a canal, b is the base of the canal channel.

In addition to route right of way, land is also required, usually in lesser quantities, for terminal facilities—stations, yards, warehouses, maintenance sheds, transfer facilities, etc. Airports also require large landing areas and runways (but no intermediate route land), and dams for canals and canalized rivers may cover thousands of acres.

Specific Carrier Requirements

Railroads. Railroad rights of way vary from 30 to 100 ft for normal situations. Roadbed widths range between 18 and 24 ft for single track lines, plus an additional 14 ft center-to-center spacing for each track of multiple track lines. Large yards will require areas 2 to 5 miles long and $\frac{1}{4}$ to 1 mile wide. Land devoted to railroad transportation cannot be used for other purposes. Railroads endeavor to acquire additional land adjacent to their tracks, which can be made available as industrial sites to prospective new industries with a potential for additional rail traffic.

Railroads laid in subways and tunnels do not interrupt the surface use of land but can create serious congestion for subsurface structures and utilities. Elevated lines, either on trestles or viaducts, are noisy, require considerable street and air space, cut off light, and reduce adjacent property values. The use of median strips between highway lanes offers a means of conserving land and coordinating transport while affecting a financial saving.

Highways. Township roads, farm lanes, and alleys probably take no more land area than a single-track railroad. Modern superhighways, on the contrary, require rights of way 100 to 300 ft wide on flat terrain. Additional acreage is required at interchange points and service areas. The right-of-way equation given earlier may be used if the width of subgrade is based on the combined widths of traffic lanes, median strips, and shoulders.

Waterways. Much land or none at all (except for port facilities) may be required, depending on whether the watercourse has to be improved or can be used in its natural state. A canalized river, which requires much additional land area, floods out existing properties in many instances to provide the dams with deep pools necessary for slack water navigation. Canals need no more area than occupied by the canal itself, the width of right of way containing enough space to pass two boats or tows in the channel, plus minor areas at lock sites.

Airways. Aircraft make no demands on intermediate land use except for minor amounts devoted to route markers and radio range stations. Air terminals require 10 to 20 acres for small fields to several hundred acres for large airports.

Pipelines. Pipelines require land for pumping stations and other terminal facilities. For the rest, the pipes are normally placed below ground. Land is usually secured as rights of way by easements, and the normal uses of the land may continue with little or no interruption.

Conveyors. For large scale, cross-country operation, conveyors require as much land for rights of way as railroads. The land so occupied cannot be used for other purposes.

Aerial tramways. Little interference is had with land use from aerial tramways. Cable towers and angle stations must be erected at intervals of several hundred to several thousand feet, but these structures pose no more land demand than towers for electrical transmission lines, an area of 100 to 2500 sq ft per tower.

Table 7-5 summarizes the typical land requirements for various

Table 7-5. Typical Land Requirements for Right of Way

Acres per Mile Devoted Exclusively to Transportation

Carrier	Width of Right of Way (in feet)	Acres per mile
Railroad	30–100	4–12
Highway	30–300	4–36
Waterway	100–300	12–36
Airway	—	Nominal
Pipeline	1–6	Nominal
Conveyor	25–100	3–12
Aerial tramway	25–100	Nominal

Note: aerial tramways and pipelines, like power transmission lines, may maintain a cleared right of way of 50 to 100 ft in width for ease in maintenance and access and to prevent trees and high shrubs from fouling the cars and cables.

transport routes. The *acres per mile* column includes land devoted only to transportation purposes and in level terrain. Thus the acreage for pipelines is shown as *nominal* because the land can be used for other purposes once the pipe has been placed under ground.

QUESTIONS FOR STUDY

1. What would have been the effect on transportation in general and rail transportation in particular if more than one gage of track were used in North America?

2. Highway and automotive engineers foresee the day when automobiles and trucks will be automatically guided on principal highways by inductive coupling to an electrified cable laid in the middle of each traffic lane. Discuss the full effects this could have on automotive flexibility and safety.

3. To what extent is crating and packaging an important techno-economic factor in each mode of transport? Use specific commodity examples in your discussion.

4. What problems incident to flexibility had to be met in designing double-decked rail rapid-transit equipment?

5. What problems would be involved in setting up a system of trailer interchange among trucking lines similar to that for car interchange between railroads?

6. What force is required to accelerate a train from 60 to 70 mph in 100 sec and how far will it run meanwhile? (Omit incremental steps but indicate how such steps could be used for greater accuracy.)

7. How far might an automobile travel before actual deceleration begins when the driver makes an emergency application of his brakes at a speed of 60 mph?

8. Explain why the maximum practical speed is not a good criterion for determining speed of traffic flow for a carrier.

9. What is the role of guidability in establishing the safety status of a carrier?

10. Assuming farm land is being taxed at 10 dollars an acre, what are the losses in tax receipts for a publicly built right of way 250 ft wide and 300 miles long?

SUGGESTED READINGS

1. L. K. Sillcox, *Mastering Momentum,* Simmons-Boardman, New York, 1955, Chapter 1, pp. 1–94.

2. W. W. Hay, *Railroad Engineering,* Vol. I, John Wiley and Sons, New York, 1953, Chapter 10, pp. 134–150.

3. Frank M. Cushman, Transportation for Management, *Service Characteristics of Carriers,* Prentice-Hall, New York, Chapter 3, pp. 41–90.

4. Hermann S. D. Botzow, Jr., *Monorails,* Simmons-Boardman, New York, 1960.

8

OPERATING CHARACTERISTICS— CONTINUED

PERFORMANCE CRITERIA

Various measures and indices of transport efficiency are available. No one of these is definitive. Even cost may not determine the ultimate choice or utility of a transport system. Factors of speed, capacity, availability, commodity requirements, terrain, or weather may be equally compelling. The following are suggested as giving a representative cross section of technological and operating criteria.

Net Ton-Miles per Vehicle Hour. Transport agencies exist to produce transportation. It is their only product. It cannot be stored but must be consumed as it is produced. The rate at which transportation can be produced is a fundamental measure of transport efficiency. One unit for measuring transport productivity is the *net ton-miles per vehicle hour*. It corresponds roughly to the horsepower unit in kinematics, the rate of doing work. The rate of producing transportation = *net tons* × *the speed* in miles per hour. From an operating standpoint, the weight of the vehicle must also be moved. Emphasis is then placed on gross ton-miles per vehicle hour, which includes vehicle weight as well as cargo weight.

A high value for the ton-miles per vehicle hour is achieved in several ways:

1. By placing as much tonnage as possible in one carrying unit, for example, a train or a ship. If traffic is plentiful, this involves skillful loading of the vehicle and a full utilization of the vehicle's propulsive force and horsepower. Pipeline and conveyor operation exemplify this operation. Although holding only nominal amounts of cargo per unit length, they move very large amounts by the con-

tinuous full utilization of propulsive force and horsepower. If traffic is not abundant, the vehicle may be held for loading until a full tonnage becomes available. This still gives a good value for the unit but may cause traffic delays and dissatisfied customers.

2. By making the vehicle itself large enough to hold many tons of freight. This ability is severely restricted in the case of airplanes and trucks, less restricted for bulk cargo ships and cableways, and experiences little restriction in the case of towboats and trains. The size of locks and width of railroad gages are factors.

3. By increasing the speed of the vehicle. This is the opposite of the first possibility and involves light loads combined with high speed—or the utilization of a relatively enormous power plant. Airplanes possess the factor of high speeds to the greatest degree; highway vehicles and railroads the next degree; and ships, tows, pipelines, and conveyors the least. Carriers endeavor to utilize all three methods to the limit of their technological capabilities.

Railroads make use of the net ton-mile per train hour and the gross ton-mile per train hour.

Using the statistically average train of 1958, 1430 net tons, and an average freight train speed of 19.2 mph, transportation was produced at the rate of 27,456 net ton-miles per freight train hour. Gross ton-miles per freight train hour for the same period were 60,807. In passenger service, passenger miles per passenger train hour are used. The 1958 value (approximately) for this unit was 3795.[1]

If, instead of the statistically average freight train, a modern main-line train operating on moderate grades, 0.50 or less, and running at 40 mph is considered, the value becomes approximately 2500 tons at 40 mph or 100,000 net ton-miles per freight-train hour. In hauling ore, coal, and other bulk commodities, slow speed or "drag" freight trains moving 30 mph may haul as much as 8000 to 9000 net tons for a net ton-miles per freight-train hour of 240,000 to 270,000 tons.

Highway motor trucks can average 26 mph in road haul, terminal to terminal, with 10 tons of pay load, thereby producing 260 net ton-miles per truck hour.[2] A 50-ton truck at 30 mph produces 1500 net ton-miles per truck hour. Single truck units average 2.2 net tons of

[1] *A Review of Railway Operations in 1958*, Special Series 93, Bureau of Railway Economics, Association of American Railroads, Washington, D. C., 1959, pp. 26–27.

[2] *Highway Practice in the United States*, Public Roads Administration, Washington, D. C., 1949, p. 73, Table 2.

load per vehicle; tractor-trailer combinations 11.0 tons. A few heavy-duty ore trucks will hold 30 to 50 tons.[3] A record haul from coal mine to railroad tipple of 80 net tons is being made in a tire-mounted wagon pulled by a six-wheeled, tire-mounted tractor at 30 mph, 2400 net ton-miles per vehicle hour.[4]

Great Lakes freighters may be assumed to have an average port-to-port speed of 10 mph (knots are seldom used in Great Lakes' terminology). A vessel with 10,000 tons of cargo would thus produce 100,000 net ton-miles per ship hour. The largest ships on the Great Lakes today can carry 20,000 tons of cargo at 15 mph and produce 300,000 net ton-miles per ship hour.

Ocean-going ships have even greater capabilities. Vessels holding 40,000 to 50,000 cargo tons and moving at 15 to 20 mph produce 600,000 to 1,000,000 net ton-miles per ship hour. Even larger vessels are on the ways. A majority of such large ships are in the bulk-cargo trade, carrying mainly petroleum but also ore and coal.

Net ton-miles per towboat hour, based on a conventional speed of 8 mph and ten 2000-ton barges, amounts to 160,000. Tows of even greater tonnage and speed up to 22,500 tons at 12 mph pool speed are attained, giving approximate maximums of 270,000 net ton-miles per towboat hour.

Pipelines vary considerably but two typical operations may be noted. An 8-in. line at 1 mph will produce 1000 ton-miles per pumping-station hour. The same line at a speed of 4 mph (more powerful pumps being required) produces 4000 net ton-miles per pumping-station hour. A 24-in. line at 1 mph will produce 9300 net ton-miles per pumping-station hour. The same line at a speed of 4 mph produces 37,000 net ton-miles per pumping-station hour.

Airplanes have a low unit load capacity but fly that load at high speeds. The DC-6A flying at 300 mph with 15 tons of pay load produces 4500 net ton-miles per airplane hour and the Globemaster flying 25 tons at the same speed produces 7500 net ton-miles per airplane hour. The Douglas DC-8 transport, powered by four turbojet engines offers a maximum speed of 598 mph with a payload of 35,000 lb for 10,665 net ton-miles per airplane hour. Other modern jet transports afford similar capabilities.

[3] *Public Roads*, Vol. XXVII, No. 11, December 1953, p. 241, Public Roads Administration, Washington, D. C.

[4] Ralph Kress, "LW-75 Biggest Coal Hauler in the World," *The Co-operator*, LeTourneau–Westinghouse, Peoria, Illinois, March 1958, p. 8.

Helicopters, as exemplified by the Sikorsky S-56, can carry a pay load of over 11,000 lb, 5.5 tons (or 36 men), at a cruising speed of 130 mph for 715 net ton-miles per helicopter hour.

Conveyors are not yet standardized for cross-country haul, but a typical installation indicates 6530 net ton-miles per conveyor flight hour for a 42-in. belt running at 6.5 mph. The proposed 72-in. Great Lakes–Ohio River conveyor is estimated to be able to handle 6500 tons per hour at a maximum speed of 1000 ft per minute (but only 600 fpm is contemplated). With the longest flight 11,000 ft pulley centers, about 13,500 net ton miles per conveyor flight hour would be produced.

Cableways are also nonstandardized, but a figure of 300 net ton-miles per cableway hour may be offered for comparison. An aerial tramway capable of moving 100 net tons per hour at approximately 6 mph has been projected for a mining enterprise in Africa. The transportation production of this installation would be 600 net ton-miles per mile of cableway per hour.

Table 8-1 recapitulates these several values for this important index of transport capacity.

These figures relate only to road-haul time. Terminal delays and unusual road delays are not included. This gives unit and as-

Table 8-1. Net Ton-Miles per Vehicle Hour

Carrier	Unit	Quantity
Railroads	Net ton-miles per train hour	25,000–270,000
Trucks and semi-trailers	Net ton-miles per truck hour	260–2,400
Ships—Great Lakes	Net ton-miles per ship hour	100,000–300,000
Ships—deep-water	Net ton-miles per ship hour	100,000–1,000,000
Towboats	Net ton-miles per towboat hour	100,000–270,000
Airplanes—propeller-driven	Net ton-miles per airplane hour	4,500–7,500
Airplanes—jets	Net ton-miles per airplane hour	8,000–10,600
Helicopters	Net ton-miles per helicopter hour	200–700
Pipelines	Net ton-miles per pumping-station hour	1,000–37,100
Conveyors	Net ton-miles per flight hour	600–13,500
Cableways	Net ton-miles per mile of cableway per hour	50–600

sembled-unit carriers a statistical advantage over continuous-flow carriers and ships, which may have a low hourly ton-mile output. The latter group generally operate 24 hours a day with only minor cessations of movement except for major breakdowns. A low figure for net ton-miles per vehicle hour may, nevertheless, be compensated by continuous delivery. A greater output tonnage can thereby be delivered in each 24-hour period than can be delivered by carriers in the first group, which deliver only intermittently. Unit and assembled-unit carriers make runs from terminal to terminal and then experience delays of varying length before going out again.

Horsepower per Net Ton of Pay Load. The horsepower required to move 1 ton of pay load 1 mile is a significant factor in determining capacity and cost. Horsepower costs money. A high ratio of horsepower to net tons as compared with the ratio of horsepower to gross tons indicates that only a small percentage of the power goes to providing transportation, that is, moving pay load. The major percentage may go to overcoming the resistive forces of the power plant and cargo containing space. The figures cited for this unit are based on conventional conditions, equipment, and practice.

The statistically average freight train in 1955 contained approximately 79 cars and 1430 net tons (3167 gross tons including cars and contents), a low figure because it lumps together branch-line, way-freight, lightly loaded high-speed trains and slow-moving, heavily loaded tonnage trains. Such a train on a 1-percent grade, the maximum desirable grade on United States railroads (but not the maximum grade) would require a 4500-hp locomotive (three 1500-hp units) to haul it at a speed of 40 mph. This is an average of 3.15 hp per net ton. However, if the lightly loaded branch, way, and expedited trains are excluded, a modern freight train may be considered as consisting of 5000 gross tons and 2270 net tons. A 6000-hp diesel (four 1500-hp units) would be required to pull this train on an 0.4 to 0.6 percent ruling grade for a horsepower-per-ton value of 2.64. Even better performance, 1.00 hp per net ton, can be had with lower than 0.5-percent ruling gradients where trains of 8000 net tons (13,000 ± gross tons) are operated by 8000-hp locomotives.

Passenger trains averaged 95.2 persons per train in 1955. Assuming an average horsepower of 3000 and an average maximum speed of 60 mph, the horsepower required per passenger is 31.5. However, passenger trains carry many empty seats, and this figure should be determined on the basis of a full train. This might be taken as 600

passengers (ten cars, 60 passengers each) pulled by a 3000-hp locomotive and requiring therefore 5.0 hp per passenger.

Truck capacities (pay load or net tons) vary from 0.50 to 50.00
tons. About 45 percent have a gross vehicle rating of 5000 lb; 4 percent over 26,000 lb. Horsepower ratings vary from 100 to 356. The
conventional over-the-road semitrailer and tractor combination can
haul about 28 net tons in a trailer containing approximately 1900
cu ft of capacity. It will be pulled by a 180-hp tractor furnishing
6.4 hp per net ton. The average load in a semitrailer, however, is
more likely to be 10 to 15 tons. This average load gives a horsepower-per-ton ratio of 11.33. These ratios, higher than for railroads,
reflect the higher propulsive resistance of highway vehicles. Passenger cars possess to an even greater degree than trucks the limitation of horsepower to pay load, 200 hp per ton or 15 hp per passenger
for a 90-hp, 6-passenger vehicle. The ratio is even greater for modern
high-horsepower automobiles.

Modern lake freighters carry as much as 20,000 tons of cargo
(ore, coal, grain, etc.), and, powered by 7000-hp engines, have a horsepower-per-net-ton ratio of 0.35, one of the lowest. The largest ocean-
going tankers and bulk-cargo carriers built to circumnavigate the
Suez Canal haul 40,000 to 50,000 cargo tons with engines of 12,500 to
14,000 horsepower, a horsepower-per-net-ton ratio of 0.31 to 0.28.

River transport can combine a 2400-hp towboat with as many as
ten or more 2000-ton barges, a total of 20,000 tons of pay load. The
ensuing ratio of 0.14 hp per net ton gives an even lower relation than
do the lake and oceanic carriers.

However, this heavy loading is not customary, and less favorable
ratios are the rule. The slow rate of speed is also a factor. Nevertheless, even with a six-barge tow, a common loading, the combination
gives 12,000 net tons for a ratio of 0.20 hp per net ton.

Airplanes are single-unit carriers with a high horsepower-per-ton
ratio. The DC-6A for example carries a pay load of 32,900 pounds
but requires an engine capacity of 10,000 hp. The ratio is 667 hp
per net ton. For overseas transport, where more weight capacity
must be devoted to fuel, the pay load drops to 22,000 pounds and the
horsepower-per-net ton increases to 910. The Douglas Globemaster
(C-124A) carries 50,000 lb at 300 mph, utilizing 14,000 hp, a ratio
of 650 hp per ton of pay load.

For passenger service, the DC-7 has a seating capacity of 60 persons, which gives a horsepower-per-passenger ratio of 217. The
current jet transports, cruising at 590+ mph have approximately

20,000 hp available (10,000 lb of thrust) to haul 100 to 140 passengers for a ratio of 200 to 140 hp per passenger.

The horsepower-per-ton ratio is not so obvious with pipelines. The quantity of oil depends principally on the size of pipe and pumping pressures (see chapters 5 and 6). A 10-in. line under 700-psi pressure will deliver 800 bbl of oil per hour, equivalent to 116 tons. A 250-hp pumping unit is required—2.2 hp per ton.

A conveyor of conventional design moving granular bulks will require 800 to 1200 hp varying with the lift and speed to move a 42-in. belt of 2450-ft flight with a belt load of 70 tons, a ratio of 11.4 to 17.1 hp per net ton. In descending flights, the motors may be performing solely a braking function rather than providing propulsion.

Cableways may have a load of 8 to 30 tons on the system powered by a 30- to 60-hp unit. The ratios are 0.27 to 2.00. Cableway design is so dependent upon terrain, that is, elevation, that one can hardly pick out any operation as typical. As with conveyors, the driving motors may actually be acting as brakes on descending flights.

Table 8-2 summarizes the foregoing ratios for typical situations.

The reader should note that the foregoing relations may also be stated in reverse, that is, the number of tons (net) that can be moved by 1 hp. This value would be of interest when the potential of a fixed or otherwise limited horsepower was in question.

Table 8-2. Typical Horsepower-per-Net-Ton Ratios

Carrier	Horsepower per Net Ton	Horsepower per Passenger	"Typical" Average Horsepower
Railroads—freight	3.15–1.00		2.64
Railroads—passenger		31.5–5.0	5.00
Highway trucks and semitrailers	11.33–2.13		7.00
Passenger automobiles		60.0–6.0	15.00
River tows	0.20–0.14		0.18
Bulk-cargo ships	0.35–0.22		0.25
Airplanes—freight	667–240		500
Airplanes—passenger		230–140	160
Pipelines	2.00–3.00		2.50
Conveyors	10.00–20.00		15.00
Aerial tramways (cableways)	0.20–2.00		1.50

Dead-Load-to-Pay-Load Ratio. Chapters 5 and 6 have implied that the lighter the tare or dead weight of the vehicle as contrasted to pay load, the more efficient from all standpoints is the operation. Designers strive to reduce dead load by the use of lightweight materials and the elimination of all nonessential equipment and gadgets. Limits to this effort are imposed by considerations of safety, passenger comfort, and the relative costs of maintenance. Sometimes a radical change in design may be introduced to decrease dead weight, for example tubular construction with lightweight materials or the even more radical designs incorporated in the Talgo-type trains.

The problem is further complicated when fuel constitutes a large part of the load. Much of the gross lifting force of an airplane is lost in fuel carriage, especially on long-distance and overseas flights. Similarly, there arises a significant relation between the cruising and cargo-carrying capacity of a ship. The greater the distance between ports, the more fuel required—and the less space available for cargo. Faster speeds consume fuel more rapidly for a given distance of travel and require more fuel space in relation to cargo space. (The reader should recall that these problems finally get back to questions of propulsive resistance and the horsepower required to provide the necessary overcoming propulsive force.) Railroad trains and highway vehicles, in contrast, carry little fuel in proportion to their pay load because their runs are relatively short and it is convenient to stop from time to time for refueling. Also, their unit propulsive resistance is low in contrast to that of ships and airplanes. Pipelines, conveyors, cableways—and electric railways—do not face this problem. All vehicle space is available for stowage. The power plant is stationary and in all cases the fuel or its equivalent electrical power is brought to the source of propulsive force rather than being carried along with the cargo. An exception to this is the situation where pipeline pumps may be operated with diesel fuel drawn from the cargo being pumped through the line. Without further analysis, the several components are presented in Table 8-3.

As was true for the preceding table, these values may also be shown in reverse by computing the tons of dead weight per ton of pay load.

CAPACITY

Meaning of Capacity. The preceding section has discussed various criteria for measuring transportation ability. For example, a carrier's ability to produce transportation can be measured by its ton-

Table 8-3. Tons of Pay Load per Ton of Dead Weight—Typical Values

Carrier	Tons of Light, Tare, or Dead Weight	Tons of Pay Load	Tons of Pay Load per Ton of Dead Load
Railroad freight cars	20–25	50–80	2.0–4.0
Railroad passenger cars	40–60	2.3–4.5	0.06–0.08
Highway trucks	2–8	4–20	2.1–2.5
Highway tractor-trailer combinations	6–15	8–30	1.3–2.0
Automobiles—6 persons	1.5–2.0	0.45	0.30–0.22
Motor buses—28–45 persons	5–16	2.10–3.18	0.21–0.42
Great Lakes bulk-cargo carriers	6,000–11,500	9,000–20,000	1.5–1.74
River barges	1,000–1,500	1,000–3,000	1.1–2.1
Towboat with 10 barges (Pusher-boat weight = 1,000–1,400 tons)	10,000–16,400	10,000–30,000	1.0–1.8
Airplane—freight	12–50	3.6–24	0.3–0.5
Airplane—passenger (28–150 passengers)	12–50	2.1–11.3	0.18–0.22

miles-per-vehicle-hour ratio. The final criterion in many situations, however, is the quantity of freight or number of passengers that can be moved per hour or per day between two points by a given combination of plant and equipment. A railroad may have a high ton-miles-per-train-hour figure, but inadequate motive power, rolling stock, track layout, or signaling may limit the number of trains and/or the total net tonnage that can be moved. More often the problem appears in reverse, namely, to determine the size and design of plant and equipment required to move a given volume of traffic. This ability to move quantities of freight and passengers in a given time, usually an hour or a day, is a carrier's traffic capacity.

Traffic capacity depends on the load per vehicle and the number of vehicles that can be operated in a day. The number of vehicles is a function of the number that can be present on a route at any one time (route capacity) and on speed and the system of operation and control. For most types of transport, vehicle performance involves three basic factors: vehicle miles, gross ton miles, and road time expressed in vehicle hours. Road time may also be expressed in terms of hours per trip or hours per 100 vehicle miles.

Vehicle Performance. The time T in hours to move a cargo over a distance of S miles with a given horsepower at a speed of V mph is $T = S/V$. Earlier chapters on propulsive and resistive forces have shown that as the load is increased, speed decreases and the minimum time per trip or per 100 vehicles also increases.

In the following examples, a somewhat-hypothetical wheeled land vehicle is assumed, weighing 30 tons empty, having a cross-sectional area of 144 sq ft, and a 250-hp engine, moving upon a smooth concrete pavement of level grade over a 100-mile trip distance. Rolling resistance is assumed to be 20 lb per ton. (A tractor-trailer combination weighing 30 tons empty, accelerating to 45 mph when empty and to about 30 mph when carrying 80 tons of pay load is in use near Peoria, Illinois, hauling coal from a strip-mining operation to the railroad.) Figure 8-1 shows the simple relation between gross vehicle load and speed.

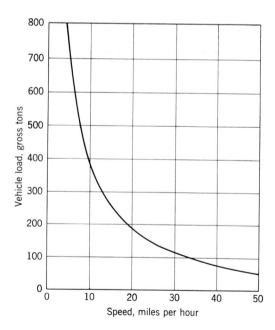

FIGURE 8-1. Maximum gross vehicle loads with variations in speed.

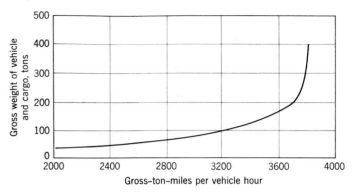

FIGURE 8-2. Variations in gross ton-miles per vehicle hour with changes in vehicle loading.

A curve may be plotted (Figure 8-5a) by assuming various average speeds, determining the corresponding load, and then determining the minimum time for a trip with each loading. Such time values for any carrier can be computed in advance by use of acceleration curves (noted in the preceding chapter), by plotting velocity profiles (not considered in this text), or by an analysis of actual vehicle performance from field tests or dispatchers' records.

Figure 8-2 shows variations in gross ton-miles per vehicle hour for different weights and corresponding speeds. The product of the *gross weight per vehicle* $\times$ *length of trip* $\div$ *hours per trip* $=$ *gross ton-miles per vehicle hour*, or $GTM/T_v = (W_v + W_c)S \div T_s$, where $W_v =$ vehicle weight in tons, $W_c =$ cargo weight in tons, and $T_s =$ time for one trip. As the loading increases, the gross ton-miles per vehicle hour increase, up to a certain speed, at which point the decrease in speed resulting from the heavier load *may* bring about a decrease in total gross ton-miles per vehicle hour. Figure 8-2 has been plotted for the same equipment and conditions as Figure 8-1. Here the increase in time per trip due to lower speed has been compensated by the increase in propulsive force at the lower speed, which permits heavier loads. This is usually the case.

The total tonnage moved per vehicle in a day is: tons per vehicle $\times$ number of trips $= (W_v + W_c)N_t$, where $N_t =$ number of trips $= 24/T_s$, with $T_s =$ time for one trip. Returning to the simple speed-time-distance relation which opened this section, $T_s = S/V = S \div (375 \times \text{hp} \times e)F_r$ where $F_r =$ resistive force at maxi-

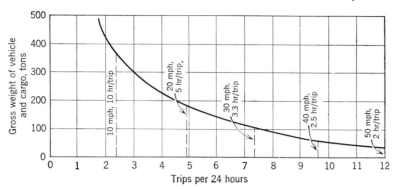

FIGURE 8-3. Number of trips per day per vehicle for various loads (and speeds) per vehicle.

mum load for a given speed. For a given horsepower, the variables are load and speed. The total number of vehicles required to move a given tonnage for any given vehicle $= W/(W_v + W_c)N_t = N$, where $W =$ total tonnage to be moved in 24 hours and $N =$ the number of vehicles required to move it. Given an expanded form, $N = W \div (W_v + W_c)24/(375 \times \text{hp} \times e/F_r)$, the resulting variations are shown in Figure 8-3. The economic aspect of this problem is to determine what loading will require the least number of vehicles to move a given tonnage in a day.

These analyses are predicated on having a fixed type of motive power and horsepower and a fixed route and system of operation with constant speeds and no traffic or other interference. Such assumptions are largely theoretical.

Traffic Interference. The foregoing analysis is particularly applicable to pipelines, conveyors, and cableways, where there is no interference between individual transport units. It might also apply to ships, airplanes, trucks, and trains, where there are not enough units of traffic to cause traffic interference and where the minimum and average times and speeds are approximately equal. It would also apply where traffic interference is caused by other carriers outside the scope and control of the carrier in question, presenting a "constant" factor to be reckoned with in determining minimum and average speeds, trip times, etc.

At this point, speed requires further definition. The maximum-allowable or the cruising speed may be acceptable where there are no delays en route—as in nonstop airline flight or a point-to-point ship's passage in good weather. The point-to-point speed is actually the effective speed. It is less than the cruising speed because of speed reductions, port or station stops, and propulsive-effort variations due to weather conditions, individual engine efficiency, and the way the operator handles his equipment. The average speed for the trip (or 100 vehicle miles) for a given set of conditions—motive power, load, route layout, profile, etc.—will be a maximum under ideal performance, conditions. The time for the trip will be a minimum. Other trips, under less ideal conditions, will take a greater length of time depending on all of the foregoing variables and on delays from traffic interference of other units using the same route. Some of the elapsed times will approach the minimum time, some will extend far beyond it. The majority of times will be concentrated around an average point. Since the variations in conditions and performance are largely accidental, the similarity of a plot of number of vehicles against road time to one half of a probability curve has led to the vehicle-hour performance diagram.

The vehicle-hour performance diagram has a sampling of trips, 100 trips for example, arranged and plotted in order of elapsed times as shown in Figure 8-4.* (*Note:* use of the probability curve makes for simple computations. Dr. Mostafa K. K. Mostafa has shown that a more precise representation is that given by the first integration of the probability curve.[5]) However, plotting actual data from test results and dispatchers' records is often as easy as processing the same data in order to plot a curve mathematically.

When traffic becomes heavy, especially as a route's maximum capacity is approached, the problem of traffic interference becomes of much importance in creating delays and increasing minimum and average times per trip. It should be recalled that the fewer the tons per vehicle, the more vehicles will be present (in moving a given

* Mr. E. E. Kimball, Consulting Engineer, General Electric Company, developed this concept as a train-hour diagram in studying train performance. Its application to any transport operation is obvious. Mr. Kimball's work is found in the *A.R.E.A. Bulletin*, Vol. 47, No. 462, Nov. 1947, pp. 125–144 (and ensuing *Proceedings*); in *Track Capacity and Train Performance,* a report of a subcommittee, Mr. E. E. Kimball, Chairman of the A.R.E.A. Committee 16 on Economics of Railway Location and Operation; and in earlier studies and reports noted therein.

[5] Mostafa K. K. Mostafa, Actual Track Capacity of a Railroad Division, Ph.D. thesis, University of Illinois, Urbana, Illinois, 1951.

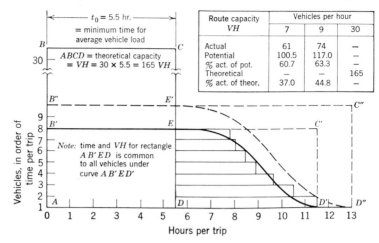

FIGURE 8-4. Vehicle-hour performance diagram. (After E. E. Kimball and the
A.R.E.A.)

tonnage) to cause traffic interference. Also, the slower speeds of
heavily loaded vehicles may be a source of interference. A private
industry deciding between ten fast-moving trucks with light loads
and six slower-moving trucks with heavy loads need not be greatly
concerned about traffic interference among those few vehicles. It
would be a small item compared with the dense flow of other traffic
on a public highway. Traffic interference would be an important factor, however, in determining the hourly and daily capacities of that
busy highway. It would also be important in determining traffic
capacity of a heavily used, narrow road from a mine to a railhead.
It is an important factor in railroad operation, especially on single-
track lines and on rapid-transit lines.

Mr. E. E. Kimball, in analyzing the problem for train operation,
presents the theory, supported by statistical data, that the average
interference time for a given set of conditions is proportional to the
number of trains operated in a given time. From this theory he developed the straight-line equation, $T_{av} = T_0 + kN$, where T_{av} = average road time, T_0 = minimum road time (without traffic interference
in ideal conditions), N = number of trains in a given time, and
k = an interference factor depending on track capacity and miscellaneous conditions.

Professor A. S. Lang has pointed out an oversimplification in

Kimball's studies.[6] This arises from Kimball's considering the average time as being represented by the foregoing straight-line function. This relation assumes that delay time varies as the number of trains on the line per day, whereas, according to Professor Lang, it varies as the number of trains on line during the time a particular train in question is on line. Thus $t_{av} = t_0 + k(N/2)(t_{av}/24) = t_0 + kNt_{av}/48$, whereby $t_{av} = t_0/(1 - kN/48)$. This relation is curvilinear rather than linear, a relation not incompatible with the scatter of the Kimball plots. The matter is undergoing further study in A.R.E.A. Committee 16, where Mr. Kimball's work originated.

The following presentation is based on Mr. Kimball's more simple if less accurate procedure as illustrating the general relations when this type of analysis is extended to other types of carriers. The factors governing t_0 have already been considered. Kimball's t_0 is the T_s of the preceding pages where theoretically perfect operation was considered. When the increased number of lightly loaded vehicles or the slower speeds of heavily loaded vehicles is a traffic interference factor, a variation of that foregoing speed-time discussion must be invoked. The vehicle load and speed that will result in the minimum time per trip (or per 100 vehicle miles) must be determined.

Figure 8-5a presents, as a straight-line representation, the hours per trip for various vehicle loadings—as already explained in the section entitled Vehicle Performance. The average load of 200 tons with a computed road time of 5.5 hours represents theoretically perfect performance ($t_0 = 5.5$ hours) is indicated by point b.

In Figure 8-5b, the number of vehicles required to handle a given 10,000 tons per day is presented, using the hours per trip and vehicle loadings of Figure 8-5a. The similarity of this diagram to Figure 8-3 should be noted.

In Figure 8-5c, the average road time *from test results or dispatchers' records* is found to be 8 hours rather than 5.5 hours. This is a 2.5-hour increase due to traffic interference. Point b' is plotted and extended to $t_0 = 5.5$ hours and a performance line drawn through the two points. Performance under traffic-interference conditions for other vehicle weights of Figure 8-5a is obtained by plotting their minimum road times from Figure 8-5a and drawing performance lines through those points parallel to the average performance line passing through point b'.

[6] Letter to the author dated August 4, 1958, from A. S. Lang, Professor of Transportation Engineering, Massachusetts Institute of Technology, Cambridge, Massachusetts.

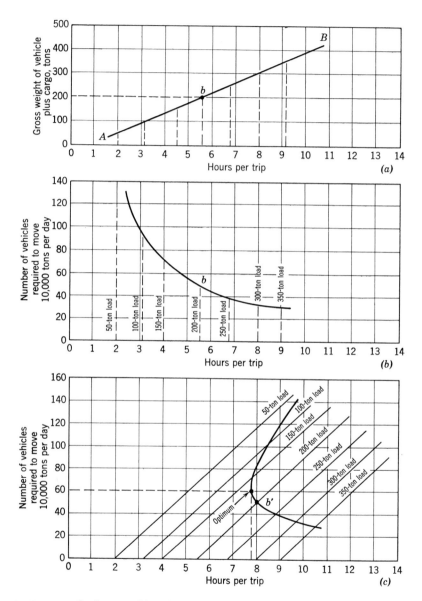

FIGURE 8-5. Optimum vehicle load: (*a*) gross load versus hours per trip; (*b*) number of vehicles versus hours per trip; (*c*) optimum vehicle load for minimum hours per trip. (After E. E. Kimball and the A.R.E.A.)

To determine how the average time will vary with different vehicle weights and traffic densities for a given volume of traffic, project from the number of vehicles (Figure 8-5b) to the corresponding performance line on Figure 8-5c and locate thereon the point corresponding to the number of vehicles. The curve EF drawn through these points indicates that a minimum time of 7.75 hours per trip will be obtained with approximately 55 vehicles of 175 net tons each. This represents the optimum vehicle load for minimum trip time. Some other minimum may, however, be desired. If total vehicle hours are to be minimized, the low point at D is chosen on the basis of the maximum load per vehicle.

Route Capacity. The number of vehicles (trains, trucks, automobiles, etc.) that can be on a given route (track, highway, etc.) is a factor of route capacity. Route capacity can be expressed in vehicle hours, VH, per day, that is, $24n$, where n is the number of vehicle sections, spaces, or blocks available. Highway vehicular capacity is usually expressed as the number of vehicles that can pass a given point in an hour—but the basic relations are the same.

A saturated condition of route occupancy (for one lane in one direction) is indicated in Figure 8-6a, where each vehicle is nosed against the vehicle in front. The total capacity would be $VH = (L_r/L_v) \times 5280 \times 24$, where $L_r =$ miles of route and $L_v =$ vehicle length in feet. This represents an almost impossible operating situation (although some city streets and approach highways are not far removed from it at certain hours). The number of vehicles is of course $N = (L_r/L_v) \times 5280$. Practically, some headway must be allowed between vehicles as in Figure 8-6b. The space controlled by one vehicle is represented by the distance $L_v + S_d$, where S_d is the space between vehicles, usually stopping distance or some variation thereof depending on driver perception and reaction times, brake application time, breaking distance, sight distance, and a factor of safety. The number of vehicles is now $N = (L_r/L_v + S_d) \times 5280$ and the vehicle capacity is $24N$. This is similar to the early basic equation for highway capacity, $C = 5280 \, V/S$, where $C =$ capacity in cars per hour of a single lane, $V =$ speed in miles per hour, and $S =$ the average distance from the front of one vehicle to the front of the one behind.

In a block system, such as is used on high-speed railroads and rapid-transit systems, the factors of stopping distance are all taken into account in establishing the minimum length of block. See Figure 8-6c.

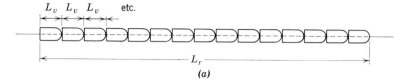

(a)

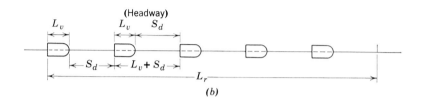

(b)

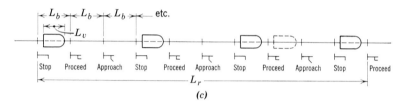

(c)

FIGURE 8-6. Theoretical route capacity: (a) route occupancy—complete saturation; (b) route occupancy—headway between vehicles; (c) route occupancy—two-block system.

A three-block headway is maintained if trains are in the position indicated by the solid lines. Route capacity (track capacity) is then VH (or train hours) $= L_r/3L_b \times 5280 \times 24$. If the following train advances to the dotted position, each train is commanding two blocks, and route capacity is $VH = L_r/2L_b \times 5280 \times 24$; but a train in the dotted position runs the risk of having its speed reduced by an approach signal if the leading train does not move into the next block quickly enough. On multiple-track lines, $VH = (L_r + L_o)/2L_b \times 5280 \times 24$, where $L_o =$ miles of other main track. For double-track lines, $L_r = L_o$ and $VH = L_r/L_b \times 5280 \times 24$. Similarly, for single-track lines without automatic block, the vehicle or train capacity is $VH = 24n$, where $n =$ the number of sidings (thereby determining the number of track spaces).

On double-track lines, trains can be operated theoretically on any headway or none at all. Practically, trains in the same direction are usually operated at least one train length apart, two train lengths between head ends. Signals are spaced accordingly. A further limitation on headway and signal spacing is that headway and speed must be so related that a following train has room to stop short of the train ahead (in the next block). The minimum headway must then be stopping distance for the maximum authorized speed at the point involved. More elaborate signaling systems in congested territory may shorten the blocks by spreading stopping distance over two or more blocks.

The foregoing discussions have been limited to obtaining theoretical route capacities. The vehicular-hour diagram of Figure 8-4 represents by the area under the curve the actual number of vehicle hours incurred. The rectangle $AB'C'D'$ represents the potential vehicle hours (theoretical) if a greater number of vehicles could have been operated with the same maximum road time maintained. However, because of traffic interference, an increase in number of vehicles operated would require a longer maximum road time—and a longer base AD'' to the rectangle. The ordinate or altitude AB' of the rectangle would therefore be decreased accordingly. A limiting value of AB versus AD, establishing the maximum practical vehicle capacity, will finally be reached. This will always be less than the theoretical as the area under the curve will be less than the circumscribing rectangle.

Theoretical and mathematical solutions should be tempered by the criteria of observation and experience. With train orders alone or with manual block, no more than 25 to 30 trains should be operated in 24 hours on a single-track railroad. When one attempts to run more, excessive interference delays are likely to occur. When automatic block signaling is used, the number may increase to 40 or 50 trains. Mr. L. F. Loree told of putting 60 trains a day over a single-track line without specifying the type of operation or signaling.[7] The South African Railway, using a station-to-station system of operation, regularly handles 30 to 40 trains on single track, but train interference causes frequent delay. The addition of Centralized Traffic Control (CTC) will increase capacity 50 to 100 percent and may permit as many as 100 trains to run over a single-track line in 24 hours under favorable conditions. Double-track main lines can handle as many as 90 to 100 trains daily with manual or automatic block and up to 200 with CTC. Four tracks are desirable when as many as 150 trains are being operated, even with automatic block

[7] L. F. Loree, *Railroad Freight Transportation,* 1931 edition, D. Appleton and Company, New York, p. 25.

(but without CTC). The four-track New York Division of the Pennsylvania (more than four tracks in some places) has regularly handled 340 to 360 trains daily, and a four-track New York subway system operates over 400 trains per day. One passenger train requires about the same track capacity as two freight trains when the two are run on the same track. The capacity of any line is being exceeded when traffic interference causes such delays that trains continually fail to maintain schedules.

Obviously, the highway capacity as expressed by the number of cars that pass a given point in an hour will vary with the speed and headway. Studies have indicated that the driver of an automobile tends to increase the headway as his speed increases.[8] A slow speed gives close headway but, because of the slow speed, few cars. High speed also gives few cars because of the greater spacing. There must therefore be an intermediate or optimum speed that will permit the maximum number of cars per mile of roadway per hour, or allow the maximum number to pass a given point in an hour. Studies by the Highway Research Board have determined capacities of various groupings of traffic lanes as shown in Figure 8-7. These studies have shown the maximum theoretical capacity of a single traffic lane to be about 2000 vehicles at 30 mph. Other maximum capacities are given in Table 8-4. In general, the highest volumes occur at speeds between 30 and 40 mph. It should be noted that maximum capacity is not synonymous with maximum density. In fact, maximum density (maximum congestion) often leads to reduced capacity to move a large number of vehicles. The ultimate in density occurs where there are so many vehicles that movement is completely halted. See Figure 8-6a.

As traffic volume increases, other conditions being equal, speed will decrease. In practical operation, all drivers do not drive at the same speed. Unless the slowest-moving vehicle is to establish the rate for a group, there must be an opportunity for faster-moving vehicles to overtake and pass those of slower speed. This opportunity is afforded by a second lane in the same direction as in four-lane highways or in the opposing lane of a two-way, two-lane highway when opposing traffic is light. However when the traffic density increases to a point where there is no room for safe overtaking and passing, all traffic must move at approximately the same speed and

[8] O. K. Normann and W. P. Walker, *Highway Capacity Manual*, Bureau of Public Roads, U. S. Department of Commerce, Washington, D. C., 1950, p. 27.

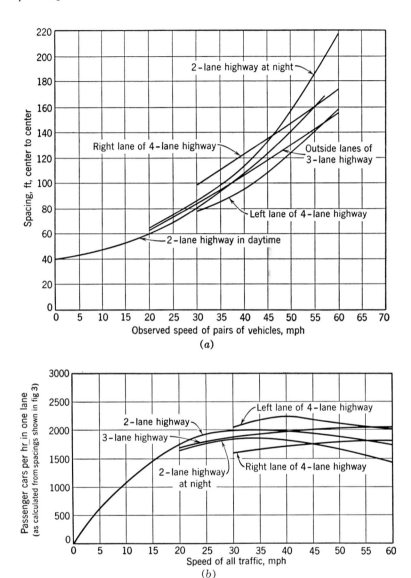

FIGURE 8-7. Maximum capacity of a traffic lane. (*Traffic Capacity Manual,* Bureau of Public Roads, Department of Commerce, Washington, D. C. Courtesy of L. I. Hewes and C. H. Oglesby, *Highway Engineering,* John Wiley and Sons, 1954, p. 144, Figures 3 and 4.)

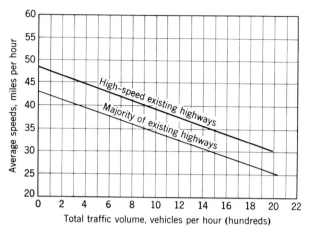

FIGURE 8-8. Average speed of all vehicles on level, tangent sections of two-lane rural highways. (Courtesy of Traffic Capacity Manual, Bureau of Public Roads, Department of Commerce, Washington, D. C.)

the relative speed between vehicles will approach zero. (Incidentally, the problem of overtaking and passing is common to all transport not operating on fixed tracks or confining routes.) At this point the critical or optimum density has been reached and any increase in density will lead to a reduction in speed and in traffic volume. See Figure 8-8.

Unless the opportunity for free overtaking and passing is present, the maximum theoretical capacities will seldom be reached. There are various types of traffic interference that operate to reduce the maximum to a more easily attained value. Cross interference comes from two streams of traffic crossing at grade. Stop signs and stop lights may here have a controlling effect upon speed and capacity, especially on city streets. This aspect of the problem is not a part of this study. Marginal interference occurs between moving persons and vehicles or objects along the roadway edges. Internal interference occurs between cars moving in the same direction (the overtaking and passing problem), and medial interference occurs between cars moving in opposing directions with no separation between lanes. All these tend to reduce the maximum capacities to the practical design capacities for uninterrupted flow given in Table 8-4. These capacities, based on 12-ft lanes, are further reduced by narrow lanes (marginal interference). An 11-ft lane has only 86 percent of the

Table 8-4. Route Capacities

Route	Ave. Speed	Train or Vehicle Hours	No. of Trains, Vehicles, etc.
Railroads: (100-mile district)			
Single-track (theoretical)			
10 sidings	10 mph	240	24 per day
	20 mph	240	48 per day
	40 mph	240	96 per day
20 sidings	10 mph	480	48 per day
	20 mph	480	96 per day
	40 mph	480	192 per day
Single-track (practical)			20–30 per day
(potential)			40–50 per day
(CTC-practical)			45–60 per day
(CTC-potential)			80–100 per day
Double-track (theoretical)			
1-mile train length,			
2-train headway	20 mph	2400	480 per day
	40 mph	2400	960 per day
1-mile block,			
2-block headway	20 mph	2400	480 per day
	40 mph	2400	960 per day
1-mile block,			
3-block headway	20 mph	1600	320 per day
	40 mph	1600	640 per day
Double-track (practical)			
Manual or automatic block			
(potential)			60–80 per day
Manual or automatic block			
(potential)			80–120 per day
Centralized Traffic Control			160–200 per day
Four-track (practical)			300–360 per day
(potential)			360–460 per day
Highways: (Theoretical basic maximum, passenger vehicles)			
2-lane, 2-way	30–40 mph		2000 per hour
3-lane, 2-way	30–40 mph		4000 per hour
4-lane, 2-way	30–40 mph		8000 per hour
1-lane maximum, 1-way	30–40 mph		2000 per hour
(Practical-design capacities, passenger vehicles)			
2-lane, 2-way	45–50 mph (operating speed)		900 per hour
3-lane, 2-way	45–50 mph (operating speed)		1500 per hour
4-lane, 2-way (rural highway)	45–50 mph (operating speed)		1000 per hour in direction of heaviest flow
4-lane, 2-way	45–50 mph (operating speed)		1500 per hour in direction of heaviest flow

(*Note:* The foregoing highway capacities are from the *Highway Capacity Manual*, 1950 edition, Bureau of Public Roads, United States Department of Commerce, Washington, D. C., pp. 45–50.)

Airplanes: (Airway flight, instrument rules, 10-minute headway)	6 per hour
(Airport landings and departures)	1000–2500 per day
Pipelines: (For 40-A.P.I.-gravity, 0.825-sp-gr petroleum with a viscosity of 40 Saybolt universal seconds)	
Pipe diameter: 2 in.	4–150 bbl per hour
4 in.	10–400 bbl per hour
6 in.	50–2000 bbl per hour
8 in.	100–4000 bbl per hour
10 in.	100–4000 bbl per hour
12 in.	400–5600 bbl per hour
Belt conveyors: (actual, carrying slack coal, etc.—Capacities vary with types and densities of materials being handled)	
Belt width—24 in. 200 fpm	65 tons per hour
400 fpm	130 tons per hour
600 fpm	196 tons per hour
Belt width—48 in. 200 fpm	325 tons per hour
400 fpm	649 tons per hour
600 fpm	974 tons per hour
800 fpm	1298 tons per hour
Aerial tramways:	6–100 tons per hour

(*Note:* Data for belt conveyors is from the *Handbook of Belting: Conveyor and Elevator*, 1953 edition, The Goodyear Tire and Rubber Company, Akron, Ohio. Section 6.)

capacity of a 12-ft lane on two-lane roads, 97 percent on multilaned roads. Correspondingly, a 9-ft lane has only 70 and 81 percent. Commercial vehicles usually move at slower speeds than passenger cars, especially on ascending grades. A truck or bus reduces total passenger-car capacity by two at 20 mph and by eight at 60 mph. Referring to the foregoing studies and capacities, one commercial vehicle will have the same effect as two passenger cars on level grades, four passenger cars on rolling profiles, and eight passenger cars in mountain territory.[9] Slow-speed lanes on ascending grades have helped.

Traffic is seldom heavy enough on open waterways to impose any serious route-capacity restrictions. However, narrow channels, locks, and harbor entrances may impose rather severe restrictions. Traffic is then limited to that which can move through the limiting section in a given time according to the general principles just set forth. In open channels, a headway limited by stopping distance must be observed. In passing through locks, a headway equal to the time it takes to lock through a vessel or tow is automatically imposed. The time may vary from 20 minutes to an hour or more depending on the size and flow capacity of the lock and on the number of units in the tow.

Federal airways obtain maximum safe air capacity by dividing the skies into 1000- and 500-ft levels and assigning each kind of craft by direction and class to its proper level. The ability of a landing field to receive and discharge planes has traditionally imposed limitations upon route capacity. Landing capacity is especially restricted when bad weather forces instrument landings, more time consuming than contact landings under some conditions, and incoming airplanes have to "stack up" over the field, that is, fly a prescribed waiting pattern bringing them lower and lower over the field until their turn comes to land. Nevertheless, increased numbers of planes in the air and the increasing speeds of flight, with a corresponding increase in the air space required for safe flight and maneuverability, are already imposing air-route-capacity limitations.

All planes flying above 10,000 ft, which includes most domestic trunk-line flights, now fly on instrument-flight rules.[10] In addition to the 1000-ft vertical separations noted earlier, air-traffic-control regulations for instrument flight have required a 10-minute headway

[9] *Ibid.*, p. 57.

[10] *Air Transport Facts and Figures 1959,* Air Transport Association of America, Washington, D. C., p. 9.

between airplanes flying the same route and elevation (plus a 10-mile lateral spacing). At a speed of 180 mph, a headway of 30 miles is thereby imposed; at 300 mph, a headway of 50 miles. For the $600\pm$-mph speeds of jet transports, an equivalent headway would be 100 miles. According to this calculation, no more than three such airplanes could be in the air at any one time on a given route and elevation between New York and Buffalo. Jet transport speeds are becoming too fast for safe contact navigation and the more stringent regulations and space requirements of instrument flight must be observed, including landing approaches. A conventional propeller-driven transport plane requires from 12 to 15 square miles for approach maneuvering at airports. Jet transports require over 1000 square miles. Three new cross-country superskyways connecting New York and Washington with San Francisco and Los Angeles have been established by the C.A.B. at altitudes between 17,000 and 22,000 ft. No airplane can use or cross these routes without specific permission from the traffic-control center involved. Radar separation is being provided for aircraft operating above 24,000 ft.

The route capacities of pipelines are a function of the capacity of one line, already described as depending on pumping pressure and flow resistance, etc., and the number of lines. Many systems are composed of two, three, or even four or more lines of pipe. The capacity is then a multiple of the capacity through one line.

Capacities for conveyors are based on the load per foot of belt (a function, in turn, of the width and strength of the belt) and its speed. These matters too have been considered in earlier chapters.

Cableways have a relatively fixed capacity as there is little speed variation for a given installation. Capacity depends on the load per carriage, the number of carriages, and the speed of the cable. These are all fixed within rather narrow limits for most installations. More cars may be added to a cable but not many more because the design of the cable, strength of its supports, and allowable sag between towers are based on a given number of loaded cars, which cannot be exceeded with safety.

SUMMARY OF OPERATING CHARACTERISTICS

Utility. Each of the numerous operating-technological characteristics described in preceding pages have their peculiar and detailed value in design and operation. The over-all significance, however, is what these bring about in the way of transport usefulness or utility.

How do these characteristics, all in combination or because of the overwhelming significance of one or two individually, make one mode of transport more suitable than another for a given type of traffic or group of transport conditions?

The simplest approach is probably to discuss and eliminate first those modes with the most obvious and significant utility patterns.

Aerial tramways offer few comparative advantages. They have high initial construction cost, due primarily to the long, heavy cables used. Their transport productivity is low in net ton-miles per flight hour and in total tons moved per day. They have poor flexibility in regard to route, cargo types, and fluctuations in volume of traffic.

Aerial tramways do offer two significant advantages, nevertheless—a low horsepower-per-net-ton figure and, of most importance, adaptability to terrain where no other type of transport can penetrate with reasonable ease and economy. The principal field of usefulness for aerial tramways is therefore in overcoming rugged terrain where there is sufficient volume of traffic to warrant the expense of a continuing operation, acting as a feeder to other modes of transport, and overcoming poor hourly productivity by steady, continuous delivery.

Conveyors, with expensive belting, also pose the problem of high initial costs, to offset which, a large continuing volume of traffic is necessary. These combine with low-flexibility of route and of cargo types, principally granular bulks. Although the net ton-miles per flight hour are not many, by continuous delivery, the belt conveyor can move large quantities of freight economically over any reasonable terrain with a safety and dependability inherent in conveyor design and operation. The use of belt conveyors as moving sidewalks for passenger movement is barely at the threshold of a potential application to urban transport.

Pipelines are directly analogous to conveyors within the field of fluid transportation. Water, sewage, gas, and petroleum and its products have thus far been the only fluid commodities moved in sufficient quantities to warrant extensive pipeline transport. The introduction of suspended solids to pipeline movement is still largely on trial but opens the possibility of a greatly broadened area of pipeline usefulness, especially among granular bulks such as coal and ore. Again there must be sufficient volume of traffic for continuous movement over an extended period of time.

Airplanes are at the other end of the scale. With a high propulsive

force per ton to overcome, a high horsepower-to-pay-load ratio, and
an unfavorable dead-load-to-pay-load ratio, the net ton-miles per
airplane hour have not been high despite a high speed factor. Limited
flexibility of landing for commercial transports and uncertainties due
to weather are additional handicaps. Nevertheless, the one technological advantage of speed gives overwhelming favor to air transport
for a large segment of the traveling public and a somewhat restricted
group of shippers. The latter include those for whose shipments time
is of the essence—emergency shipments of any kind, lightweight
perishables such as cut flowers, exotic foods, drugs, and printed and
filmed news. Items with high value in proportion to weight and
bulk—gold, currency, gems—are carried also. Many shippers take
advantage of the ability to ship safely by air with a minimum of
crating and packaging, a favorable characteristic of unit-type carriers. Bulk commodities, large, heavy objects, and freight of low
value compared to bulk and weight are clearly outside the present
scope of airway advantage. Larger airplane capacity and the commercial approach to supersonic speeds are, however, extending the
range of airplane utility.

Water transport offers many technological advantages—high productivity in net ton-miles per ship or towboat hour, extreme flexibility in respect to cargo type, high cargo weight–to–dead weight and
low horsepower-per-ton ratios. Water transport includes three major
disadvantages: lack of route flexibility, slow speed, and interruption
of service by bad weather and winter ice. The slowness of movement
and, for inland transport, the interruption from winter conditions have
made water transport of little importance in the movement of passengers, merchandise, livestock, perishables, and general cargo. This
has limited inland water transport to low-grade freight of all kinds
for which speed is less important than quantity movement, especially
to bulk commodities in an unfinished or semiprocessed state. Ocean
movements of all commodities must continue as the only practical
method available, but air transport is well into the passenger business
and is also taking considerable general cargo. It should be noted
that water routes are becoming more ubiquitous each year, making
most of America's larger cities available by water.

Highway transportation has a hold on the American interest and
fancy that is a little out of proportion to its technological advantages.
High horsepower-per-ton (and per passenger) and high dead-weight-
to-cargo-weight ratios, combined with a low net-ton-miles-per-

vehicle-hour figure, are not enhanced by a high accident rate and susceptibility to unfavorable weather. Despite these facts, the private automobile has become the outstandingly principal carrier of passengers, and motor trucks carry a high percentage of the nation's freight.

The outstanding feature of highway transport is detailed flexibility. Few persons can afford a private airplane or ship for personal transportation. No one has a railroad for that purpose. Almost everyone can have in his personal possession a means for modern, economical, rapid transportation, a means which he can use equally well to run to the corner drugstore or to travel from coast to coast. No other transport available today can compete on this personal basis—although there is ample possibility for effective competition in many areas of personal travel.

The flexibility inherent in motor transport similarly recommends it for a wide range of uses. For general cargo in intercity haul, the freedom from heavy packing and crating and the ability to drive directly from the shipper to the consignee with no intermediate transfer (for truck- or trailer-load lots) are economical advantages. The truck's usefulness in terminal movements has already been noted. Its low pay load-to-dead-load, high horsepower-to-net-tons, and low net-ton-miles-per-vehicle-hour ratios are handicaps in the movement of mass traffic of any type but especially the long-distance haul of bulk commodities. Three hundred 20-ton trucks would be required to haul the contents of one freight train of 6000 net tons; 1000 would be required to haul the contents of one Great Lakes bulk-cargo carrier —besides, there are the problems of returning the vehicles and providing adequate roadway. The use of trucks for hauling masses of bulk commodities is generally advantageous only when the distance is short, as in feeder operation, or when the total amount to be moved is too small to warrant investment in other facilities, or for local distribution, a tank truck making deliveries to gas stations, for example.

Trucks have a definitely advantageous position in the transportation system for feeder service, for terminal and local distribution and pickup, for a great variety of small miscellaneous jobs (earthmoving in construction work for example), and for general cargo haul over short and medium distances of 50 to 500 miles. Trucks can and are being used for long-distance hauling also.

Railroads offer a major technological advantage of low propulsive

Table 8-5.   Technological Utility

Carrier	Principal Technological Advantages	Field of Usefulness
Railroads	Minimum propulsive resistance and general flexibility, dependability, and safety	Bulk-commodity and general-cargo transport, intercity; of minimum value for short-haul, intraterminal traffic
Highways	Flexibility, especially of routes; speed and ease of movement in intraterminal and local service	Individual transport; also transport of merchandise and general cargo of medium size and quantity; pickup and delivery service; intraterminal and short-to-medium intercity transport; feeder service
Waterways	High net-ton-mile-per-ship (or towboat)-hour productivity at low horsepower per ton	Slow-speed movement of bulk, and low-grade freight where waterways are available; general-cargo transport where speed is not a factor or where other means are not available
Airways	High speed	Movement of any traffic where time is a factor— over medium and long distances; traffic with high value in relation to its weight and bulk
Pipelines	Continuous flow; maximum dependability and safety	Transport of liquids where total and daily volume are maximum and continuity of delivery is required; have potential for future use in movement of suspended solids
Belt conveyors	Same as for pipelines	Transport of granular bulks where total and daily volumes are a maximum and continuity of delivery is required; have potential future development as carriers of urban passengers
Aerial tramways	Not greatly affected by terrain; low horsepower per net ton-mile	Useful only where terrain makes any other type of transport uneconomical or impossible; perform a feeder service

resistance and thereby achieve a low horsepower-per-net-ton ratio and a high net-ton-mile-per-train-hour ratio. These advantages are coupled with dependability of movement (resulting largely from the system of flanged wheel guidance), good flexibility of route and movement, and outstanding flexibility in regard to cargo types and quantity. Technologically speaking, there is no field of transportation, with the exception of detailed terminal movements, where railroads cannot perform a serviceable function.

Table 8-5 gives a brief summary of these techno-utility comparisons. Factors of cost have been generally ignored throughout this discussion because other than technological factors enter into the cost. Cost and its relation to technological factors will be considered in a later chapter.

Fuel Economy. The cost of fuel is one of the big items in transportation operating expense. Economy dictates the need to get as much transportation, net ton-miles per ton or gallon of fuel, as possible. An initial factor is thermal efficiency as discussed in Chapter 6. High efficiencies are obtained with a central steam or diesel generating plant feeding electrical energy to electric locomotives, trolley buses, and rapid-transit trains. Turbo-electric drive on ships approaches the same efficiency. Direct utilization of diesel-engine drive also makes for high thermal efficiency. Direct steam drive in ships and locomotives gives the lowest. Losses in power transmission also enter the picture as in the 50-percent losses in ships' propellers and shafting and the 20–40 percent losses in airplane propellers.

The horsepower-per-net-ton ratio and dead-load-to-pay-load ratios are also factors that enter into over-all fuel economy. These are related, in turn, to the unit propulsive resistance for each type of transport. The question arises, how much fuel is consumed simply to overcome friction and move dead weight? It gives rise to another question, what modes of transport should be encouraged in the interest of conservation of national resources? Mr. A. K. Branham, Research Associate, Joint Highway Research Project, Purdue University, is reported as saying:

The average automobile consumes approximately one gallon of fuel for each 15 miles. The average passenger load of the automobile is in the range of 1.5 to 1.7. If we assume 1.6 to be the average, then 1 gal of fuel will generate about 24 passenger miles. The average Class I intercity bus consumes about 1 gal of fuel for each 5.3 miles. The most popular size of intercity bus, when fully loaded, carries 37 passengers. Thus in assuming a full load, the bus may use 1 gal of fuel in generating 196 passenger miles. With a 50 percent load, this bus generates 92 passenger miles, or about four times that of the private automobile. For economy of our national resources can we justify intercity travel by private automobile? [11]

Another measure is the amount of fuel taken by various carriers to move a given tonnage the same distance. Mr. James M. Symes, President of the Pennsylvania Railroad, is quoted in excerpts from his testimony before the Senate Subcommittee on Surface Transportation as presenting the following tabulation of the amount of fuel necessary to move 100,000 tons of freight from New York to San Francisco.[12]

Fuel	Rail	Highway	Water	Air
Gallons	832,300	3,366,300	4,346,100	20,801,200
Ratio to rail	1.0	4.0	5.2	25.0

Costwise, the question of how far a given tonnage can be moved on 1 dollar's worth of fuel might be asked. The following answers have been given to the question of how far 40 tons can be moved for 1 dollar's worth of fuel: [13]

40-ton freight car	151 miles
40-ton railroad coach	116 miles
Two 20-ton trucks	11.9 miles
Twenty 2-ton automobiles	2.9 miles
40-ton, 4-engined airplane	3.1 miles

Figure 8-9, taken from the same publication, p. 84, Chart Z, shows the weight moved and fuel consumed by various carriers in 1952.

Considerably more study and research are needed to determine not only the most efficient and economical transport systems from this point of view but also the relation of one of the country's heaviest users of fuel and the available supplies of that fuel.

[11] A. K. Branham, "National Transportation and Research Applied to Some Highway Transportation Problems," *Highway Research Abstracts*, April 1950, p. 19, Highway Research Board.

[12] James M. Symes, "The Next War: We Could Lose It on the Rails," *Railway Progress*, March 1958, p. 7, Federation for Railway Progress, Washington, D. C.

[13] *A Ten-Year Projection of Railroad Growth Potential*, prepared by Transportation Facts, Inc., for the Railway Progress Institute, Chicago, Illinois, 1957, Table 8.

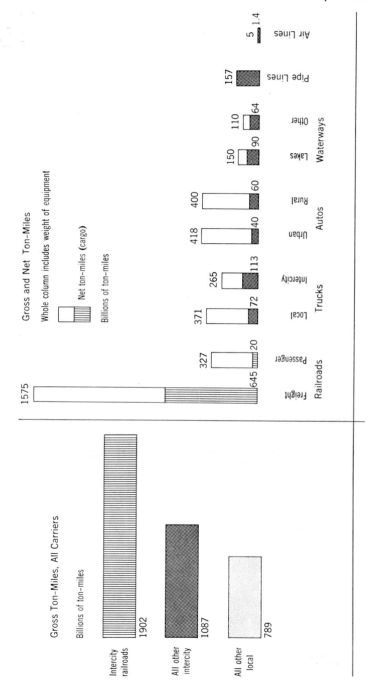

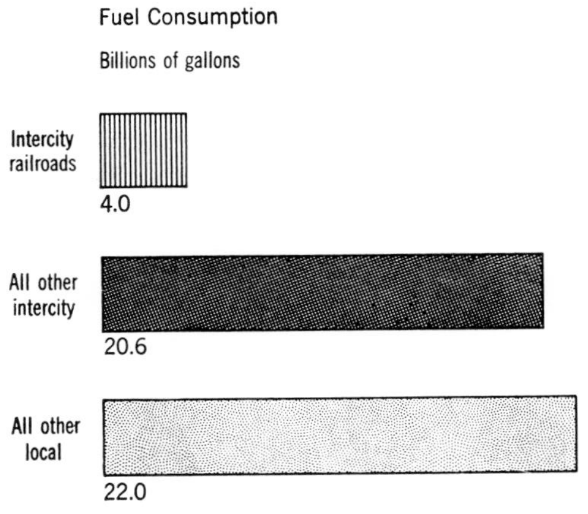

80 %

Fuel Consumption
Billions of gallons

Intercity railroads — 4.0

All other intercity — 20.6

All other local — 22.0

Weight Moved and Fuel Consumed

All figures in billions	Cargo ton-miles	All (gross) ton-miles	Gallons of fuel used	Percent of total Cargo	Percent of total gross	Percent of total Fuel
Total Railroads	665	1902	4.0	52.7	50.3	8.6
Freight	645	1575	3.0			
Passenger	20	327	1.0			
Total Trucks	185	636	11.0	14.7	16.8	23.6
Local	72	371	6.0			
Intercity	113	265	5.0			
Total Autos	100	818	30.0	7.9	21.7	64.4
Urban	40	418	16.0			
Rural	60	400	14.0			
Waterways	154	260	0.6	12.2	6.9	1.3
Great Lakes	90	150	0.3			
Rivers & canals	64	110	0.3			
Pipelines	157	157	0.4	12.4	4.2	0.8
All Airlines	1.4	5	0.6	0.1	0.1	1.3
All Intercity	1150	2989	24.6	91.1	79.1	52.8
Local Only	112	789	22.0	8.9	20.9	47.2
Total	1262	3778	46.6	100.0	100.0	100.0

Source: Various industry records for the year 1952.

FIGURE 8-9. Weight moved and fuel consumed by various carriers. (Courtesy of *A Ten-Year Projection of Railroad Growth Potential*, 1957, Chart Z, p. 84, prepared by Transportation Facts, Inc., for the Railway Progress Institute, Chicago.)

QUESTIONS FOR STUDY

1. Using typical or average values for vehicular capacities, determine how many units for each mode of transport would be required to move 10,000 tons 50 miles. *Note:* vehicles must make the return trip empty and travel at speeds appropriate to each vehicle.

2. How much horsepower is being used to move dead weight in a train of 8000 gross tons, assuming empty cars to weigh 22 tons, 44 tons of pay load to be in each car, and the train to be pulled by an 8000-hp diesel-electric locomotive (4-2000-hp, 110-ton units)?

3. What reduction in horsepower, still giving the same ton-mile performance, would be possible if a truck with a 240-hp engine and gross vehicle weight of 40,000 lb had the weight of the 20,000-ton vehicle reduced by 10 per cent? What added cargo weight could be had with the same 240-hp engine?

4. Determine, for the several modes of transport, typical values for net ton-miles per vehicle mile and explain the significance of this figure.

5. Determine the theoretical track capacities and number of trains per day for (*a*) A single-track-railroad district 120 miles long, with sidings spaced 12 miles apart, and trains running at an average speed of 24 mph. (*b*) A double-track-railroad district 120 miles long, blocks 1.5 miles in length, each train commanding three blocks, and trains running at an average speed of 40 mph.

6. Given: the following data for a railroad operation in which 40,000 gross tons per day must be moved over a 100-mile district: Minimum road time for a train of 4000 gross tons average weight is 2.35 hours. Average road time is 4 hours. Road times for trains of 2500, 3000, 5000, 6000, 7000, and 8000 tons are respectively 1 hour, 55 minutes; 2 hours, 5 minutes; 2 hours, 38 minutes; 2 hours, 56 minutes; 3 hours, 14 minutes; and 3 hours, 32 minutes. Determine the optimum road time and the interference time for the optimum among these several trains. (Based on data used by E. E. Kimball.)

7. Using the times for the trains of Question 6, prepare a train-hour diagram and determine therefrom the track capacity in train hours actually utilized by these trains.

8. Compute the basic maximum and the practical design capacities for (*a*) a two-lane, two-way highway of 11-ft-wide lanes. (*b*) a six-lane, two-way road with 12-ft-wide lanes. (*c*) The same road as in (*a*) but with 10-ft lanes.

9. A mining company desires to move 32,000 tons of ore per 8-hour day to a lake-front site 40 miles away. Assuming an average speed of 20 mph, how many trucks and how many lanes of highway would be necessary for this movement? If a railroad were used instead, how many tracks and how many trains would be required? Could a conveyor be used for this movement? How many ships per 8-hour day would be needed to move the ore down the lake?

10. Given the following traffic to be moved, determine which mode of transport should be used from the standpoint of utility and explain why. (*a*) Six million tons of ore yearly from Labrador to the Pittsburgh-Youngstown area. (b) An average of 1500 gal of gasoline per day to each of 26 service stations located within a 20-square-mile rural area. (c) A new ring gear for a broken-down power shovel in Fargo, North Dakota, the spare part to come from Milwaukee, Wisconsin. (d) 96,000 bbl of oil per day from the Gulf Coast area to a New Jersey refining center. (e) 800,000 tons of aggregates to a dam-construction site over rolling terrain from a borrow pit 10 miles away. (f) 6,000,000 tons of ore annually from a mine pocketed within an extremely rugged mountain range; no means of transport presently available. (Note: the reader should be warned that the foregoing situations have been overly simplified to permit a generalized application of the principle of utility.)

SUGGESTED READINGS

1. *Track Capacity and Train Performance*, a report of Subcommittee 1, E. E. Kimball, Chairman, Committee 16, American Railway Engineering Association, Bulletin 462, November 1946, pp. 125–144, A.R.E.A., Chicago 5, Illinois.

2. *Proceedings of the A.R.E.A.*, Vol. 22, 1921, pp. 744–759, Vol. 32, 1931, pp. 643–692, American Railway Engineering Association, Chicago 5, Illinois.

3. Unpublished Ph.D. theses, Civil Engineering Department, University of Illinois, Urbana, Illinois:

Mostafa K. K. Mostafa, Actual Track Capacity of a Railroad Division, 1951.
Meng-Te Chang, Effects of Traffic Capacity and Locomotive Performance, 1949.
Wai-Yum Yee, Centralized Traffic Control as a Means of Accelerating Train Movements, 1943.
Wai-Chiu Chang, A Study of the Traffic Capacity of Railways by the application of the Relation between Delays to Train Operation and Number of Trains Operated, 1941.

4. O. K. Norman and W. P. Walker, *Highway Capacity Manual*, written for the Committee of Highway Capacity, Highway Research Board, Bureau of Public Roads, U. S. Department of Commerce, Washington, D. C.

CHAPTER 9

TERMINALS

TERMINAL FUNCTIONS

At this point a study of techno-cost relations might logically follow the materials of the preceding chapters. However, a glance (and only that) at the more important aspects of terminals and operational control will give fuller understanding and depth to the rest of this study.

Definition and Function. Terminals have been variously defined. In a limited sense, a terminal is simply the end of the line for a transportation operation. The term is also applied to specific structures used for transportation purposes. The author here considers terminals as the sum total of facilities and their locale where road-haul traffic is originated, terminated, and/or interchanged before, during, or after the road-haul movement, including the servicing of facilities for the vehicles and equipment in which the traffic is moved. Such a grouping of facilities does, true enough, usually occur at the end of a route, but it also occurs frequently at one or more intermediate points along the route.

Terminals are as important in the transportation picture as line haul. In fact, terminal problems often surpass those of line haul in extent and complexity. Line haul, furthermore, has no significance except as there is traffic to move, and a terminal is the operational origin or destination of that traffic, or the point to which it is usually brought from outlying areas for consolidation prior to road movement or for distribution to those outlying points following a road haul.

From the standpoint of time alone, terminals possess more significance than line haul. The average daily movement of a railroad freight car is about 44 miles. This is a distance that can normally be run in 1 hour or less. In other words, a freight car spends only 1 hour out of 24 in road movement. Most of the remaining 23 hours are spent in or at some terminal activity or facility—in yards, at the shipper's or consignee's door, in transfer, on repair tracks, etc. Bulk-cargo carriers will spend about 15 percent of their time in port on the Great Lakes but defer maintenance and repairs to the three winter months, when they don't sail at all. General-cargo ships may spend as much as 50 to 65 percent of their time in port. Airplanes spend far more time on the ground than in the air. Much motor truck operation is confined solely to terminals, and a trailer will often require as much time for stripping and stowing as to make an overnight run.

The variety of terminal facilities needed or available and the investment therein is extensive. Railroad yards, freight stations, piers, wharves, transit sheds, grain elevators, produce terminals, icing docks, car dumpers, tank farms, coal and ore docks, and shops and servicing equipment are among the more obvious of such facilities. The railroads' investment in these facilities is about 1,000 million dollars. A partial listing of the terminal facilities owned and constructed by the Port of New York Authority, including airports, motor freight terminals, a bus terminal, and a union rail freight terminal amounts to 76 million dollars. If to this is added the highway bridges and tunnels giving access to and through the terminal area, the total increases to 319 million dollars. Corresponding investments could be cited for other cities and for the investments in railroad yards and in port facilities not owned by railroads.

Types of Traffic. It is pertinent to a study of transportation to mention a few of the most important characteristics and requirements of terminal operation and planning. The types of traffic passing through a terminal have important effects on the operation and the facilities required (this is also true for road haul). One may distinguish between commodity and traffic types and the peculiar needs of each. Perishable fresh fruits and vegetables must be moved rapidly, kept cool by ventilating or icing in summer and warm by charcoal heaters in winter. Precooling plants for railroad cars, icing docks, and produce terminals are typical of the facilities required. Frozen foods, fruit concentrates, and meats must be kept frozen by mechanical refrigeration, both in cars and trucks and in terminal buildings. Granular bulks require grain elevators, coal docks, car dumpers, and conveyor loaders for storage and transfer. Hulett unloaders and bridge-mounted bucket cranes unload granulars from ships. Petroleum is stored in tank farms. Livestock must have wayside loading pens and intermediate and/or terminal unloading chutes, pens, and water and feed facilities. Bananas and other perishables require holding and reconsignment yards and extensive communications so that cars may be diverted, en route, to the best markets.

Coal, grains, and other dusty products pose problems of neighborhood nuisance and the hazards of explosion and fire. The latter hazard applies equally to petroleum and chemicals. Livestock movements are accompanied by offensive odors. The list of commodities and the special problems presented by each in terminal handling could be expanded almost indefinitely.

The classification of freight into carload (CL)—or truckload—and less-than-carload lots (LCL) has already received comment in Chapter 3. In addition to Commodity types, one may further distinguish between general and bulk cargos, especially in water transport. General cargo, as the name implies, includes all types of cargo—processed, semiprocessed, and manufactured goods, and small shipments of what is usually termed bulk freight. Bulk freight applies principally to raw materials being moved in quantities and requiring special facilities for handling, transfer, and storage. Coal, ore, grain, petroleum, sulfur, molasses, etc. are a major part of this category, usually handled at private docks.

Loading and Unloading. A principal terminal function is that of loading and unloading the transport unit. Terminals at the Upper Lake ports load ships with ore, grains, and aggregates. Those at the Lower Lake ports provide unloading facilities plus car dumpers to load coal into some of the upbound vessels. Freight and transit sheds perform loading and unloading services for cars, trucks, and ships. Grain elevators, petroleum docks, etc. carry out these functions for specific commodities.

Traffic Concentration. An important principle and function of terminals is the concentrating of traffic to permit efficient and economic handling. Only trucks and airplanes, because of their small individual capacity, are suitable for the individual movement of single small shipments. Even with these it is helpful if freight can be concentrated in one freight house, or passengers in one airport. In this respect, every freight facility, whether in a metropolitan center or a country cross roads performs a terminal function. The country grain elevator concentrates grain from many farms so that freight cars can be loaded and sent on their way without the delays attendant on piecemeal loading. Similarly, grain is concentrated at terminals in train loads, tow loads, or ship loads in the secondary grain markets and elevators at Minneapolis–St. Paul, Duluth–Superior, Chicago, Winnipeg, and Port William–Fort Arthur, and at the export elevators at Seattle, Montreal, New York, Galveston, and Houston. In addition to the grading, drying, blending, and storage functions performed, the grain elevator brings about rapid loading and unloading of ships and cars, keeping turn-around and terminal time to a minimum.

Ore and coal docks concentrate quantities of those commodities, thereby permitting rapid loading of ships and cars for quick turn-around and efficient use of equipment. Where such docks are not available, stock or surge piles perform the same function albeit with somewhat less efficiency.

LCL freight is similarly accumulated and concentrated into large tonnages in freight houses of railroads, motor freight lines, airlines, and freight-forwarding agencies. General cargo is concentrated for water movement in transit sheds and other water-front storage areas or in loaded cars in nearby supporting and holding yards.

Another aspect of traffic concentration is the act of pickup or collection. Individual freight shipments must be brought to the freight house or transit shed by rail or highway, or barge. Local LCL freight may be brought to the freight house in the shipper's own trucks, in the vehicle of an independent for-hire trucker, or in the vehicle of a pickup-and-delivery service provided by the line haul carrier in its own or contracted vehicles.

Car lots moving by rail are concentrated in railroad classification yards for make-up into trains. Individual cars for loading are ordered by the shipper through the freight agent, usually from that same yard, and brought to the shipper's door (or to a public delivery yard) by local switching service called switch runs. Switch runs also take the loaded cars back to the classification yard. In river traffic, individual barges are loaded at industrial docks or public-transit sheds and brought together to make a tow, either by small pusher tugs, or by the principal towboat. Often one industry has enough traffic to load a complete tow.

Truck loads, being in unit-type carriers, are usually not thus concentrated, but trailers for carload lots may be left for loading while the tractor performs services elsewhere.

The concentration of passengers at airports, railway stations, and passenger piers by private automobile, taxi, bus, and local rapid-transit trains is too well known to need more than this brief mention.

In making detailed deliveries, the reverse of the foregoing opera-

FIGURE 9-1a. Petroleum concentration and interchange—petroleum concentration in tank farm at Beaumont, Texas. (Courtesy of *The Oil and Gas Journal,* Tulsa, Oklahoma, and Texas Eastern Transmission Corporation.)

FIGURE 9-1b. Petroleum concentration and interchange—tank-car loading rack. (Courtesy of *The Oil and Gas Journal,* Tulsa, Oklahoma, and the Arkansas Fuel Oil Company, Shreveport, Louisiana.)

tions prevails. Inbound freight is unloaded and concentrated at transit sheds, freight houses, railroad yards, and in stock piles and tank farms preparatory to detailed distribution to the consignees by switch runs, delivery services, or the consignees' own trucks or agents. Warehouses, elevators, tank farms, and stock piles hold quantities of goods in central locations for detailed distribution over longer periods of time as required.

Interchange. Much freight reaching a terminal is destined for another point and requires transfer to a similar or different mode of carriage to complete the journey. This is a function of classification yards from which carload transfers to other railroads are made, of the transfer platforms of freight houses, and of transfer piers and lighters. Railroads coordinate the interchange of bulk granulars with ships at ore and coal docks, grain elevators, etc. Pipelines interchange with ships and barges and with railroads through tank farms and flexible nozzles at loading docks, Figure 9-1.

Classification. One last highly important terminal function is classification. This reaches its highest state of development in railroad classification yards, where cars are sorted into groups of like destination (or grade, commodity, or similar grouping). Thence the cars are placed in trains of appropriate destination. A freight house or transit shed performs a similar sorting or classifying function for the shipments there tendered so that LCL freight of like destination is placed in a car or truck going to that destination.

Figure 9-2 shows the relation between road and terminal movement.

CHARACTERISTICS

Turn-around Time. A factor which reflects the efficiency of terminal operation is the over-all time for a vehicle to be placed empty for loading, moved to its destination, and unloaded ready for another load. Line-haul time is usually a small proportion of the total time thus consumed. A variation in this measure of terminal efficiency, especially for tramp steamers and gypsy truckers, is reflected in the time to arrive in a terminal at the place of unloading, unload, take on another load, and be under way again. This time will vary greatly in individual cases but average times are known for some carriers. A railroad car, for example, requires 10 to 14 days. Ships will be in port varying lengths of time depending on tonnage—4 to 12

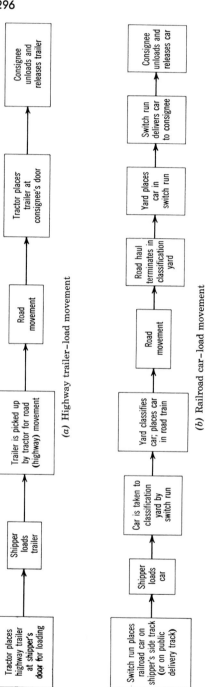

(a) Highway trailer–load movement

(b) Railroad car–load movement

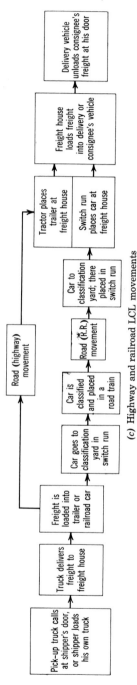

(c) Highway and railroad LCL movements

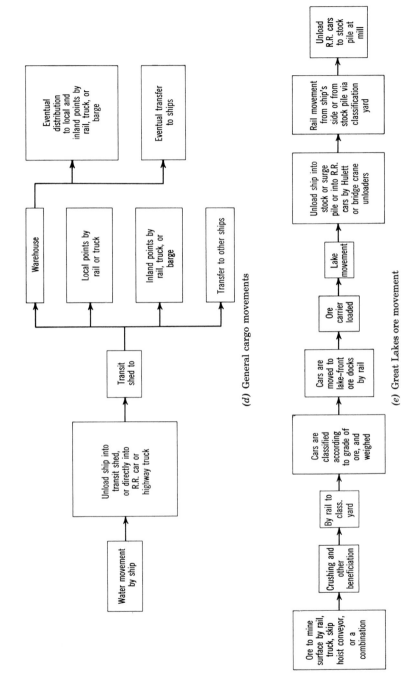

(d) General cargo movements

(e) Great Lakes ore movement

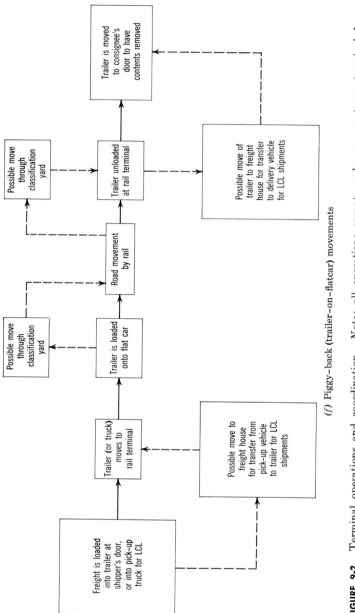

FIGURE 9-2. Terminal operations and coordination. *Note:* all operations except road movement are terminal functions or operations. Road movement may be interrupted by one or more handlings through classification yards or across freight (transfer) house platforms.

(f) Piggy-back **(trailer–on–flatcar)** movements

hours for bulk cargo carriers on the Lakes, 6 to 10 days for an 8000-ton general cargo ship. Truck trailers will arrive loaded at a freight station in the morning and go out loaded again that night when traffic is moving freely. The differences in time reflect in part the efficiency of the terminal (example: ships may have to await their turn at a wharf) or the technological characteristics of the carrier of which size is of considerable importance. A railroad car that has to pass through one or more intermediate terminal yards before reaching the yard that will classify it for road haul is not going to show a favorable terminal-time figure. A poor harbor channel may require a ship to lie at anchor outside the entrance waiting for favorable tides and currents. Flexibility in detailed terminal movements has been pointed out as an inherent techno-operational advantage for trucks and automobiles; lack of that flexibility is a disadvantage for railroads. Long hours of ground crew inspection and maintenance are behind the excellent safety record and low point-to-point flight time of commercial air lines.

Turn-around time has an obvious relation to the amount of equipment required. Shortening the average turn-around time of a railroad freight car would be equivalent to adding thousands of additional cars to the existing car fleet. Cutting turn-around time in half would permit a truck, ship, or airplane line to handle the same volume of traffic with approximately half the number of vehicles.

One element in turn-around time beyond the direct control of those carriers affected is the abuse of equipment—railroad cars, barges, motor trailers—by shippers and consignees. Where a car is placed for unloading on Friday at a plant working a 5-day week, the car will remain idle and under load until an unloading crew reports for duty Monday morning. Once unloaded, the car may be held several days to receive an outbound load, the shipper fearing a car will not be available when he orders it. Other abuses include holding the cargo units for storage, ordering more units than are immediately needed, leaving a unit dirty and filled with dunnage after unloading. All these and other delays increase turn-around time and the number of units required to give service. Unit-type carriers are less subject to this delay than assembled unit carriers. Pipelines, conveyors, and aerial tramways do not have the problem at all.

Terminal Costs. The total costs of transportation may be divided into (*a*) road-haul costs and (*b*) terminal costs. Within certain limits, road-haul costs will vary with the distance hauled, the unit cost usually decreasing as the distance increases. Terminal costs bear no relation to the distance to be hauled. The costs of terminal service will be the same whether the pay load is being moved 10 or 1000 miles in line haul. The I.C.C. has calculated the 1957 terminal costs for Eastern railroads as $64.38 for an average gondola car with a 47.5-ton load.[1] The line-haul cost was 33 cents per mile. Terminal costs were thus equivalent to a 195-mile line haul. However the terminal costs would have remained the same had the car made only a 50-mile line-haul move. The dollar amount may vary but the principle is the same for all modes of transport including the often-excepted pipelines, conveyors, and aerial tramways.

Terminals versus Land Use. Terminal location in relation to land use is presently plaguing both transportation and urban planners. It is axiomatic that terminal facilities, when ideally located, are in close proximity to sources of traffic. With lack of adequate zoning in the past, industry and commerce have located in widely scattered parts of many urban areas. The result has been a complex crisscrossing of rail, truck, and canal routes, often invading residential areas, crossing central business districts, and introducing blighted neighborhoods, safety hazards, and mutual traffic interference.

A large city with an established land-use pattern can do little to improve the situation except at great expense. Placing rail lines and expressways on elevated structures, in depressed open cuts, or in tunnels has given relief in some situations. Consolidation and abandonment of duplicate facilities have been carried out to advantages. Union truck and bus terminals reduce cross haul and duplicate truck routes.

Where the community is small enough to admit adequate readjustments of land use, industrial and commercial areas are defined and transport routes planned to give the maximum service to those areas with a minimum of interference to other land uses of the community. Switching and truck service to an industrial park area can be made as complete as the situation requires without interfering with resident, shopping, CBD and civic-center areas. The noise, dirt, traffic interference and hazard and other objections peculiar to certain types of traffic are thus localized.

A feature of terminal location and land use is the large amount of land required by terminal facilities. A motor freight terminal in a

[1] *Railway Age,* June 1, 1959, p. 38, Simmons-Boardman Publishing Company, New York.

large city will occupy most or all of a city block. One to five square miles or more are needed for railroad yards and servicing facilities. Wharves and piers often take up an entire water front. Airports of today require 5 to 10 square miles or more, and the jet transports now flying and to come present land-use demands which are likely to place such airports farther away from urban centers, whereby several communities will be served from one airport with shuttle service to and from the central areas of each.

TERMINAL FACILITIES

Design and operation of specific facilities, as these reflect technological characteristics, are of some interest at this point. Typical of terminal facilities are ports and harbors, railroad freight yards, and the ubiquitous freight house and transit shed for rail, truck, water, and air transport.

Freight Houses. Freight-house planning is based on a design tonnage from which the requisite floor or platform space, berths, car spots, tracks, and truck tailboard room is developed. The design tonnage may be the anticipated yearly average, reduced to a daily or shift basis, plus a factor—usually 15 to 20 percent—to cover peak periods and traffic increases. Design tonnage may also be based on the expected arrivals of an estimated or scheduled number of ships or other units of a given capacity. The ideal location should include land area for future expansion when the traffic increase so justifies.

For an outbound-only rail or truck house, the floor need be only wide enough to receive freight and move it across to the waiting line-haul vehicle, 30 to 50 ft. Inbound freight is customarily allowed 24 to 48 hours of free storage, so more space is required. The area may be calculated as so many square feet per ton of freight—130 sq ft per ton has sometimes been used—but depends on the weight-volume relation of the type of freight handled. Live loads of 300 to 500 psf are usually considered. About 30 percent additional space is needed for aisleways.

Platforms are generally placed about 3 ft-9 in. above the top of rail and 4 ft-0 in. above tops of pavements.

For rail freight, the platform length is based on two factors: the number of car spots required on one side of the platform and tailboard room for trucks and trailers along the other side. For motor freight alone, tailboard room must be provided on both sides. See

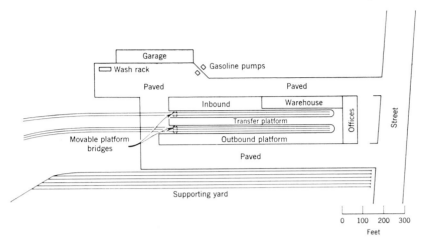

FIGURE 9-3. Typical freight-house design.

Figure 9-3. The tonnage for an LCL car varies from 6 to 10 tons and is not much less for trailers. This tonnage, divided into the daily or shift tonnage, indicates the car spots required per day or shift. With tailboard room satisfied, an economic balance is obtained between annual costs of construction and operation for varying lengths of platform and corresponding number of spots per track and length of track. The optimum design will give the length for minimum combined costs.

Tailboard may be determined in several ways. The A.R.E.A. has recommended 1.12 tons per foot of platform length in their manual. Thus a daily average of 100 tons would require approximately 90 ft of platform length or ten 9-ft spaces. By state law, trucks cannot exceed 8 ft in width. The 9-ft allowance provides only a 1-ft clearance between any two maximum-width trucks. For ease and safety in maneuvering, this width should be increased to 10 or 12 ft, and the platform correspondingly lengthened. If service and maintenance are to be performed on the truck or trailer while it stands at the platform (thereby reducing terminal time), then as much as 14 ft of space per truck is desirable.

Transit Sheds. A transit shed is a freight house for water-borne general cargo. It performs the same function as a freight house with concentration assuming more importance. It operates on a longer turnover cycle and often with heavier weights of traffic. Floor capacities are based on the number of ships to be served during a given period. The floor space must not only accommodate, with appropriate stacking, what is required to load the expected ships upon arrival but must also hold the cargo which is off-loaded from the ships before they can take on new cargo. Covered-space requirements can be reduced by the anticipated tonnage that can be stored out of doors on open wharf areas or that will be loaded directly into railroad cars, lighters, barges, or trucks.

A transit shed designed to handle two 8000-ton ships (common cargo capacities are 8000 to 10,000 tons) would have to provide space for accumulating 16,000 to 20,000 tons of outbound freight. In addition, space would be necessary for another 16,000 to 20,000 tons to be off-loaded before the outbound tonnage could be put aboard (less tonnages that are given open storage or handled directly from another carrier to or from a ship's hold). A total of 32,000 to 40,000 tons would thus have to be accommodated at a rate of 300 to 400 lb of cargo per square foot plus about 33 percent of the loaded space for aisleways. It is usual for United States sheds to permit 5 days free storage for accumulating outbound cargo and 10 days free distribution for inbound tonnages. About 80,000 to 120,000 sq ft of covered transit-shed space are required per ship berth; note again that not all cargo has to be under cover.[2]

If, in the foregoing example, another two ships were expected 5 days after the first two were unloaded, the shed would have to accommodate additionally what still remained undistributed from the first two. Cargo to be held beyond the 10-day free storage period is usually taken to a warehouse, which should be reasonably close to the transit shed (and is sometimes included in the same structure). About 2.5 to 5.0 percent of all general cargo handled annually in the United States passes to a warehouse from or through the transit shed, and 10 to 20 percent of that will be warehoused on the water front for about 3 months.[3]

Ports and Harbors. Harbors provide a safe anchorage, protecting ships from the open seas. Typical harbor locations are mouths of rivers, natural bays and inlets, the interiors of coral reefs, and man-made breakwaters and tidal basins. Tide variations, currents, silting,

[2] Maurice Grusky, "Harbor Engineering," in R. W. Abbett, *American Civil Engineering Practice,* Volume II, John Wiley and Sons, New York, 1956, Chapter 21, pp. 78–81.
[3] *Ibid.*

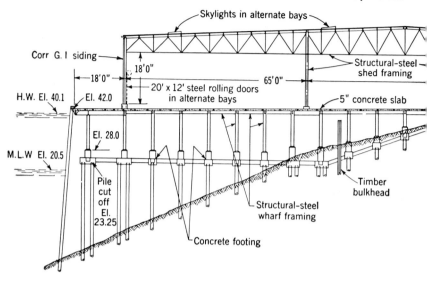

and wave action are problems that enter into the design and operation of harbors.

A 26-ft depth of harbor is said to be adequate for about 80 percent of the world's shipping. Hence the selection of that depth for the St. Lawrence Seaway. Depths of 33 ft are desirable but depths of 36 ft are necessary to dock the largest passenger liners and maximum-tonnage oil tankers. Deep-draft vessels may dock at high tide in some shallow harbors, then wait until another high tide before casting off. Another solution to shallow harbors is to anchor the ship away from shore in deep water and shuttle cargo between ship and shore in shallow-draft, light-tonnage lighters or barges. Where exceptionally high tides prevail, those exceeding 6 to 12 ft variation, tidal basins may be built. These are landlocked basins bordered by wharves. There is a gate at the entrance which is closed during low tide to maintain a constant high-tide level in the basin. Ships enter and leave only when the gates are open at high tide. The deck of a wharf is usually kept about 7 ft above high spring tide.

A port combines harbor protection with facilities for concentrating cargos to be loaded, for loading and discharging cargo and interchanging with other carriers and places where the ship may take on fuel and other supplies and be repaired.

The principal feature of a port is the wharf across which goods to

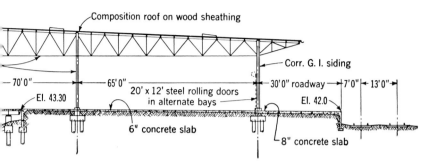

FIGURE 9-4. Cross section of typical wharf and transit shed. (Robert W. Abbett, editor, *American Civil Engineering Practice*, Vol. II, John Wiley and Sons, 1956, pp. 21-82 and 21-83, Figure 67.)

and from the ships are moved. The wharf may be of the pier type built over the water, or a quay built on shore or a filled-in extension of the land into the water. A wharf may also be partly on land, partly over the water, depending on topography of the shore line. A transit shed is a usual feature of most wharves. Other elements include an apron between the ship and shed with one or more railroad tracks and paved for land vehicles, tracks and pavements in or at the rear of the shed, and, sometimes, a rail-mounted gantry or portal crane of the rotating or turret type on the dockside apron. Figure 9-4 shows the cross section of a typical wharf layout.

Piers are used where shore space is limited or where there is ample room in the harbor channel. Quay-type wharves find use where channels are narrow or where land and shore line are plentiful. Berthing is much simpler with quay systems. Slips are the open spaces between adjoining piers or docks.

The capacity of a terminal must be based on the pattern of ship arrivals. Pier and wharf lengths are functions of the number of ships to be berthed there at one time. The usual length of vessel to be accommodated must be determined in each situation, but for a normal 10,000-ton vessel of 520-ft length, 600 ft of berth space would be required. United States design is based on vessels with five cargo hatches, loading or unloading 300 long tons per hour for an 8-hour working day, 200 days per year.[4] The longer the pier, the wider it must be to accommodate the increased tonnage moving shoreward, or vice versa, from the far end. Recommended widths for a pier with

[4] *Ibid.*

one ship on each side are 350 ft minimum (for one-story sheds) and 450 to 500 ft desirable. With two 10,000-ton ships on each side, a minimum width of 450 ft is required, but a width of 500 to 600 ft is desirable. Included in these widths are 30- to 40-ft aprons.[5] Marginal wharves should have widths similar to those for a two-ship pier.

Mechanization. The movement of freight from ship to shore, on aprons, in transit sheds, and in motor freight and railroad freight house was once performed by hand. Most of that drudgery has been removed, accidents and damage reduced, and economic speed and efficiency brought forth by mechanization. For very small houses, the old hand truck still prevails, but in most freight and transit sheds, small tractor-pulled trucks are used for detailed movements. The introduction of pallets to which shipments may be attached for handling as a unit permit the use of fork trucks for moving and stacking the pallets with a more economical use of floor space. Where large volumes of freight prevail, mechanical conveyors move individual trucks around a closed path. A continuous moving chain, placed either above or below the floor, has hooked projections to which the handle of the truck may be attached. The truck is moved along to its proper location and unhooked from the chain.

Where heavy or oddly shaped cargo is to be handled, special gantry, turret, or other types of cranes of 5 to 20 tons capacity may supplement the foregoing. For unusually heavy lifts, tractor cranes up to 50 tons may be kept available. Rail-mounted locomotive cranes will lift up to 250 tons. A few of the largest ports have floating cranes of similar capacity.

Yards. Railroad yards serve the varied purposes of storage, holding, reconsignment, public delivery, and supporting industrial, waterfront, and switching activity. The principal type of yard, and its function, is the classification yard, which also performs a concentration function by accumulating enough cars to fill out a train. Classification includes the receiving and break-up of trains and the sorting and classifying of the cars into new trains for road haul, transfer to other yards or railroads, or local delivery. These last two functions are distribution factors. A large classification yard usually contains three yard units: the receiving yard, into which trains are moved from the main line preparatory to sorting; the classification yard proper, where the sorting or classifying into blocks of common desti-

[5] *Ibid.*

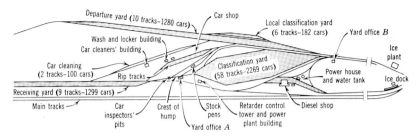

FIGURE 9-5. Plan of a classification yard. (Courtesy of *Railway Signaling and Communication,* Simmons-Boardman Publishing Co., New York, March 1955.)

nations takes place; and the departure yard, in which the sorted groups or blocks are made into trains and held pending main-line movement. Small yards consist of only one general yard, certain tracks within that one yard being assigned to receiving and departure purposes. See Figure 9-5.

The track lengths of the receiving and departure yards are obviously based on the number of cars in the average- and maximum-length trains (at 50 ft per car) plus length of locomotive (50 to 200 ft), and caboose, 40 ft; plus 200 to 300 ft as a factor of safety in stopping. The number of tracks is based in part on arrival rate of inbound trains but is governed fully as much by the rate of classifying, the rate at which cars can be taken from the receiving yard and sorted into groups or blocks, and assembled into trains in the departure yard. The final assembly of trains involves combining the blocks from various tracks in station orders, front-to-rear or rear-to-front depending on the set-out operation employed.

In the classifying unit, each track is assigned a given "destination," and cars going to that destination, and no others, are sorted into it. Classifying rates vary with the method of operation. Small yards are flat switched, that is, the engine pushes and pulls a cut of cars in and out of the various tracks, sorting the cars onto the proper tracks at a rate of 30 to 60 cars per hour. Gravity yards make use of an artificial hump placed between the receiving and classification yard over which cars are pushed at a speed of about 3 miles per hour, uncoupled, and allowed to roll into the assigned track. Gravity yards are seldom used where less than 1500 cars a day are to be classified.

In manually operated gravity yards, now largely obsolete, a rider mounts each car and controls its speed into the body track with a brake club in the handbrake wheel. The classifying or humping rate for such a yard has been 60 to 120 cars per hour.

Semi-automatic yards have retarder units placed on leads to groups of tracks. The retarders control car speed by pressing brake shoes, electrically or electropneumatically, against each side of the wheel as the car moves through the retarder. Tower operators judge the cars' speeds and, by push-button arrangement, control the amount of braking pressure which will be applied. In this type of yard, classification rates will vary from 100 to 150 cars per hour.

Completely automatic yards use electronic and radar devices to measure the weight and speed of each individual car and automatically apply the proper retardation. The electronic computer in which the control is set thus takes into account temperature, wind effects, rolling resistance, and, by additional measurement, the distance the car must roll to couple to the cars already standing on a particular track. The safe coupling speed which will not cause damage to car or contents is about 4 mph. The operator needs only to push a button indicating the proper track for each car, and the switches are aligned and control exercised from there on by the electronic control. The most recent designs can feed an entire teletyped switch list for a newly arrived train into the machine with no need for the track-designation buttons to be pushed. Classifying rates of 200 cars per hour can be obtained when there are no delays due to external causes. It should be noted that technical know-how is already available to operate the locomotive pushing cars over the hump by remote control and uncouple them. Thus the human element can be removed almost entirely from this phase of the operation.

An essential part of every yard is a comprehensive system of communication. Use is currently made of telephone, loud speaker, and talk-back systems, radio, inductive telephone, teletype, television, and pneumatic tubes. Consists of trains are sent by teletype from the point of origin to the destination terminal so that switch lists and consists for the new trains to be built can be prepared in advance of the train's arrival.

The problem of yard location in an urban area includes proximity of the yard to industrial, water-front, and other traffic sources and to other rail routes, land values and availability, taxation, and opportunities to expand. These are rather obvious and highly important. Of even more significance to rail operation, however, is the location with respect to other yards on the system. Involved here are problems of traffic patterns, scheduling of trains, and how far in advance of final destination and in what detail sorting should occur. The tendency today is to have a few large strategically placed yards equipped with all the modern devices for rapid car handling instead of many small yards scattered over the system.

Airports. The principal feature of an airport is its runways, a prime necessity in landing and take-off for all present-day airplanes. A large, well-equipped airport will have, additionally, hangars for storage, inspection, and maintenance, fuel and oil facilities, fire-fighting equipment, hard standings for airplane parking, and taxiways leading from hangars, terminal building, or standing area to the run-ways. An operations center, control tower, offices, freight and ex-press platforms, ticket sales and waiting rooms, amenities for the passengers, and adequate automobile parking are also included. These facilities, in addition to their other functions, serve to concen-trate in plane-load quantities passengers who are interchanging or transferring from one flight to another.

Airports require extensive land areas and clear air space with good visibility approaching those areas. Proximity to traffic sources and to main roads are further considerations. The large runways and approach areas and the noise nuisance of jet operation are likely to

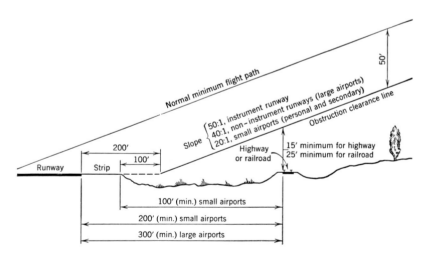

FIGURE 9-6. Vertical clearance for approach paths. (Robert W. Abbett, editor, *American Civil Engineering Practice*, Vol. I, John Wiley and Sons, 1956, p. 5-06, Figure 2.)

place airports designed for their use definitely in the regional category, with helicopter and conventional-type feeder service to adjacent communities. Clearance and glide paths for various types of operation and classes of runways are shown in Figure 9-6.

The lengths and widths of runways vary with the type of traffic (and airplane) and are so classified by the F.A.A.

Personal airports handle small aircraft up to 3000 lb in weight and may have unpaved runways of 1500 to 2300 ft in length with a minimum strip width of 200 ft and actual runway width of 50 ft.

Secondary airports take weights up to 15,000 lb in nonscheduled flying on runways 2301 to 3000 ft long with minimum strip and runway widths of 250 and 75 ft respectively.

Feeder ports serve certificated feeder lines with runway lengths of 3001 to 3500 ft, widths of 300 and 100 ft, and pavements designed for single-wheel loadings of 15,000 and dual-wheel loadings of 20,000 lb.

Trunk-line ports serve small cities on trunk lines with lengths of 3501 to 4200 ft, widths of 400 and 50 ft, and loadings of 30,000 and 40,000 lb.

Express ports are at important cities or interchange points on trunk lines with lengths of 4201 to 5000 ft, widths of 500 and 150 ft, and permissible loadings of 60,000 and 80,000 lb.

Continental airports serve domestic flights on runways of 5001- to 5900-ft lengths, 500- and 200-ft widths, and 60,000- and 80,000-lb loadings.

Intercontinental ports terminate long-distance international flights on lengths of 5901 to 7000 ft, widths of 500 and 200 ft, and bearing supports of 75,000 and 100,000 lb.

Intercontinental-express are the largest type of port for intercontinental flight. Lengths are 7001 to 8400 ft, widths are 500 and 200 ft, loadings 100,000 and 125,000 lb.

The foregoing lengths have been established for sea-level altitude and 59 degrees Farenheit temperature and for level gradients. The length should be increased 7 percent for every 1000-ft increase in elevation above sea level. A further increase of 0.5 percent is made for each degree that a long-time average of the hottest month exceeds the standard temperature. The sum of the foregoing is additionally lengthened by 20 percent for each 1 percent of grade.

Runway orientation must be such as to permit take-offs and landings with or into the wind and with 95 percent of such operation free of cross-wind components exceeding 15 mph (20 to 30 mph if only heavy transports are involved).[6] This requires a study of prevailing winds, usually plotted on the radial lines of a so-called wind rose, which shows the percentage of time winds of different velocities blow from the radial directions. To achieve freedom from cross winds, more than one runway may be required for alternate use as the wind changes direction. Runways should also be placed in such a way as to avoid conflict between two being used simultaneously, especially if one or more are designed for instrument landings—as at least one should be at the larger ports.

From a traffic standpoint, the number of runways is based on a peak load of 40 to 60 landings and take-offs per hour under visual conditions and 25 to 35 landings and take-offs per hour under instrument conditions.[7] These top capacities will probably be increased as navigational and control methods and equipment are further improved.

Access to the planes from the terminal building affects the over-all speed of transport and the passengers' convenience and comfort. Characteristically the planes are reached via a long concourse and then out into the weather. Moving sidewalks have shortened concourse transit time and effort in some ports. Another device is to bring planes close in to overhanging galleries with telescoping walkways that can be extended directly to the door of the plane. At the San Francisco airport, one airline brings its first-class passengers from the planes' cabins to the concourse over a "jet walk" and into a monorail gondola. Freight and express are carried from the receiving platform and vice versa on trucks with lift platforms or raised and lowered to the hatchway by portable conveyors.

Service and Repair. Service and repair facilities are usually provided by the carrier except in water transport, where heavy repairs are made by contract. Drydock companies give the ship's hull, rudder, and propellers (as well as its internal fittings) a thorough overhaul. Similarly, lighter vessels and barges are hauled from the water on marine railways. Running repairs on rail equipment is performed in engine houses and car-repair shops with major repairs being made in centrally located heavy-repair or back shops. Airlines

[6] Phillips Moore, "Airport Engineering," in R. W. Abbett, *American Civil Engineering Practice,* Volume I, John Wiley and Sons, New York, 1956, pp. 5–11.
[7] *Ibid.,* pp. 5–14.

maintain elaborate inspection and repair facilities in company hangars at airports. Bus and truck maintenance is performed at company garages at principal terminals; some of it is contracted. A few large truck lines have erected intermediate maintenance garages along their routes.

Locomotive fuel, sand, water, and lubricants are placed at the engine-house site and at other convenient terminal and on-line points. Fuel for water transport is usually obtained at privately owned shore points. At airports, fueling is performed by an oil distributor having a concession contract with the airport. Trucks and buses use their terminal facilities for fuel and oil but also make use of regular gasoline stations along the road.

QUESTIONS FOR STUDY

1. A railroad inbound freight house is planned to handle 100 tons per day. What area of floor space should be provided? How many car spaces?
2. Assuming platform length has been designed on the basis of adequate tailboard space for the delivery trucks to distribute the inbound freight of Question 1, how many tracks will be needed and how many car spots on each if the tracks are pulled only once a day and average car contents weigh 10 tons?
3. What is the floor space required of a transit shed to handle two 10,000-cargoton ships at a time, assuming all the cargo will first be delivered to the shed?
4. What warehouse space would be required for the Question 3 situation if three ships at a time came to the transit shed planned originally for two?
5. How many receiving yard tracks would be needed to hold 80-car trains arriving at the rate of two per hour during one 8-hour shift (with light, scattered arrivals throughout the rest of the day), using a classifying rate of 120 cars per hour?
6. If the 120 cars per hour of Question 5 are uniformly distributed in a ratio of 10, 10, 20, 20, and 40 percent over each of five classification groups or blocks, how many tracks and of what standing-room length would be needed in the classification yard to handle the traffic of the 8-hour shift?
7. How many tracks would be required in the departure yard, assuming 100-car trains outbound and the trains moved into the departure yard as soon as sufficient blocking becomes available? Assume each train spends 1 hour in the departure yard having the air tested, the caboose and locomotive attached, and waiting for orders to move onto the main track.
8. Explain the presence of grain elevators, ore docks, and coal docks in the light of the principle of concentration. What do these facilities have to do with questions of car, truck, and barge supply?

9. A union truck terminal receives 180 tons of freight daily inbound from 90 semitrailers that carry an average of 20 tons per vehicle. How many delivery vehicles will be needed to make local distribution of that 1800 tons if each truck averages 5 tons per load and requires 4 hours for each round trip? What reduction in number of vehicles would be made if the time for each round trip of a delivery vehicle could be reduced to 2 hours, 30 minutes.

10. What are advantages of having industrial activities concentrated in a limited number of zones in an urban area?

SUGGESTED READINGS

1. "Yards and Terminals," Chapter 14, *Manual of the A.R.E.A.*, American Railway Engineering Association, Chicago, Illinois.

2. E. W. Coughlin, *Freight Car Distribution and Car Handling in the United States,* Association of American Railroads, Washington, D. C.

3. Charles A. Taft, *Commercial Motor Transportation,* Business Publications, Chicago, Illinois, 1955.

4. *Principles of Freight Terminal Operation,* American Truckers Association, Washington, D. C., 1950.

5. Wilbur G. Hudson, *Conveyors and Related Equipment,* Third Edition, John Wiley and Sons, New York, 1954:
Chapter 1, "General Principles"
Chapter 12, "Storage and Transport"
Chapter 13, "Bins and Bunkers"
Chapter 14, "Unloading Water-Borne Cargoes"
Chapter 22, "Dust and Explosion Hazards"

6. "Design of Ore Docks," *Proceedings of the A.R.E.A.,* Vol. 36, 1935, p. 288 ff., American Railway Engineering Association, Chicago, Illinois.

7. Harold M. Mayer, *The Port of Chicago and the St. Lawrence Seaway,* University of Chicago Press, Chicago, Illinois, 1957.

8. C. L. Sauerbier, *Marine Cargo Operations,* John Wiley and Sons, New York, 1956.

9. R. W. Abbett and E. E. Halmos, "Harbor Engineering," in R. W. Abbett, *American Civil Engineering Practice,* Volume II, John Wiley and Sons, New York, 1956, Chapter 21, especially the section entitled "Marine Terminals" by Maurice Grusky.

10. "Classification Yards," *Proceedings of the A.R.E.A.:*
Vol. 30, 1929, p. 762 ff.
Vol. 31, 1930, p. 1014 ff.
Vol. 32, 1931, p. 210 ff.
Vol. 34, 1933, p. 177 ff.

11. "Hump Yard Systems," *American Railway Signaling Principles and Practices,* Signal Section, Association of American Railroads, Chicago, Illinois, Chapter 21.

12. "Retarder Layout and Profile Design," *"Union" System Description,* Number D7.1.1, 1956, Union Switch and Signal Division, Westinghouse Airbrake Company, Swissvale, Pennsylvania.

13. Charles Froesch and Walter Prokosch, *Airport Planning*, John Wiley and Sons, New York, 1946.

14. H. Oakly Sharp, G. Reed Shaw, and John A. Dunlop, *Airport Engineering*, John Wiley and Sons, New York, 1944.

15. Phillips Moore, "Airport Engineering," in R. W. Abbett, *American Civil Engineering Practice*, Volume I, John Wiley and Sons, New York, 1956, Chapter 5.

CHAPTER 10

COORDINATION

COORDINATION PRINCIPLES

Definition and Significance. The ideal transportation is usually considered to be that of loading a shipment into a container (freight car, ship, truck, etc.) or into a transport system (pipeline, conveyor, etc.) at the shipper's door and performing no other operation than a single road haul before the freight is turned over directly to the consignee at his door. Such an ideal is not always realized, possible, or even desirable in practice.

Earlier chapters show how each carrier type possesses certain inherent technical and economic advantages and disadvantages. These advantages can often best be realized, or the disadvantages overcome, by combining two or more carriers to perform a joint or coordinated transportation service. Such coordination can bring about faster or more dependable service for the shipper and economies for the transport agencies, some of which may be passed on to the public through lowered rates.

Union rail and bus stations, the collection and delivery by trucks of line-haul freight, and the travel to and from an airport by automobile, bus, taxi, or helicopter are well-known examples of coordinated transport services. Many others are not so well known to the general public.

The value of coordination is, in many situations, clearly evident through the avoidance of duplicate facilities, the sharing of costs, or the utilization of a less costly service. In other situations, the actual value may be apparent but hard to determine. In still others, the presence of any value may require much study and analysis. Each arrangement is a problem to be settled on its merits. The reader can gain some concept of the possible savings through coordination in only one branch of the industry by reading of the many schemes pro-

315

posed by Federal Coordinator of Transportation Joseph B. Eastman in his reports submitted to the Congress in 1936.[1] It is probable that the administrative savings occasioned by coordination have been overemphasized. At the same time, the possibilities for more economical, rapid, convenient, and dependable service through coordination are far from realization.

Coordinative Factors. What are the factors or combination of conditions that bring about coordination?

Extension of service has been one of the prime factors. Airplanes cannot take off and land in the center of a large city or its central business district. Their service must be extended into that potential source of traffic by use of the earlier-mentioned modes of transport. Rail lines lack the flexibility required to serve individual shippers at their doors by rail delivery and pickup. The flexibility of trucks is therefore used to extend their service to the shipper's door. Much of the feeder service to line-haul routes falls into this category.

Impossibility of other means of service. The intervening presence of a large body of water may require joint rail or highway and water service to reach a destination. Rail movements to Cuba or across Lake Michigan must have ferry service as an integral part of their route. A railroad may penetrate a rugged mountain area as far as the terrain permits. Beyond that a cableway or conveyor system will have to be used to cross ground impassable by rail.

Speed. The use of combined modes of transport to produce a speedy passage is exemplified in the surburban dweller who drives his car to a parking lot on a commuter or rapid transit line and rides the train into town.

Convenience. The desire to offer a more convenient service, often for competitive reasons, has led to such types of coordination as truck pickup and delivery for rail and highway motor freight and the substitution of truck delivery for trap- and way-car delivery from break-bulk points. Coordination carries out the principle of concentration discussed in connection with terminals by permitting a large- or bulk-shipment carrier to accumulate freight in large quantities in stock piles, tank farms, or warehouses and make small-lot distribution therefrom by other means of transport. The use of a belt line or switching service to give all rail carriers unbiased access to all shippers in an area, and vice versa, is even more illustrative.

[1] Fourth Report of the Federal Coordinator of Transportation on Transportation Legislation, 74th Congress, 2nd Session, House Document No. 394, 1936.

Economy. The simple urge for economy may, in some instances, bring about coordination. Two types of economy—land use and financial—are likely to be involved. The joint use of the same right of way by different types of transport illustrate land-use economy. Rail lines have been proposed, and placed, in the median strip between two highway lanes. The placement of rail lines over highways and vice versa has also been proposed and carried out. Some pipelines have recently been laid on railroad rights of way, and more such pipelines are proposed. In Wuppertal, Germany, a monorail is suspended over a waterway.

Financial economy may be the reason for a union rail or bus station or for a terminal service for all railroads provided by a single terminal system within an urban area. The capital, operating, and administrative costs of duplicate facilities are thus avoided.

It should be evident at this point that several or all of these factors are usually present at the same time to bring about a particular type of coordination. Economy in land use, for example, usually (but not always) leads to financial economy as well.

Limitations on Coordination. Important as it is, coordination has no value for its own sake. It should be utilized only when it makes a real contribution to over-all economy and efficiency of movement. Combination frequently involves interchange and/or rehandling of equipment or lading. Each such interchange or rehandling involves additional expense and loss of time. Each rehandling increases the possibility of loss or damage to lading. Trans-shipment of coal, for example, by means of a car dumper to a ship and then via a bucket crane back to a railroad car involves breakage of the initial lumps into smaller particles and loss of original tonnage through dust and the leakage of fine particles. The design of interchange facilities and operations should always be based on a minimum amount of rehandling and reverse movements. When harmful rehandling cannot be avoided, other measures may be required. One of the taconite-grade-ore producers in Minnesota has placed its beneficiating plant near the mills at the lower end of the lakes and ships raw ore to it because it was found that the ore pellets formed by the sintering process did not stand up under the impacts of trans-shipments required by shipments from upper-lake ports.

The most efficient and economical transportation is usually that of one single movement from shipper's door to consignee's door. Car-load movements from private side tracks or direct truck-load movements exemplify this operation. However, the car may be interchanged with several lines with an accompanying loss of time, with added expense, and with wear and tear on the car. A trailer-on-flatcar combination can, on the other hand, avoid transfer and rehandling at intermediate freight houses entirely.

No hard and fast rule can be laid down except to note that the costs of rehandling and the time consumed must always be taken into account as offsetting factors for the advantages of coordination. These costs and time factors will vary with the situation, facility, commodity, and system of operation.

Freight Handling. Even where several carriers are involved, the actual freight should be handled as little as possible—whether during a road or freight-house operation, or in transfer from one carrier to another—because of the dangers of loss, attrition, and damage mentioned in the preceding section. The use of containers is one method to avoid rehandling. By interchanging barges, cars, or trailers, large shipments can be moved from one carrier to another without disturbing the contents. This is one justification for interchange and for the use of trailer-on-flatcar or piggy-back and car and trailer ferry service.

For smaller shipments, containers of many different types, shapes, and sizes are being tried. The use of palletized loads is an application of this principle.

Special Facilities. Coordination, to be truly effective, requires special facilities and a coordinated design of equipment. The function of standardization has already been noted in promoting interchange of railroad cars and highway trailers. A completely nationwide system of piggy back must be similarly standardized in regard to length and trailer capacity of flatcars, hold-down devices, and the fifth-wheel connection to tractors. Interchange between rail and ship has called forth the greatest degree of special facilities in the form of ore and coal docks, car dumpers, bridge cranes, Hulett unloaders, stock-pile stackers, and a variety of other highly specialized equipment.

TYPES OF COORDINATION

Intracarrier. Coordination is carried out between different companies of the same mode of transport. Railroad coordinates with railroad, trucker with trucker, and airline with airline. Such coordination usually takes one or more of the following forms.

Joint use of terminals. The union depot for rail, bus, or airline, the union freight station for rail or motor freight, and the transit shed serving both river and lake traffic are examples of joint terminal use. Advantages include convenience of transfer, provision of better facilities than an individual carrier might be able to afford, and avoidance of cross hauls and duplication of facilities.

The economies of a union passenger station arise from the tax, interest, maintenance, and operating expenses avoided at individual stations. Not all of this can be counted as net saving, however, as each tenant must contribute to the costs of the joint facility, but not in the same proportion.

At a union freight station, the freight can be moved from one road-haul line to another directly across the platform in a single operation. With individual stations, the freight would move across one platform into a transfer vehicle, move in the transfer vehicle to another freight house, and then from that vehicle across the second platform and into a second road-haul vehicle. The latter operation requires twice as many handlings as the union-depot performance.

A union freight station saves mileage and the number of vehicles required. It reduces the number of calls made at the door of an individual shipper. The Port of New York Authority estimated a saving from use of its lower Manhattan motor-freight house of 1,830,000 truck miles per year, 15,600,000 tire miles, and 336,000 gal of gasoline. At the same time, the over-the-road truck capacity was increased about 20 percent because of faster terminal turn-around. A shipper served by the Newark terminal had had up to 18 trucks a day with an average load of 1900 lb each call at his shipping-room door. With union-depot operation, four trucks of 8500-lb load each were all that were needed.

A single freight house might not have enough capacity to justify mechanization, whereas the combined traffic of several carriers could serve as an adequate warrant. For example, the use of fork-lift trucks with palletized loads has been estimated as effecting 30 to 65 dollars per carload in savings.[2] The same principle holds for other types of union-station operation.

Disadvantages include the scarcity of large land areas often re-

[2] "Better Materials Handling, etc." *Railway Age,* August 10, 1959, Simmons-Boardman Publishing Company, New York.

quired in central locations to provide adequately for the enlarged capacity of a joint facility. The coach yards of rail terminals, for example, may therefore have to be located some distance from the station with expensive deadhead running to and from the yards. The attempt to handle commuting and line-haul traffic in the same station may cause excessive congestion at the platforms during commuting rush hours, when line-haul operations will also be in progress. Additional platforms may have to built to stand idle and unproductive most of the day.

Other disadvantages are some loss of individual carrier identity, loss of economic advantage from an individual location, difficulties in apportioning user costs and charges, and excessive charges required for small operators who may not require the elaborate facilities provided.

Joint terminal use is common in large cities, where land is scarce and expensive and congestion is intense, for railroads, bus lines, and airlines. Water carriers and motor-freight lines have given up their individual facilities and locations in only a few cases. Typical examples of joint terminals are the Union Station in Chicago, the Union Bus Terminal and the Consolidated Truck Terminals operated by the Port of New York Authority, and the National Airport of Washington, D. C.

Coordination of schedules. Passenger and freight schedules of one carrier may be arranged to connect with those of other carriers. This more often occurs where the carriers share a union terminal or where one carrier acts as a feeder or bridge line for another. Railroads coordinate their schedules as a routine practice where they interchange large volumes of freight traffic. Entire trains may be moved from one railroad to another on predetermined schedules.

Interchange of equipment. Truck and barge lines interchange trailers and barges to a limited degree. This practice and its advantages are most fully realized in railroad operation, where cars and contents move freely from one carrier to another. Such interchange saves rehandling costs and loss of time in transferring freight. The necessity of standardized features to permit interchange is again noted. Disadvantages include difficulties of securing return of equipment, unfavorable equipment account balances with carriers having a deficiency in ownership of cars, trailers, or barges, maintenance of foreign or off-line equipment, and determining and collecting user costs for use and maintenance of foreign equipment.

Trackage rights. Owing to their technical and economic features, railroads offer additional opportunities for intracarrier coordination. When two rail lines are approximately parallel, trackage rights granted by one permit the other to use its tracks. The excess capacity usually available in most track layouts permits additional trains to be added with little or no extra capital outlay. If capacity is a problem, two parallel single tracks may be paired to give the advantages of double-track operation. As an alternative, the institution of Centralized Traffic Control may permit one track to carry the added load and the other to be abandoned. Savings due to abandonment lie in the recovery of scrap value of rail and fastenings (40 to 60 dollars a ton) and a saving in taxes (500 to 5000 dollars a mile) and maintenance (3000 to 4000 dollars a mile). There may also be a saving on operation if more favorable grades are encountered on the host's tracks and if train order and block stations can be closed. Not all of this is clear saving, however, since the tenant road must contribute to the cost of maintaining the tracks and operation used. Payment may be on a per-train, a gross-ton-mile, a per-car, or a straight-percentage-of-operating-cost basis.

Service railroads. Service railroads, acting as terminal, belt-line, interchange, switching, and bridge companies, are organized and owned jointly by several railroads, by a municipality, port authority, or industrial group to reduce congestion and duplication in crowded areas or to give unbiased service to all shippers in an urban, industrial, or port area. Examples of these are the Kansas City Terminal Railway, the Terminal Railway Association of St. Louis, the Union Railroad of Pittsburgh, and the Cincinnati Union Terminal Company. The Belt Railway of Chicago operates the Clearing Yard for interchange of traffic between the several carriers entering Chicago as well as performing a belt-line function.

A single railroad may perform all switching services for several railroads in a port or industrial area, charging so much per car switched. Other roads may perform a similar service in other parts of a city on a reciprocal basis. Unfortunately the result is sometimes poor service for the shipper who is not giving the switching line the road-haul business. Such poor service is often hard to pinpoint but may appear as delays in settling claims, delays in placing and moving cars, and difficulty in getting an adequate supply of cars, especially in times of car shortage. A railroad is sometimes given the road haul in order to overcome these deficiencies. Belt railways or switching lines, whether owned jointly by the railroads or by a municipal, port, or industrial group are planned to serve connecting carriers and shippers alike without bias.

Tugs and towboats and local trucking lines perform functions that correspond in many ways to those of terminal railroads. The parallel is especially close in the case of a pickup and delivery service for a consolidated truck depot.

Other types. A considerable amount of economic and administrative coordination supplements and aids in developing physical coordination. Joint maintenance of equipment has developed between a few truck and bus lines and also between some airlines. Joint rates covering interline movements permit an economical routine billing and accounting procedure for the carriers, convenience for the shipper, and a concentration of traffic over selected routes and gateways.

Intercarrier. More obvious examples of coordination are found between carriers of unlike types—between rail and highway, rail and waterway, pipeline and waterway, highway and air, or a combination of all of these and even with borderline types of transport. Several of the intracarrier types of coordination are also common to intercarrier operations. Representative of these are the joint use of terminals, coordination of schedules, joint and through rates, and common maintenance facilities. Buses and railroads using the same terminal are not uncommon. Bus service to and from an airport it commonplace. In some large terminals rail, bus, and rapid-transit lines converge as in the Pennsylvania and Grand Central stations in New York or the Pennsylvania Railroad Station in Newark. Some terminals already include moving sidewalks, conveyors, monorails, and helicopter service.

In addition there are coordinating procedures possible only with unlike carrier types.

End-to-end movement. The features of this have already been presented as *extension of service*. Freight moving part way by water moves to its final destination by rail or truck. Passengers alight from train or airplane and rent a drive-it-yourself automobile for local travel. Crude and processed petroleum moves by pipeline to a waterfront loading dock for transfer to river barge or deep-water tanker.

An important characteristic of this type of coordination is the need for special facilities for transferring freight from one carrier to the other, especially for such bulk commodities as coal, ore, phosphates, aggregates, grain, and petroleum. An example of such a combination of carriers and facilities is given in the next section.

Supplemental and auxiliary services. In supplemental service, one carrier type is used to perform transportation services that are only incidental to the road haul. The use of buses and ferries to carry passengers between Manhattan Island points and rail terminals in New Jersey exemplifies this kind of service.

Another example is the pickup and delivery of railroad freight. LCL shipments are brought by truck—rail owned or operating under contract with the railroads—to the railroad freight station, moved by rail to the city of destination, and then delivered to the consignee's door by a truck delivery similar to the pickup service. In the same vein is the use of trucks to replace the way car of local freights. LCL shipments are sent in carload lots to centrally located break-bulk points from which detailed distribution is made to local freight agencies along the rail line. The way freight is used then only for carload business.

Truck service is sometimes offered by the railroads in lieu of unprofitable branch-line service by rail—when regulatory bodies permit. A somewhat similar service is the use of trucks as feeder lines to railroads, whether rail owned or not; for example, farmers hauling grain and cattle to the railroad elevators and loading pens.

The most recent full-scale example of rail-highway coordination is the trailer-on-flatcar service already mentioned. This, however, is hardly a supplemental service. Other examples of incidental services include lighterage, car ferries, auto and helicopter taxis, and highway transport to and from airports and wharves. More will be said about trailer-on-flatcar service in a later section.

Joint use of right of way. The possibilities in joint use of rights of way are only recently receiving adequate attention. From time to time, proposals have been made that a highway be built over the tracks of a railroad right of way on an upperdeck or viaduct. Similarly, railroads over highways have been proposed. The loads for the latter are heavier to support, up to 80,000-lb axle loadings for railroads as contrasted with 18,000- to 20,000-lb axle loadings for trucks. As an offsetting factor, a railroad structure need only provide 14 to 16 ft of clearance over the highway, whereas a highway structure would have to allow 22 to 24 ft of clearance for the railroad. The railroad grades are usually more suitable than highway grades. In fact a railroad couldn't operate over some of the grades that would thus be established even by high-class highways.

Present attention is being directed to the use of the center mall or median strip of expressways and superhighways as railroad rights of way, primarily for rapid-transit systems. A two-track, standard-gage system would require 29 to 32 ft of median strip width, 13 to 16 ft more than required by minimum A.A.S.H.O. standards for interstate highways in urban areas but well within the 40 ft of width recommended for expressways and the highest-class construction. If additional land is required, it can be obtained far more easily and cheaply when the highway land is being purchased than it could if obtained separately. Several of the Chicago expressways have center malls designed for future rail rapid transit. An unfortunate aspect of this coordination is that urban, and other, expressways may parallel an existing railroad already prepared to give service.

Another aspect of rail-highway location is the desirability of keeping noncoordinated rail and highway routes far enough apart through industrial zoning to permit adequate development of industry on both sides of each. A highway and railroad closely paralleling each other prevent or seriously hinder any industrial access or development between them. Various separation distances have been proposed ranging from 300 ft to a quarter of a mile.

Pipelines are adaptable to location on rail and highway rights of way, especially rail. Pipe of the Southern Pacific Pipe Line Company has already been placed alongside the tracks of the parent company and more is in prospect. The railroad or highway provides easy access to the line during construction and for maintenance when it is operating. Where severe development curvature is present, the pipeline may cut across country, bypassing one or more of the curve loops. The lines should always be buried deep enough to avoid breakage and a disastrous fire in the event of train derailment.

Another recent proposal has been for the railroads to use low-flying vertical-take-off-and-landing-craft (VTOL) airplanes, using rotors set in the wings for take-off and landing, which would skim along over the railroad right of way and land at regular railroad terminals.[3]

Great Lakes Rail-Water Coordination. Outstanding examples of end-to-end movement are the handling of iron ore and coal via the Great Lakes. Ore is brought from the pits to the surface by skips, belt conveyors, trucks, or rail. At the surface, it is crushed and loaded into railroad cars, classified as to grade of ore by cars, moved to the lake front, and dumped into the pockets of the ore docks. Each ore-

[3] News item, *Railway Age,* August 10, 1959, p. 26, Simmons-Boardman Publishing Company, New York.

FIGURE 10-1a. Ore-transfer equipment—ore running from ore-dock pocket to hold of Great Lakes bulk-cargo carrier. (Courtesy of Pittsburgh Steamship Division, U. S. Steel Corp.)

FIGURE 10-1b. Ore-transfer equipment—Hulett unloader at docks of Pittsburgh and Conneaut Dock Company, Conneaut, Ohio. This machine has just dumped a bucket of ore into a chute that weighs the raw material before depositing it in the railroad car. (Courtesy of Pittsburgh Steamship Division, U. S. Steel Corp.)

dock pocket is 24 ft long and each ore car is 24 ft long, just covering the pocket. These dimensions also correspond to the 24-ft hatchway spacing on most ore boats. Because some boat hatches are spaced on 12-ft centers and in order to provide loading flexibility, chutes from the ore-dock pockets are spaced on 12-ft centers. The movement of ore trains, classification into various grades of ore by cars in the classification yard, and dumping and blending of ore at the ore docks are all coordinated with the arrival and departure of the ore boats. Ore-boat movement is, in turn, closely watched and scheduled by ship-to-shore radio telephone.

At the other end of the run, ore-unloading facilities are located at Gary, Indiana Harbor, Detroit, Toledo, Sandusky, Lorain, Cleveland, Ashtabula, Conneaut, Erie, and Buffalo. Gigantic bridge cranes and Hulett unloaders, taking 10 to 20 yd at a bite, unload the vessels into stock piles or into railroad cars for rail movement to the steel mills of Gary, River Rouge, Cleveland, Canton, Youngstown, Pittsburgh, and adjacent areas. See Figure 10-1.

From these same Lake Erie and Lake Michigan ports, coal brought by railroad to the lakes moves north and west, often in the same boats that bring down the ore. Car dumpers pick up the cars of coal and pour their contents into the hold of a vessel, like sand is poured from a toy sand bucket. At Detroit, Duluth, Superior, and intermediate ports, bridge cranes and similar specialized devices unload the coal into stock piles or into railroad cars for further land haul.

A question might be raised at this point as to why lake haul of ore predominates when rail service, at least from the Lake Superior region, is also available. The following example will help to establish the pattern. The rail distance from Duluth, Minnesota, to Gary, Indiana, is approximately 490 miles; the water route, about 800 miles. The cost of Great Lakes transport is usually estimated at 0.002 to 0.005 dollars per ton-mile. Using the higher figure, the cost of moving the contents of one 20,000-cargo-ton carrier would be

$$20,000 \times 800 \times \$0.005 = \$80,000$$

Unloading costs with a Hulett unloader are estimated at $2\frac{1}{2}$ to 5 cents a ton. Loading costs could be conservatively taken as a similar amount. Terminal costs then are

$$2 \times 20,000 \times \$0.05 = \$2000$$

The total cost of the shipload is \$80,000 + \$2000 or \$82,000.

Rail costs on the same tonnage at an average rail cost of $0.015 per ton-mile would be

$$20,000 \times 490 \times \$0.015 = \$147,000$$

Without assessing terminal and one or more intermediate yard costs to the rail operation, there is an immediate saving of 65,000 dollars. In addition, considerable expense would be involved in making existing rail lines capable of handling the continued movement of bulk tonnages such as now move down the water lanes of the lakes.

Thus the answer to the question is simple. A water segment is inserted into the possible rail route because of the economy offered by water transit to bulk movements, an economy made possible by the low propulsive resistance, high net-to-dead-weight-tonnage ratio, and to existence of a waterway that requires no maintenance or operating costs from the carriers. *Note:* costs, not rates, are used in the example above.

Similar examples could be cited for the rail-water haul of grain from the Lake Superior ports to mills at Buffalo via portside elevators or through the Welland Canal and St. Lawrence Seaway or by way of the New York State Barge Canal and the Hudson River for overseas shipment. Along rivers and canals, coal, ore, limestone, grain, aggregates, sulfur, molasses, and petroleum move by combined rail and water routes as origin and destination permit, with necessary transfer facilities established at terminal points.

Piggy Back and Ferry Service. The term "piggy back" is a crude but popular term used to describe a type of coordination which has come into common use only recently, especially on railroads. It is, actually, simply a form of ferry service in which the transport unit of one carrier is moved by another. The system of rail and automobile ferries across Lake Michigan and the movement of railroad and highway vehicles by car floats and ferries in New York and San Francisco harbors are examples. An elaborate example is the system which ferries railroad cars from Gulf and Atlantic coast points to Cuba and other off-shore islands as well as between the two coasts. A train between London and Paris is moved in its entirety across the English Channel by boat.

The trailer-on-flatcar service provided by the railroads finds a counterpart in water carriers which haul motor trailers. A service has recently been inaugurated from Seattle to and from Alaskan points. In a few localities, on the Pacific Great Eastern in British

Columbia for example, the railroads perform a ferry service, hauling highway vehicles between two nonconnecting highways.

The trailer-on-flatcar (TOFC) or piggy-back service is simple enough in concept. Highway motor freight trailers loaded at terminal points are brought by tractor to a railroad loading platform, placed on flatcars, and hauled in trains to their destination. The trailers are then unloaded and terminal delivery is made by tractor over the city streets.

Certain advantages of this coordination are fairly obvious. With the line-haul time of merchandise trains approaching or even equaling that of passenger trains, TOFC line-haul service is faster than highway haul, while the terminal times are practically equivalent. Much of the expense and nuisance of highway haul—traffic congestion, personnel problems, traffic violations, accident hazards, delays in small communities, and restrictive limitations on weight and size—are avoided or markedly reduced. The truck operator can also reduce his pool of tractors and drivers and his tractor maintenance.

Five systems of TOFC are generally recognized.

Plan I. Vehicles of common carriers only are hauled.

Plan II. Only the railroad's vehicles are carried.

Plan III. Anyone's vehicle, including the individual and private trucker, may ship.

Plan IV. An intermediate or forwarding agency or broker secures the freight, loads it into trailers and onto its own flatcars, and turns it over to the railroad to haul.

Plan V. Plan I plus joint rail-highway rates with the highway carrier.

Students of economics and management will be interested in the details of these several methods. To the engineer, only a few questions arise.

The advantages of TOFC cited earlier accrue mainly to the trucker. Railroads, in hauling common-carrier and privately owned trailers, gain in securing a portion of the revenue that would otherwise have gone entirely to a competitor. When railroads haul their own trucks, additional advantages accrue. If merchandise traffic is picked up in railroad trailers and taken directly to the loading ramp, terminal make-up, transfer, and break-up, which now give truckers a big delivery-time advantage, will be avoided and the speed advantage of railroad line haul will be maintained. Big metropolitan freight houses with their high operating costs might in time become obsolete.

One railroad has estimated a saving of 7 dollars per ton by thus keeping merchandise freight out of the freight houses entirely.[4]

Dr. L. K. Sillcox, pointing up these savings, has quoted testimony of the Pennsylvania Railroad (I.C.C. Docket 32533) as to costs of LCL loading across an inland platform at their Thirty-Seventh Street Station, the originating terminal: [5]

Cost to load car of 7.9 tons at $4.72 per ton	$37.29
Less tariff charge of $4.09 per ton	32.31
Net cost to load car of 7.9 tons	$ 4.98
Float bridge—37th St.	2.63
Floating—37th St. to Harsimus Cove	33.82
Float bridge—Harsimus Cove	5.13
Switching cost—Harsimus Cove	13.44
Total per car (excluding switching at 37th St.)	$60.00

Dr. Sillcox then made a comparison with the same operation under Plan III (piggy back) at the Kearny, New Jersey, piggy-back terminal:

Loading two trailers	$ 9.46
Clerical and supervision expense— Kearny Truck-Train Terminal	5.68
Switching loaded car to road train (includes cost of placement)	4.23
Total	$19.37

Since this loading would average 25.9 tons, the foregoing is equivalent to loading three box cars at Thirty-Seventh Street. Dr. Sillcox thus finds a cost of 180 dollars for conventional practice as compared to the foregoing $19.37; a savings ratio of 9.3 to 1. This is a per-ton saving of $6.24 as compared with the $7.00 per-ton saving quoted earlier. Not all merchandise operations may be as complex as the Thirty-Seventh Street operation but the pattern is discernible.

Costs of operating a tractor-trailer combination have been estimated at 25 to 33 cents a mile for a 15-ton load, with a median of 28.5 cents. Not all of this can be saved by piggy back because expenses of trailer ownership, insurance, terminal-area operations (after the rail haul), and other overhead expenses will amount to about 20

[4] Nancy Ford, "Piggy-Back Spreads Out," *Modern Railroads*, December 1955, p. 69, Modern Railroads Publishing Co., Chicago.

[5] "Trucks by Train," printed account of address presented at the Canadian Railway Club, Montreal, Quebec, April 13, 1959, by Dr. L. K. Sillcox, pp. 14 and 15.

percent (5.7 cents of the 28.5 median cost).[6] Also deductible is the cost of the rail haul, approximately 10.2 cents per trailer mile with trailers loaded two to a flatcar.[7] This leaves a possible saving by piggy back of 12.6 cents per mile for the 15-ton load.

If the railroads haul only their own or trailers of common carriers, Plans II and I, there will be an assured pool of tractors and drivers to move the trailers at the end of each rail run. This may not always be true for private or Plan III truckers for whom a protected parking area would have to be provided. Problems of nonstandard equipment may arise with private operators.

Railway-owned trailers (Plan II) replacing the waycar for local delivery of LCL freight, can be hauled piggy back to the break-bulk point under load. The trailer then proceeds by highway to make detailed deliveries. The way freight is used only for handling carload business.

Not only does TOFC offer relief to freight operation, it also suggests the possibility of eliminating classification-yard service for Class I, II, and III loads. Cars brought from line haul to the unloading ramps are re-used in place for outbound trailers. The trailers can be loaded in whatever station order or blocking is desired without reference to individual cars. The loaded cars are then made into trains from the loading tracks or, if the total number is small, into a complete block (or complete blocks) to set independently on a train after its other consist has been assembled. This possibility may not work so smoothly in every case where Plan IV shipper-owned trailers and trailer cars are used. The economies gained from these procedures are self-evident if one assumes yard costs of 10 to 20 dollars per car.

The methods of loading and types of ramps to be used are still nonstandard. Some roads use end loading. The trailers are pushed up a ramp and along a string of flatcars. The space between cars is bridged by portable ramps and access from the ground is by portable or fixed ramps. Loading can proceed from one, or at the most, both ends. An additional reverse gear in the tractor gives a smoother performance going up the ramp.

With end loading, a trailer in the middle of a string cannot be

[6] J. S. Gallagher, Jr., " 'Piggy-Backs'—Good or Bad?" *Railway Age,* April 20, 1953, Simmons-Boardman Publishing Co., New York.

[7] John R. Meyer, Merton J. Peck, John Stenason, and Charles Zwick, *Competition in the Transportation Industries,* Harvard University Press, 1959, pp 151–153.

given special handling without disturbing the whole track. Side loading permits several or all of the trailers to be loaded or unloaded simultaneously. Portable side ramps or hinged aprons permit movement from the loading dock to the cars.

Originally, ordinary 35-ft trailers on standard 40-ft flatcars equipped with hold-down devices were used—and still are. Special designs of cars have been more efficient for large-volume movements. A 75-ft car can hold two 35-ft trailers; an 85-ft car holds two 40-ft trailers or a 35-ft and a 45-ft trailer. Many of both sizes are in use. The general requirements for a suitable trailer car call for a two-trailer capacity, shock-absorbing elements, fast, simple hold-down devices, a lowered floor to provide clearance for the 12-ft, 6-in. standard height of trailers, and, of course, conformity to A.A.R. interchange rules. See Figure 10-2.

Piggy-back traffic is placed in solid high-priority trains when volume is sufficient or, for lesser quantities, in fast merchandise trains. Trailer cars have even been placed in passenger trains. The passenger station is not, in many locations, a convenient spot from which to remove piggy-back cars and delays to passengers would ensue if the cars were removed in the yards. Nevertheless the plan has possibilities.

TOFC has two major technological objections: (a) the trailer capacity is too great for some shippers so that their small shipments must still be consolidated across a freight-house platform—also, the trailers are too large to place in an airplane or hold of a ship; (b) TOFC requires the hauling of one vehicle upon another, thereby decreasing the pay-load-to-dead-load ratio to 3 to 1 or worse (from a possible 4 to 1).

As a solution to the first problem, special low-capacity containers are being used but without any standardization. Capacities vary from 5 to 20 tons, limited by the weight allowance of highway-vehicle axles and capacities of ships' gear. Containers are of many sizes and shapes in the form of demountable car or truck bodies or simple boxes to be set on flatcars or in gondolas. The individual freight items loaded in the container need not be rehandled from the time the container is sealed by the shipper until the seal is broken by the consignee. Such a procedure represents the final step in eliminating large-scale freight-house operations. The ultimate in this direction is an all-purpose or universal container that can be used equally well for shipment by rail, highway, ship, or airplane.

FIGURE 10-2. Piggy-back trailers in place. (Courtesy of the Erie Railroad.)

The second problem has two solutions, one of which stems from the foregoing in the shape of a demountable car and trailer body or container that can be transferred from the chassis of a railroad car to a truck or trailer chassis. The container can be left at any point for loading or unloading while the chassis is used to move other containers. This is the basis of the Flexi-Van service used for hauling merchandise, express, and mail on the New York Central, Milwaukee,

FIGURE 10-3. Rail-van service. These units are adaptable to either rail or highway travel and the dual sets of wheels can be interchanged easily. (Courtesy of the Chesapeake and Ohio Railway.)

and other roads. The transfer from truck to rail chassis, or the reverse, can be made, unaided, by the driver (a basic requirement of efficiency with these services). A variation requires a highway truck or chassis to be spotted under a special gantry crane parallel to a railroad gondola car. The truck driver can operate the crane to move the container from car to truck or return.

A different approach to the problem involves the use of self-contained units that can either be used as highway trailers or made into trains on the rails. The cars are equipped with the usual rubber-tired wheels for highway travel and also with dollies equipped with flanged-steel wheels for rail travel. These wheels can be lowered when rail movement is intended. The cars also have a fifth wheel for tractor coupling, train air brakes, and other I.C.C. safety requirements. A prime requisite is structural strength adequate for operation in trains. The Rail-Van type of operation has capacities of 8 to 14 tons and a pay-load-to-dead-load ratio of up to 7 to 1. See Figure 10-3. These designs in various forms are undergoing test and development on the Rock Island, Chesapeake and Ohio, and other railroads. Designs are not yet standardized and not all problems are solved but the future possibilities appear bright.

ESTABLISHMENT OF COORDINATION

How Coordination Occurs. Although generally desirable, many apparently sound schemes for coordination have never been put in effect, for the following reasons.

1. In many situations, the carriers feel they would be losing competitive advantages and their identity by giving up established routes, locations, and services when entering into combinations with other carriers.

2. Laws prohibiting the immediate reduction in personnel as a result of consolidations make estimated savings unattractive.

3. The lack of immediate and extensive saving, plus a certain apathy in some quarters, make the carriers loath to abandon present methods in favor of vaguely defined savings and a period of trial and development.

Most coordination has been the result of self-interest. The use of motor trucks for pickup and delivery service by the railroads arose from the competition of the truckers. Trackage-rights agreements derive from hoped-for economies, access to new traffic, or other self-interest, often a reciprocal track or traffic agreement elsewhere. Facilities for interchange of granular bulks are often provided by an individual company to assure an adequate share in the traffic.

When an industry is large enough to have its own transportation system, it selects whatever coordination best meets its needs. The large oil producers have their own pipelines to ports, their own barges and deep-water tankers, and, for distribution of refined products, their own tank trucks and railroad cars. The U. S. Steel Corporation has a well-coordinated system for moving ore. The Oliver Mining Company surfaces the ore with trucks, hoists, and conveyors. The Duluth, Missabe, and Iron Range Railroad hauls the ore to its ore docks at Duluth and Two Harbors. The Pittsburgh Steamship Division's fleet of ore boats carries the ore to lower lake ports, principally Gary and Conneaut. From Conneaut, the ore is moved to the Pittsburgh-area steel mills via the Bessemer and Lake Erie and the Union railroads.

Some small amount of coordination, that is, access to a particular terminal or station, has come about by regulatory order.

Extension of Coordination. Three possible ways of extending the advantages of coordination and joint operation are by intercarrier agreement, horizontal integration, and vertical integration.

Agreement. Agreements between carriers come about by recognized self-interest, by order of a public regulatory agency, or by force of public opinion.

Horizontal integration. Intracarrier coordination is more readily achieved between carriers with a common management. It is more easily attained when one carrier owns a significant or controlling interest in another or when both are under the control of a parent company.

Vertical integration. Vertical integration is the combination of several unlike types of transport into one agency. Outstanding examples are the Canadian Pacific and Canadian National railways and the South African Railways, which directly or through subsidiaries control and operate railways, airways, truck and bus lines, and steamship lines.

In the United States a few railroads have approached the extent of foreign companies. The New Haven has owned or controlled truck and bus, steamship, and interurban lines. The Southern Pacific has similar holdings plus pipeline and airline operations. There is vertical integration in the iron and steel industry. These varied operations are sometimes carried on directly, but more often by means of holding or subsidiary companies. Under existing statutes and regulatory procedures, vertical integration offers only limited possibilities to common carriers. The Interstate Commerce Act as interpreted by the I.C.C. and the courts prohibits ownership of one carrier type by another except as supplementary and incidental to the carrier's normal operation.[8] There are a number of instances where rail carriers do operate over-the-road truck and bus service. These operations were begun before the passage of the Motor Carrier Act of 1935, and, by the "Grandfather Clause" of the act, are permitted to continue —but no new operations can be instituted.

QUESTIONS FOR STUDY

1. Diagram or show schematically all the coordination involved in bringing iron ore from a mine in Labrador to a steel-mill furnace in Pittsburgh, Pennsylvania.

2. Diagram or show schematically, possible systems of coordination in moving petroleum from Texas oil fields to New Jersey refining points.

3. Estimate the probable savings in operating costs to haul ore from Superior, Wisconsin, to Buffalo, New York, by water instead of by rail.

4. What are trackage rights and what conditions are conducive to this type of coordination? Why?

5. What advantages do belt lines or switching railroads offer as compared with reciprocal switching?

6. Account for the success of deep-water rail ferries moving freight in railroad cars from point to point along the Atlantic and Gulf coasts and between the mainland and Caribbean islands.

7. Using the approximate cost data contained in this chapter, tell how much circuity of line would have to be saved to justify moving railroad cars in a 30-car-capacity ferry across a body of water.

8. A flatcar weighing 18 tons with a load capacity of 60 revenue tons holds two highway trailers, each containing 20 revenue tons and weighing 8 tons apiece when empty. What changes in dead-load-to-pay-load ratios are made in the flatcar capacity by this use for piggy backing? If the result is disadvantageous, how can it be improved?

9. Explain how the development of Plan II TOFC could lead to the eventual elimination of large-capacity freight houses.

10. Explain how Plans I, II, and III for TOFC could do away eventually with much classification-yard operation. Why doesn't Plan IV fit into this pattern?

[8] I.C.C. vs. Parker, 326 U.S. 60 (1945). Rock Island Purchase of White Line Motor Freight Co., 40 I.C.C. 456 (1946).

SUGGESTED READINGS

1. Wilbur G. Hudson, "Conveyors and Related Equipment," Third Edition, John Wiley and Sons, New York, 1954, Chapters 12 to 18 inclusive.

2. L. K. Sillcox, *Trucks by Train*, privately printed, 1959; contact author through New York Airbrake Company, 230 Park Ave., New York, N. Y.

3. "Canada's New Railroad," *Modern Railroads*, December 1954, pp. 55–91, Modern Railroads Publishing Company, Chicago, Illinois.

4. J. W. Rice, "Floating Rails," *Wheels*, March–April 1951, American Car and Foundry Company, New York.

5. A. E. Gibson, "Ore and Coal Handling on the Great Lakes," *Civil Engineering*, December 1944, pp. 503–506, American Society of Civil Engineers, New York.

6. *Transportation of Oil*, Petroleum Administration for Defense, Washington, D. C., 1951.

7. *The Mass Transportation Survey Report, 1959, National Capital Region*, Government Printing Office, Washington, D. C.

8. D. C. Wolfe, "Huge Oil Pier Built in Open Water," *Engineering News-Record*, May 25, 1950, pp. 34–39, McGraw-Hill Publishing Company, New York.

9. "The New Orleans Union Passenger Terminal," various articles, *Railway Age*, April 26, 1954, pp. 22–31, Simmons-Boardman Publishing Company, New York.

10. "P.R.R. Unveils New Ore-Unloading Terminal," *Railway Age*, March 15, 1954, pp. 45–47.

11. "Modern Lake Port Transfer Facility Open for Business at Toledo, Ohio," *Railway Age*, May 1, 1948, pp. 32–37.

12. "Phosphate—from Train to Ship," *Railway Age*, August 14, 1948, pp. 60–63.

13. "Canton Railroad Expands Ore Docks," *Railway Age*, December 15, 1952, pp. 52–53.

14. "Fuel Oil from Tanker to Tank," *Railway Age*, September 24, 1956, pp. 32–33.

15. "Faster Coal Terminal Warms Up," *Railway Age*, January 7, 1957, pp. 28–31.

16. "Sea Train's New Seamobile Goes to Work," *Railway Age*, March 30, 1959, pp. 16–17.

17. "Newest Piggy-Back Form May Be Biggest Breakthrough Yet,'" *Railway Age*, November 24, 1958, pp. 16–17, 21.

18. "Containers—Next Step in Freight?," *Railway Age*, November 24, 1958, pp. 30–35.

19. "Railvan Marries Rail and Road," *Railway Age*, May 14, 1956, pp. 47–49.

20. "Piggy-Back Roads Take a New Look," *Railway Age*, December 9, 1957, pp. 22–29.

CHAPTER 11

OPERATIONAL CONTROL

FUNCTIONS OF CONTROL

Definition and Application. Operational control is the regulation exercised over vehicles and traffic to attain the maximum in safe and efficient utilization of plant and equipment. The control may be simple or highly complex, reflecting the complexity of the operation.

Control is exercised to achieve safety and dependability of movement. Contact (collision) between vehicles must be avoided. Coupled with this is the need to move the vehicles as quickly as possible with the least delay for early and prompt arrival. These goals are sometimes conflicting. For example, vehicles cannot travel too closely together with safety at high speed. Responsible operators make safety paramount although the stress of competition and heedlessness of individuals sometimes work to the contrary.

In addition to safety, dependability and speed are the goals of maximum realization of traffic capacity. Here are involved the factors of maximum-tonnage ratings (loadings)—based on principles earlier described—maximum permissible speeds, scheduling, and effective use of route capacity. Principles governing speed and route capacity have also been considered earlier.

Control includes keeping movement records of all the vehicles—trains, airplanes, ships, trucks, buses—directing their movement in regard to meeting and passing (where appropriate), calls at sea and at airports, and pickups and setouts of cargo units and traffic. Control also includes forwarding information for operational and planning purposes regarding movements under way and contemplated.

Means of operational control include rules and regulations, standard operating procedures, use of signs and pennants, signals, communications, records, and reports. Only those involving engineering problems are considered here.

Supervising Agencies. Operational control is exercised by different groups under different situations. Railroads, conveyors, cableways, and pipelines maintain their own control. Private automobiles are subject to the safety rules of the road, signs and lights placed by communities and highway departments, and supervision by local and state police. Trucking and bus lines, in addition, control their operations through their own dispatchers and supervisors. Shipping control emanates from admiralty law, lights and markers set out by U. S. Army Corps of Engineers, the supervision of the U. S. Coast Guard, and from the ship line's own dispatchers and supervisors. Airlines are controlled by company dispatchers, by terminal control-tower personnel, by runway lighting, various radio-type navigation aids, and by Air Traffic Control Centers.

A major problem has been how much control should be left to the individual operator and how much should be made automatic. The trend thus far has been to give the operator or dispatcher as much electronic and automatic help as possible but to let him make the final decisions. The problems involved are the increasing complexity of control apparatus, sonic and supersonic speeds of some carriers, and increasing traffic densities in media of limited extent versus the reaction time and ability to comprehend and make decisions of the human mind and body. The solution to these problems lies within the realm of human engineering, where the psychologist and engineer meet on a common ground.

COMMUNICATIONS

Dispatching. Primitive systems of operation rely on customs, codes of rules, signs, pennants, and orders. Modern control of operations cannot exist without an adequate system of communications. Telegraph, and later telephone, sufficed for early transport, but today's operations require extensive systems of telephone, radio, microwave, teletype, and even television. Ship-to-shore and ship-to-ship telephones provide contacts on the Great Lakes, inland rivers, and, to some extent, the high seas. Railroads and pipelines use leased commercial lines with carrier circuits superimposed to give more paths or channels or they install their own lines and carrier channels. Microwave is beginning to be used by both these types of carriers to provide reliable communications over long distances regardless of weather.

Pole lines are susceptible to damage by avalanches and snow slides, by floods, by wind, and by ice storms. Railroad operations often have been brought to a complete standstill for several hours to several days because of such disasters. Reliance in the past has been placed on amateur and police radio for emergency communication but microwave installations, being relatively free from such interruptions, are replacing wire lines, beginning in those areas most frequently experiencing severe storms.

A primary use of communication is for dispatching—directing and keeping track of vehicular movements. Taxi cabs, contractors' trucks, service vehicles, industrial fleets, and terminal and over-the-road motor freight vehicles are under the guidance of central dispatchers who maintain radio contact with each vehicle, record movements on a log sheet, and direct the vehicles to successive tasks and new traffic contacts as required. Without radio, the drivers call from check points during road haul or as the assigned task is completed.

Ship owners and agents at ports of call are given advance letter, cable, and radio information concerning the expected arrival and cargo of deep-water ships. This is later verified and revised by radio reports from the ship itself as it nears the port. Where difficult harbor approaches (or strong unions) prevail, the ship takes on a local pilot at the harbor (or canal) entrance to guide the vessel in and out. Orders and requests for tug service are made via ship's radio or onshore agents.

Within the harbor, the harbor master assigns berthing locations and priorities at public wharves and anchorage locations in the roadstead. When fog or storm conditions make harbor operations unsafe, he may require all ship movements to halt. He keeps informed of ship movements and locations by radar as well as by port documents and radio contact with individual ships.

Bulk-cargo vessels on the Great Lakes maintain contact with each other, with their terminal and intermediate offices (which direct the ship to the desired ports), and with lock and Coast Guard personnel. Knowing the arrival time, speed, type, and capacities of ships makes it possible for ore and coal docks, grain elevators, etc. to be prepared with sufficient cargo and supplies on hand for prompt loading and refueling and for minimum time in port. At the destination point, sufficient railroad cars, barges, or storage space will be held available.

Flights along and across the Federal System of Airways are under the direct supervision of some 30 or more Air Traffic Control Centers strategically located across the country. Before leaving the ground, the pilot files an approved flight plan and adheres to that plan while in the air. He makes regular check-ins to the Control Centers and to his own company dispatchers, who log the progress of the flight, stating his location and conditions of flight. Commercial airlines usually have their own dispatchers in direct touch with each flight and also coordinate activities with the Control Centers. Weather information, air-lane traffic conditions, and the ceiling and traffic at the next point of landing are given to the pilot. Permission to make changes in the flight plan as to destination, altitude, or direction must be secured from the appropriate Control Center. As the pilot nears a point of landing, the flight comes under the control of an airport control center and receives landing (or stacking) instructions as to weather, ceiling, priority of landing, and runway assignment.

The "speed-of-sound," high-flying jet transports use principally three transcontinental routes, 40 miles in width, between elevations of 24,000 and 35,000 ft to separate them from military and defense aircraft that also fly at those altitudes. The jets are separated by radar observation from installations of the Air Force Defense Command with special Air Route Traffic Control personnel assigned specifically to the control and safeguarding of jet commercial transport. No aircraft can enter or cross these lanes without an Air Route Traffic Control clearance unless the plane has a transponder, a radar beacon that gives on a scope in the aircraft a radar picture of the surrounding air space, more positively and readily identifiable than simple radar scanning. For a military plane not so equipped to enter or cross the commercial jet lanes is a court-martial offense.

Railroads operate under one of the most elaborate of dispatching systems. A train dispatcher will have control of all train movements in an assigned territory of 100 to 500 miles. Operators at train-order and block-station offices along the line report to him by wire the time each train passes his office. The dispatcher records the times for each train on a train sheet or log. Trains run according to time tables, rules, and signals. Situations arise regarding the movements of extra trains, handling of traffic, and emergencies not covered by the rules. The dispatcher then issues train orders to the trains involved, handed on to the train and engine crews by the wayside operators. The dispatcher can supersede any previous orders or rules and can annul or change schedules with a train order.

In sophisticated systems of Centralized Traffic Control, the movements of trains are indicated by lighted sections of a track diagram on a control panel before the dispatcher. See Figure 11-1. A log of

FIGURE 11-1. Centralized Traffic Control. New design of Traffic Control Center for railroad operations. (Courtesy of the Union Switch and Signal Division, Westinghouse Airbrake Company, Swissvale, Pennsylvania.)

train movements may be maintained on a train sheet, supplemented or replaced by a graphical record automatically prepared by the CTC equipment.

In yard operations, train consists are sent by teletype to the next yard before the train's arrival. Switch lists indicating the proposed assigned track for each car (by car numbers) are prepared and sent by teletype to the hump-master's office. Or tapes containing the same information are cut for transmission to an electronic control that automatically sets up the tracks and routes leading thereto for each car. Inbound trains are advised by radio of the receiving yard tracks to enter. Television may record the car numbers and initials as inbound and outbound trains enter and leave the yards. This may serve as a prime record or as a check on teletype transmission of train consists. Yard locomotives are in contact with the yardmaster by radio, inductive telephone, or talk-back loud-speaker systems and can report progress of their work, explain delays, and receive instructions on the spot. Car inspectors with walkie-talkies maintain similar contact. Transfer and switch runs use radio to keep the yardmaster advised of their progress, expected time of arrival, number of cars being brought to the yard, and cause and extent of any delay. Pneumatic tubes carry waybills from the inbound yard to the yard office and from the yard office to the departure yard.

The dispatching of oil shipments by pipeline is similar in many ways to train dispatching. A dispatcher is in direct contact with and has control over the intermediate stations along the line. He sends orders, patterned after train orders, to each station regarding time, volume, pressure, temperature, viscosity, etc. that will govern a particular movement of traffic. The station operators keep him and adjacent stations informed of the movement and operational details at their stations. An upstream station, for example, cannot begin pumping until the station next in line, downstream, has advised of its readiness to receive and handle the flow. In the event of an emergency, the upstream station may be ordered to stop the flow and accumulate what it is receiving in storage tanks. Systems of remote control, corresponding to CTC for railroads have been developed for one-man control of an entire pumping operation. More is said about this later in the chapter.

Nondispatching Communications. There is, of course, a wide area of nondispatching communication involved in transportation. Traffic solicitation, reservations for passenger-train space, ordering cars, tracing, passing reports, maintenance operations, and administrative matters require a constant use of all available facilities. Shippers and the carrier personnel issue holding and reconsignment orders on traffic already en route or in temporary storage. Consists of ships, trucks, and trains are sent ahead by radio or teletype from point of origin to destination. Stores and purchases make demands for prompt, personal contacts.

INTERVAL CONTROL

Interval Systems. A primary function of operational control is to prevent contact in the form of collisions between vehicles, especially where the operator of one vehicle may be inherently unaware of the presence of the other—as with trains, high-speed aircraft, or ships in a fog. Three general systems are followed to provide a safe interval between vehicles: (a) the time-interval system, (b) the space-interval system, and (c) the see-and-be-seen system.

The last, which is found mainly in rural highway, waterway, and slow-moving-aircraft operation, leaves the avoidance of contact up to the individual pilots and drivers. This places more demands on the operator's skill than can be expected from human effort at very high speeds, where disaster may occur before the driver or pilot is able to act. It also is of little help when fog, storm, or darkness obscures visibility. At such times, ships can rely on radar to warn them of other vessels. This is not always enough, as evidenced by occasional collisions between radar-equipped ships.

The time-interval system keeps vehicles separated by a predetermined number of minutes. Distancewise, the separation is variable, depending on the speed of the vehicles. Time-table scheduling is a familiar example of control by time interval. In air transport, aircraft of the same elevation and direction are supposedly kept 10 minutes apart. In a preceding chapter, the corresponding distances were noted as varying from 30 miles at 180 mph to 100 miles at 600 mph. Railroad rules have specified that trains must stay 5 to 10 minutes apart (varying with the railroad) and also set time clearance by which slow or opposing trains must clear the main track to let a superior train overtake or meet and pass. Rapid-transit trains and buses may be spaced on 2- to 10-minute headways.

The time-interval system has certain obvious defects. Time-table scheduling is too inflexible and does not allow for extra, nonscheduled movements. (European railways get around this by setting up in advance the maximum number of schedules or paths the route will accommodate. Extra movements are then assigned one of the paths or schedules.) Furthermore, the time interval is difficult to maintain. A faster-than-prescribed speed closes the gap between one vehicle and the vehicle ahead. A slower speed allows the following vehicle to catch up. An unscheduled stop, deviation from the route, or speed variation for any reason immediately destroys the time protection.

For pipelines and conveyors, the time interval between shipments is completely at the dispatcher's discretion. The extreme flexibility of highways makes the time-interval factor largely dependent on the volume of traffic and the psychological reactions of the drivers. Time intervals are also established indirectly by the coordinated timing of successive traffic lights and the light cycle. Ships at bottleneck points may be spaced by specific instruction or by the time to pass through a lock or narrow channel. The time interval seems to have the most significance in air and rail transport.

Space Systems. A space-interval or block system has been devised to overcome defects of the time-interval system. The route is divided into sections or blocks and only one vehicle at a time is permitted in a block except under special precautionary measures. Entrance into and through a railroad block is governed by block signal indications. The signals may be operated manually by block station-train order operators or automatically by the presence of the train. Staff systems and the station-to-station working of European and other railroads are adaptations of the block concept.

The block system has application to modes of transport other than railroads. The signal lights at street and highway intersections are a modified space or block-interval system. A further highway adaptation is the signaling of traffic lanes for one-way movements at certain hours of the day or for no movement at all in the event of emergencies on bridges or in tunnels.

Car spacing on aerial tramways is definitely a space-interval system although it may be predicated on a time-interval calculation. The geometry of cableways is one of distance.

It has been suggested that the block system has air-transport application. Vertical space intervals or layers have long been established. The air lanes would be divided into space intervals, longitudinally, and only one plane at a time would be permitted in that interval. An overtaking plane would have to reduce speed and/or stack or circle until the block ahead had cleared before it could proceed. Radio warnings beamed vertically from the ground would mark the block limits, in conjunction with Air Traffic Control Center supervision. This proposal is simply a means of maintaining more effectively the time intervals now prescribed. There are obviously a number of problems to overcome in its application.

The relations between vehicular intervals and route and traffic capacity have been indicated in an earlier chapter.

SIGNALS

A signal is, essentially, just another means of communication. It is a method of giving prompt, on-the-spot, concise information to the drivers of vehicles, pilots of ships and aircraft, and enginemen of trains. Where traffic is light, the way is wide, and speeds are slow, "rules of the road" supplemented by oral or written directions (orders) may suffice. For dense, high-speed traffic, signals are an invaluable aid in maintaining safe movement at maximum capacity.

Systems of Signals. Signals have no direct application in the operation of aerial tramways, conveyors, or pipelines. The dispatcher and intermediate operators may, however, be provided with a panel control board which indicates speed, temperature, and other information and permits the dispatcher to exercise personal control over these factors from his chair.

In water navigation, signals have a long-established place. Channels are indicated by buoys with lights, bells, or whistles attached for night indication. Danger points—shoals, submerged rocks, etc.—are also marked by similar buoys or by lighthouses. Lighthouses also mark headlands and harbor or channel entrances as navigational "fixes" or bearings. The development of powerful lenses and dependable lights for these devices has called for the best of engineering in the fields of applied light and optics. Signal lights are used also at some canal locks to indicate when a vessel should stop or proceed and the condition of the gate openings. Range lights, set in line with prescribed courses, are a help in aligning a ship or tow on its proper course. River tows may depend largely on these in some river-crossing situations. See Figure 11-2. The pilot aligns his tow with a range marker (perhaps setting his search-light beam on it at night) and steers toward the marker, then picks up another light where the next crossing is required.

Early airways were marked by towers on the ground equipped with revolving lights. By following the intersection of the paths of two adjoining lights, a pilot could find his way by night. This advantage was lost when fog or storm rendered the lights invisible. The towers have largely been superseded by radio beams except at airports.

Highway signals find a primary application aiding lateral move-

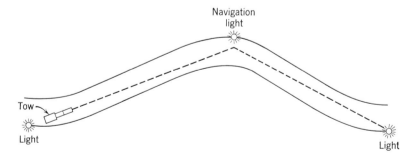

FIGURE 11-2. Navigation lights on a river.

ments of opposing (crossing) streams of traffic. They may also be set to clear intersections for left turns and for pedestrian movements. The time cycle is usually set to provide the maximum time and flow in the direction of maximum traffic. This may require a change in cycle as the traffic volume and density vary. For longitudinal control, three systems of light changes have been used: (a) all lights in a group of blocks change at the same time, (b) alternate blocks show "red" while the blocks between show "green," and (c) the lights change progressively so that a car starting with a green light and maintaining posted speed will continue to encounter green lights as it moves along. This may again require a change in time of cycle as traffic densities and volume of flow, with corresponding changes in speed, occur. The cycle may be set manually from a central control point (probably the local police station) or it may be revised automatically by electronic measure of the traffic flow fed into a computer control system.

On high-speed expressways and superhighways, cross interference is eliminated and traffic lights are not generally used. However some lights may be placed, especially in tunnels or on bridges and causeways, to stop or slow the traffic and clear lanes in the event of an emergency. Expressways carrying commuter traffic may also have signals to convert most of the lanes to inbound movement in the morning, reversing the direction of flow to take outbound traffic in the late afternoon.

Railroad Signals. Railroads maintain the most elaborate and complex system of signaling of all the carriers. Running on fixed paths, often with opposing trains in front, the tremendous momentum of a heavy fast freight train requires adequate clearance and warning to permit safe control. In light-traffic areas, operating rules, time-table authority, and supplementing train orders are sufficient. Where traffic of high volume and density is to be moved at high speed, a system of blocks and automatic block signals must be used.

Block-signal indications are given by the position of semaphore blades, colors of lights, patterns of lights, or a combination of light and pattern. The simple signal sequence behind an occupied block (and in front of it too, in single-track territory) is *Stop* (or more likely *Stop and proceed* at 15 mph looking out for train, broken rail, or other obstruction), *Approach* (which calls for a speed reduction to 30 mph or to one half the maximum authorized speed, whichever is less), and *Proceed*, at maximum authorized speed, Figure 8-6. These indications are given by a single light, semaphore blade, or light pattern. For more elaborate systems giving information about the second or third block ahead or establishing safe speeds for turnout or crossover moves, two or three blades, lights, or light patterns are used in combination to give a greater variety of *aspects* (the appearance of the signal) and *indications* (the message conveyed by the signal).

Track Circuits. A basic element in the control of any system of automatic signals for railroads or for switch and interlocking control or highway-crossing protective device is the closed-track circuit. See Figure 11-3. Closed circuits are used so that any failure in the circuit will cause it to open and give a restrictive indication. This ability to "fail safe" or "fail red" is a characteristic of all United States systems of railroad signals and interlockings. It is, actually, a fundamental concept in most designs of automatic equipment, including pipeline controls.

Simple closed-track circuits are insulated from those of the adjoining blocks, and a current is fed through the rails from a d-c battery or a-c transformer to a high-resistance relay. The up or down position of the relay opens or closes circuits that operate the semaphore blades, lights, or light patterns. When a train is in a block, the relay is shunted, because the wheels and axles of the train form a path of lower resistance than that through the relay. The armature holding the signal-control contact falls away to give the aspect for a "stop" indication. When the block is cleared, the relay is re-energized and

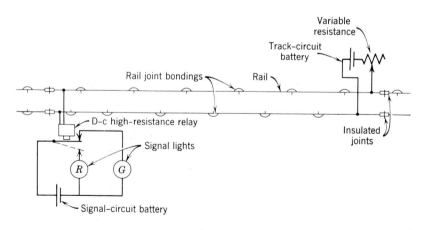

FIGURE 11-3. Closed track circuit.

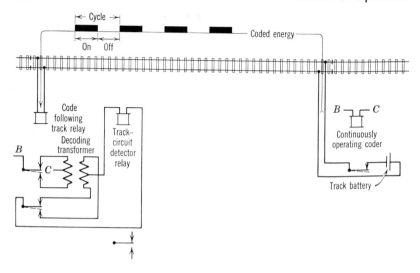

FIGURE 11-4. Coded track circuit. (*"Union" Coded Track Circuit Control,* Bulletin No. 157, July 1943, Union Switch and Signal Division, Westinghouse Airbrake Co., Swissvale, Pennsylvania, p. 10, Figure 4.)

the armature is lifted to close a circuit through the aspect for a "proceed" indication. In order to obtain the intermediate yellow or "approach" aspect and indications (and other combinations), the track relay armature is equipped with several contact points that feed back to give the desired control in circuits to the rear.

A variation of the closed-track circuit is the coded-track circuit, which makes use of codes of different frequencies to operate code-following relays and to control, in turn, the signal circuits. See Figure 11-4. The coding device that sends the various frequencies is, in turn, activated by a feedback from the circuit ahead, that is, the one that is occupied or one that has already been activated by the occupied circuit. In addition to increased sensitivity, lowered cost, less interference from stray currents, and greater flexibility, coded circuits make possible the usual types of cab signal indications displayed within the cab of the locomotive. Train stop devices, which make brake applications if the enginemen fail to respond to restrictive indications are also easily worked by coded circuits. The code is picked up inductively by pickup coils mounted on a bar just above the track and laterally under the locomotive pilot location. Both cab signals and automatic train control are thus activated.

Centralized Traffic Control. Centralized Traffic Control (CTC) provides for the direct operation of all switches and signals over a given territory varying from a few to hundreds of miles in extent. The dispatcher sits before an illuminated track diagram and panel control board, Figure 11-1. The diagram shows by lights the location and movement of trains and the position and aspects of switches and signals. By controlling these elements through buttons and levers on the panel board, the dispatcher is able to effect the most advantageous meets between trains at the various sidings, often without delay to either train. The system is applicable to multiple-track operation but has found its principal use in increasing the traffic capacity of single-track lines, often deferring indefinitely the need for double tracking or permitting the reduction of multiple-track to single-line operation.

Early CTC systems used a pair of wires from each switch and signal mechanism to the control board. With any number of units and distances, the cable and equipment became too unwieldy. Distance of no more than 20 to 30 miles could be controlled. The introduction of coded impulses sent over one pair of wires with code-following relays at each switch and signal responding only to its own code, greatly increased capacity and lengthened distances over which control could be extended. Even greater distances became available by superimposing additional carrier paths on the line wires. The same susceptibility to wind and ice storms, experienced by communication lines, holds true for signal-control lines. One solution has been to bury the wires underground. However line wires can be eliminated entirely by use of radio. Radio signals in the very-high-frequency range (VHF) are modulated to carry codes as did the line wires. Each field station must have code following, receiving, and sending equipment and a source of power supply. It should be noted that not only is an activating code sent to the field equipment but a response must be transmitted back by each switch and signal location to indicate on the control board that it has responded properly to the coded instructions.

Centralized Transport Control. Where centralized control is used for pipeline operation, the panel board before the dispatcher contains data regarding the operation of pumps at the booster stations, position of valves, bearing temperatures, pressures at selected points, etc. Flow information is shown by illuminated flow arrows. Telemetering and switching equipment indicate instantaneous changes in type of material being pumped and permit diversions to required destinations. This type of Centralized Transport Control provides the means for individual control and operation of valves and pumps for the control and routing of products.[1] The application of these same methods and principles to the one-man control of conveyors and aerial tramways is equally possible.

Other Railroad Controls. Railroad main-line switches or turn-outs as well as movable point crossings, drawbridges, and signals are usually controlled, and routes set up, at switch or interlocking plants. The operations of switch, lock, and signal controls are so interlocked that the movement of each can only be made in a safe and prede-termined order. Interlocking is designed to require all parts of a route and the signals governing it to be properly aligned and set with no conflicting routes and no conflicting signals. Routes must be set and all obstructions such as derails, open bridges, and open switches removed before a signal can be cleared to permit movement of trains. Early interlockings had the operating levers only mechanically inter-locked. Modern plants depend on all-relay control and have, in addition, interlocked protection of the switches and signals outside the plant building by means of interlocking and control circuits super-imposed upon the track circuits.

An innovation in switch control is having a route automatically set up by a train as it approaches a diversion point. The switch-operating mechanism responds inductively to a particular frequency emitted by a small transmitter. Trains taking one route emit a frequency for that route to which the switch responds. Trains requiring the switch in the opposite position emit a different frequency and get a corresponding change in switch position.

Where a switch plant becomes complicated with many crossovers and diverging routes, the manual setting up of a route is time-con-suming and cumbersome. Entrance-Exit systems of interlocking permit an entire route with all switches and signals to be aligned auto-matically merely by the pushing of a button at each end of the de-sired route.

The radio control of trains has been successfully carried out in field trials. The stage is thus set for a completely automatic opera-

---

[1] "Centralized Transport Control for Pipe Lines," from *Photographs of Progress*, prepared for the University of Illinois by the Union Switch and Signal Division of Westinghouse Airbrake Company, Swissvale, Pennsylvania.

tion of trains, especially those in rapid-transit service, with perhaps an attendant on the train but with no train or engine crews.

NAVIGATIONAL AIDS

The Need for Navigation Aids. From the earliest days of sailing, mariners have faced the problem of determining where they are. Classical solutions to this problem are, even in modern times, based on relating the ship's position to that of the sun or stars. These methods are of little help when the heavens are obscured by fog or storm. The problem becomes acute as the ship nears land with treacherous shoals, reefs, and obscured harbor entrances. The ship must then be very sure of its position. Radio direction finders and radar have added to the safety of sea transport. Radar permits a shadow outline on the radarscope of objects in the immediate vicinity, including the shore line and other ships. A radio-range compass permits a ship to determine its position, its latitude and longitude, by taking a bearing on two or more radio-range stations of known location (identified by the code transmitted), using directional antenna to determine the bearings from the ship to the stations. These have been developed to a state of almost complete automation. Sonar and other sound and radio-impulse echo devices permit taking accurate soundings as well as determining the distance from shore and other ships.

Aerial navigation shares with marine navigation the foregoing problems plus the problems of altitude and high speed and the necessity for keeping the aircraft in flight. Thus the blinding effects of fog and storm are more serious for aerial navigation. At approximate sonic and supersonic speeds, the pilot is practically flying blind since his high speed does not permit a sequence of decision making based on visual observation. The air congestion, especially around airports, is a complicating factor.

The country has long been crisscrossed with a network of routes marked by radio-range stations on the ground sending out identifying signals and by directional radio beams with which a pilot can align himself and follow to his destination. Navigation is thus possible without ground visibility. See-and-be-seen flight is kept at low altitudes, while the high-speed transports fly above all other commercial routes.

There are many electronic devices available that add to the safety

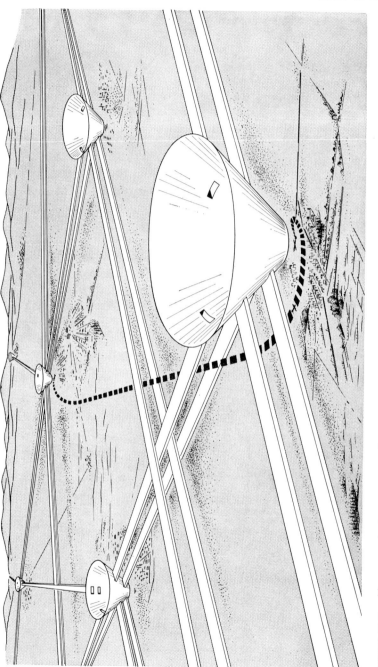

FIGURE 11-5. Airways and airport zones. Proposed division of air space below the upper, all-weather control zone. Cones of controlled air space funnel traffic between the upper controlled zone and airports on the ground. Slant airways (not shown) lead from the bottom of these cones down to the airport surface. Ribbons of controlled air space link the cones with each other. Dashed line shows separate, nonconflicting path of see-and-be-seen aircraft. (Courtesy of *Aviation Facilities Planning*, Final Report by the President's Special Assistant, Mr. Edward P. Curtis, W·I·t, D·O·M, 11·17)

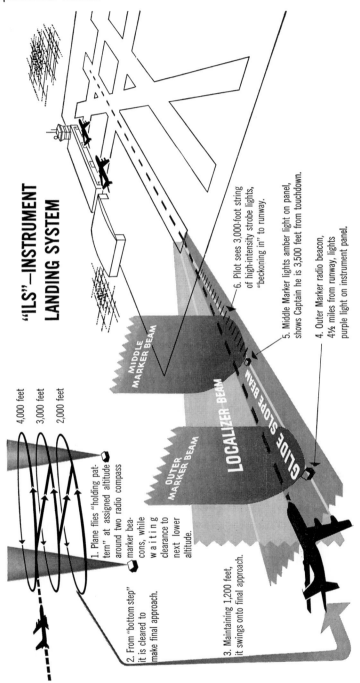

"ILS"—INSTRUMENT LANDING SYSTEM

4,000 feet
3,000 feet
2,000 feet

1. Plane flies "holding pattern" at assigned altitude around two radio compass marker beacons, while waiting clearance to next lower altitude.

2. From "bottom step" it is cleared to make final approach.

3. Maintaining 1,200 feet, it swings onto final approach.

4. Outer Marker radio beacon, 4½ miles from runway, lights purple light on instrument panel.

5. Middle Marker lights amber light on panel, shows Captain he is 3,500 feet from touchdown.

6. Pilot sees 3,000-foot string of high-intensity strobe lights, "beckoning in" to runway.

MIDDLE MARKER BEAM

OUTER MARKER BEAM

LOCALIZER BEAM

GLIDE SLOPE BEAM

FIGURE 11-6. Schematic view of landing operations. (Courtesy of *Welcome Aboard*, American Airlines, April 1957, pp. 46 and 47.)

and reliability of flying, but not all of these are afforded on even the commercial transports. Radar enables a pilot to obtain first-hand information about weather conditions ahead, and, therefore, once he has secured permission to vary his flight plan, allows him to change his course and avoid much rough weather and rough air. A transponder type of radar gives the pilot an unusually clear picture of other aircraft in his vicinity. Another device progressively traces on a map before the pilot the route he is flying. It also relays appropriate information to the Air Traffic Control Center.

Approaching an airport, the pilot enters the zone of airport control, Figure 11-5, indicated by vertically beamed radio signals, and by radio and radar contact. The pilot descends to a landing on a runway designated by the airport control tower. See Figure 11-6. If there is congestion, he flies a stacking pattern until his priority arrives. At night, the approaches to the runways and the edges of the runways will be marked with lights. Runways equipped for instrument landing may have rows of lights arranged at decreasing altitudes as the runway is neared, and transverse to it, in the approach zone to aid the pilot in establishing his altitude visually and with relation to the runway.

In making an instrument landing, the pilot follows a radio beam with a sloping approach path much as he followed a similar radio beam across country. He may receive a sound or a visual indication of adherence to the glide path depending on the system in his cockpit. The control tower, observing the plane's approach on radar, will also give helpful advice to the pilot to aid in his orientation. Landings have been made by instrument alone, with the controls electronically locked onto the glide path beam and no human control exercised at all. Cruising can also be guided automatically by an automatic pilot.

There is need for further development in these and other areas. More powerful radio stations with contact ranges exceeding the present customary 30 miles and the substitution of the longer ranged VHF for the low-frequency-range stations along all airways and in all cockpits will add much to air-flight safety and airway capacity.

QUESTIONS FOR STUDY

1. What is operational control and what are its goals?
2. What role does communication play in operational control? Explain with specific examples.

3. What factors have led to the adoption of microwave radio on sections of some railroads?

4. Differentiate, with examples, between the three methods of obtaining operational intervals between vehicles. What are the advantages and disadvantages of each?

5. What are the problems of "human engineering" in relation to operational control and what developments have brought these problems into prominence in transportation?

6. What is the importance of the train order in control on the railroads?

7. Sketch a track circuit and explain its operation. Explain fully its significance to railroad signaling and operation.

8. How does CTC differ from ordinary dispatching for (*a*) railroads, (*b*) pipelines?

9. If you were setting up a CTC system for a belt-conveyor operation, what kind of information and controls would you place on the control board before the dispatcher?

10. How may signals be used to increase street traffic capacity?

SUGGESTED READINGS

1. *The Standard Code* (of Operating Rules, Block Signal Rules, Interlocking Rules), Association of American Railroads, Chicago, Illinois.

2. *American Railway Signaling Principles and Practices* (separately bound chapters, especially Chapter III, "Principles and Economics of Signaling"), Signal Section, Association of American Railroads, Chicago, Illinois.

3. Harry W. Forman, revised by Peter Josserand, *Rights of Trains,* Simmons-Boardman Publishing Company, New York.

4. Edmund J. Phillips, Jr., *Railway Operation and Railroad Signaling*, Simmons-Boardman Publishing Company, New York.

5. *Elements of Railway Signaling,* Handbook 50, June 1954, General Railway Signal Company, Rochester, New York.

6. *Manual on Uniform Traffic Control Devices for Streets and Highways,* Public Roads Administration, Federal Works Agency, Washington, D. C.

7. *Uniform Sign Manual,* American Association of State Highway Officials, Public Roads Administration, Washington, D. C., 1959.

8. *Union Coded Track Circuits Control,* Bulletins No. 157 and 159, July 1943, Union Switch and Signal Division, Westinghouse Airbrake Company, Swissvale, Pennsylvania.

9. B. Mishelvid, "Coded Track Circuits and Cab Signaling," *The Signalman's Journal,* May 1950.

10. L. R. Allison, "A Modern Cab Signaling and Train Control System for Railroads," *Transactions of the American Institute of Electrical Engineers,* Paper No. 59-252, February 20, 1959.

11. "CTC for Modern Train Schedules," *Brotherhood of Locomotive Firemen and Enginemen's Journal,* August 1947.

12. "625 Miles of CTC in One Stretch," *Railway Signaling and Communication*, December 1949, Simmons-Boardman Publishing Company, New York.

13. "Route Type Interlocking on New York Subway," *Railway Signaling and Communication*, November 1950, Simmons-Boardman Publishing Company, New York.

14. Paul K. Eckhardt, "A New Centralized Control System to Handle Complex (Pipe Line) Dispatching," *Petroleum Engineer*, January 1955.

15. Thoburn C. Lyon, *Practical Radio Navigation*, First Edition, Aeronautical Services, Inc., Annapolis, Maryland, 1955.

16. H. E. Benham, *Aerial Navigation*, John Wiley and Sons, New York, 1945, Chapter 5.

17. Irving Conklin, *Guideposts of the Seas*, The Macmillan Company, New York, 1939.

18. G. R. Putman, *Lighthouses and Lightships of the United States*, 1933 revision, Houghton-Mifflin Co., New York.

19. Kenneth E. Applegate, "Radar for River Navigation," *The Military Engineer*, July 1948, pp. 309–311.

20. Carlyle H. Jones, "Harbor Supervision Radar for Liverpool," *The Military Engineer*, September 1948, pp. 399–401.

21. *Air Traffic Control Operator*, Department of the Air Force, June 1959.

22. *Aeronautical Statutes and Related Material*, 1959 revision, Civil Aeronautics Board, Washington, D. C., February 15, 1959.

12

COSTS OF SERVICE

Cost as a Determining Factor. The technological features of an undertaking are seldom seen in true perspective unless set against an economic background. The cost of providing (or obtaining) transportation service usually governs the final selection of carrier type except where restrictive technological conditions prevail—as where a cableway is selected because rugged terrain rules out other types of carriers. Even then, cost is probably still the controlling factor. A rail line might have been selected if the enormous costs of heavy tunneling and development had been acceptable. It is usually the over-all greater economic cost of any other alternative that underlies the technological advantages of the one selected.

Private carriers are interested directly in the cost of providing service. Investment in route and equipment and the costs of operating and maintaining the service are paramount. A common or contract carrier, in addition, is interested in costs as a factor in determining the rates to be charged the shippers. The persons who are buying transportation from a carrier look to the rate alone as their cost without any direct interest in the cost to the carrier.

Preceding chapters have discussed the technological features, the advantages and disadvantages of the several carrier types. These characteristics aid or hinder each in performing its transportation function. Differential abilities to provide flexibility, speed, safety, dependability, and economy will vary accordingly. The most efficient, technologically speaking, should be able in most instances to reflect its technological advantages in lower costs of over-all operation and therefore in lower rates.

Traffic will and should flow to the carrier that extends the lowest rate cost to the shipper, but this is subject to qualification. Low rates, for instance, may not compensate for the attendant costs of slow delivery. The high cost of speedy airline service may be economically less expensive when a much-needed spare part is being transported to prevent delays in an important enterprise. There is a class of passenger traffic that is willing to pay a premium for luxury or speed in transit. On the contrary, however, many shippers will be attracted to a low freight or passenger rate quotation in spite of a high over-all expense because they are not aware of the full economic cost. Rates and attendant problems are therefore of great importance. It matters little how technically sufficient a carrier is if its services are not utilized by the public because of its real or apparent high rates.

Rate differences, insofar as they relate to costs of service, may reflect accurately the technological characteristics. However, nontechnological factors of competition, regulation, subsidation, and even political policies enter into the formation of transportation charges and may be of more significance than technological factors in determining the rate a carrier will, can, or is permitted to impose.

Cost as a Basis for Rates. Under the classical theory of transportation charges, the rate is based on cost of service. Cost of service is understood as the actual expenses, both direct and indirect, including a reasonable margin of profit. Rates will thus vary between carriers because their costs of performing the transportation services will differ. Rates will also vary with commodities and the differing types of service required. High-speed rail service for perishables, for example, incurs more service cost and commands a higher rate than a slow-speed movement of bulk coal. The engineer has the continuing problem of assuring technological practices that will produce the minimum in costs.

A different situation is present, however, when there is an extensive lack of correspondence between the rates and the costs of service. In these instances, rates may have been adjusted to demand or to lack of demand. In the latter instance, rates may have been adjusted downward until just sufficient to cover the marginal costs of service. Examples of pricing to meet a lack of demand are frequently found outside of transportation. Power companies usually grant lower off-peak rates to consumers. "Dumping," as practiced in foreign trade, is a similar procedure. Transportation companies may offer lower than customary rates to utilize surplus capacity—as in offering excursion and weekend rates.

The importance of cost as a factor for the private carrier where profit on transportation is not a motive is self-evident. The nature of private- and common-carrier costs alike will be developed in the following analyses. It is the determining and assigning of costs to different types and classes of service that gives rise to many problems relative to rates for public carriers.

Various criteria have been used over the years as a basis for establishing transportation rates. For a time, the courts and later the Interstate Commerce Act made "a fair return on a fair value" (of the investment) the rate base. That is, the regulatory bodies permitted rate structures that would enable the carriers to earn a reasonable return on the evaluation of a prudent investment in plant and equipment. Much argument developed as to whether that valuation should be on the basis of initial cost, reproduction cost, or some compromise between the two. Another criterion has been the credit basis, whereby a carrier would be allowed a sufficient return so that it could pay dividends, thus maintaining its credit and its ability to attract capital in the money markets. Still another consideration has been the effect of rates on the movement of traffic. Outright aid has been extended, usually to products of agriculture, under "emergency" conditions, in the form of reduced rates. On other occasions, regulatory bodies have refused to permit rate increases because they thought the proposed rate would overprice and drive away the traffic on which it was imposed. Carriers, too, must consider this possibility. Attention is also given by regulatory bodies to the effect of rates on other carriers. Fear has been expressed by such bodies that lowering certain rates could undercut the prices and traffic of a competitor.

It is not the function of this text to inquire into the merits of these several criteria, some of which are highly debatable. The point to be stressed is that regardless of the importance attached to these criteria, rates must reflect costs and cannot long be kept below the level of costs without incurring disaster.

Cost of service is therefore a basic element in and the foundation of any rate structure. A carrier's rates would tend toward a common value for all commodities if costs of service for each commodity were equal. Cost differences permit and justify differential pricing, as exemplified by the higher rate charged for less-than-carload-lot freight as contrasted with carload-lot freight, or for plate glass as opposed to sand. This is not always the case however. The lower unit costs of a long haul over a short haul are generally not permitted by regulatory bodies to be reflected in common-carrier rates.

Cost is a term that needs more definition, especially when it is considered as a factor in the rate structure. One can speak of average costs, overhead costs, out-of-pocket costs, fixed costs, variable costs, capital costs, and operating costs. These will be defined and the importance of each noted in subsequent paragraphs.

Capital Costs and Operating Costs. *Capital costs* are the costs of providing the initial plant and equipment and of additions to or betterment of those facilities. Such costs can be divided conveniently into two principal groups: investment in route and structures and investment in equipment. Some carriers have an investment primarily in equipment, for example, airlines. Other agencies have investments only in way and structures, for example, turnpike authorities. Railroads have large investments in both. Capital costs include interest charges on the money invested. Usually the money is borrowed and interest is considered as a charge against income but not as an element in operating costs.

Operating expenses, the costs of conducting the transportation business, include the following:

Route maintenance, the costs of maintaining roadway and track, pavement and subgrade, rivers and harbors, channels and dams, aerial-tramway cables and towers, pipelines, etc., and the structures appurtenant thereto. Railroads refer to these costs as maintenance of way and structures. Traditionally, railroads, pipelines, conveyors, and aerial tramways build and maintain their own routes. Highways, river channels, canals, harbors, airway guides, and airports are built and maintained by governmental agencies. Route maintenance becomes an immediate cost to these latter types if, as with a mining operation for example, the route is privately owned and maintained by the carrier.

Equipment maintenance includes all costs of maintaining motive power and rolling stock—cars, locomotives, trucks, tractors, trailers, automobiles, buses, airplanes, ships, barges, pumps and compressors for pipelines, conveyor power equipment and belts, and cars and machinery for aerial tramways.

Transportation costs are all the costs of conducting transportation. Principal items are fuel and power, wages of vehicle crews, terminal costs, and the wages of those directing vehicle movements. In the case of aircraft, this last cost may be largely borne by governmental and airport traffic-control agencies. Highway traffic control is partially directed by state and local government traffic divisions and police, while control of water navigation is shared by company dispatchers with the Coast Guard and local harbor masters.

Traffic costs are the costs of traffic solicitation, advertising, publishing rates and tariffs, and administration.

General costs and *miscellaneous* take in all general office expenses, legal advice, accounting, and the salaries of general officers and their staffs.

Table 12-1 gives some *average costs* and *revenues* for various carrier types. Because these are average costs, the over-all expenses of operation are represented. The cost for any one class of traffic may differ considerably from the average. As will be seen later, actual costs may not vary directly with traffic volume as average figures would seem to indicate.

Fixed and Variable Costs. The most important cost distinctions in this study are those between fixed and variable costs. Fixed costs are incurred with little or no relation to the volume of traffic moving and may even continue to accrue when no traffic at all is moving. General office expenses fall into this category. Salaries of the president, his vice-presidents, their staffs, the accounting department, etc. continue whether ten vehicles or twenty are operated; whether there is a constant flow of traffic throughout the year or seasonal peaks and depressions. Bridges must be repainted and inspection carried out as long as any traffic moves. Tunnels must be maintained for one vehicle as well as for ten vehicles. Locks and dams must be maintained and manned without regard to volume of river traffic. Fixed costs are also referred to as overhead costs.

Variable costs, by contrast, fluctuate in harmony with traffic fluctuations. A truck driver's wages are paid only if there is a truck to drive—and the truck is ordered for the road (or purchased or rented in the first place) only if there is traffic to move in it. An airplane or freight-train crew are not called unless traffic is sufficient to fly the plane or operate the train economically. Fuel is consumed only as the vehicle operates and in proportion to the load carried by the vehicle.

Joint Costs. Joint costs are noted here because of their close relation to fixed costs. Joint costs are those costs of production that are shared by two or more products produced simultaneously, one usually being a by-product of the other. Hides, as a by-product of meat packing, are an example. In transportation, passenger and freight traffic, as on a passenger-carrying cargo ship or a railroad operation, have been quoted as examples. This is open to some criticism because it is possible to allocate many costs separately and distinctly

Table 12-1. Average Operating Costs and Revenues

Carrier	Cost per Net Ton (or Psgr.) Mile (cents)	Cost per Vehicle Mile (cents)	Revenue per Net Ton (or Psgr.) Mile (cents)
Railroads:			
Freight	1.0–1.5 [a]	300–900	1.5 [a]
Passenger (psgr. mile)			2.75–3.72 [a]
Coach	1.3–1.4 [b]		
Pullman	5–6		
Motor freight carriers:			
Class I and contract	3.0–6.0		4.6–9.8 [c]
United States average	1.25 [b]		6.0 [c]
Intercity motor buses		40 [b]	2.37
Passenger automobiles (psgr. mile)	0.63–1.33 [b]	5–8 [b]	
Airlines:			
Domestic trunk line (psgr. mile)	3.5–5.05 [b]	140–160 (est.)	4.52–5.58 [d]
Local service (psgr. mile)	4.80–6.1 [b]	140–180 (est.)	4.52–5.58 [d]
All-cargo (ton-mile)	10–18 (est.)		24–32 [d]
Waterways:			
Great Lakes bulk-cargo carriers	0.0005 *–0.0007 [e]	1000–1400 [e]	
River and canal barges	0.002 *–0.0025 [f] †	700†–800 †	
Pipelines	0.0513–0.237 (varies with throughput, line diameter, and pumping pressure) [g]		
Conveyors	1.5–2.0 (est.)		
Aerial tramways	4.0–11 (est.)		

Based on data from various sources:

[a] *Review of Railway Operations in 1958*, Bureau of Railway Economics, Association of American Railroads.

[b] Meyer, Peck, Stenason, and Zwick, *Competition in the Transportation Industries*, Harvard University Press, 1959, p. 158.

[c] *American Trucking Trends*, American Trucking Associations, 1958.

[d] *Air Transport Facts and Figures*, Air Transport Association, 1959.

[e] Meyer, Peck, Stenason, and Zwick, p. 114.

[f] *Ibid.*, p. 121.

[g] *Ibid.*, pp. 129–131.

* Vehicle operating costs.
† Fully distributed costs.

to each class of service. Return loads, when obtainable, on a normally one-way haul are perhaps better examples. A truck, hauling a one-way load must make a return journey to its point of origin whether it returns empty or loaded. If a return load can be secured, the transportation so produced may be thought of as a by-product of the out-bound load. The costs of the two loads—out and return—are joint.

A different aspect of the problem arises when multiple-purpose dams are constructed. A dam may provide power, flood control, irrigation, and slack-water navigation. When the dam is erected for navigation and one or more other purposes, the costs of the dam are jointly shared by the several services provided. The question arises as to how those costs should be apportioned. No entirely satisfactory formula has yet been devised. One method takes account of the additional height of dam required to provide additional services. The defects of this criterion are obvious. A similar problem arises in apportioning the costs of subgrade and rights of way when a rapid-transit line is laid between the two lanes of a modern expressway. The use of the same highway by pleasure as well as by commercial vehicles is still another example of joint costs.

Direct and Indirect Costs. Direct costs, sometimes termed "out-of-pocket" costs, are incurred directly by and are specifically attributable to an individual operation. The direct costs of operating an airplane are the wages of the crew, the fuel and oil consumed, landing fees, and the running repairs made between flights. Indirect costs are those incurred by the entire airline operation and attributable to an individual flight only by some more or less arbitrary method of accounting distribution. Costs of hangar and repair facilities, accounting, sales effort, and general offices fall into this category. There is therefore a close relation and similarity between direct and variable costs and between indirect and fixed costs. The terms are almost synonymous in transport operation.

Variable-Cost and Fixed-Cost Carriers. A quick résumé of operating characteristics of all carrier types indicates that each type has a certain percentage of fixed costs and a complementary percentage of variable costs. These percentages vary so widely, however, with the carrier types that one can, by a crude generalization, divide the types into fixed- and variable-cost categories. It is important to understand the reasons and justification for such a generalization.

The principal factor determining the percentages of fixed versus variable costs is the amount of fixed plant devoted to transportation service. Before a pipeline, for example, can pump even one barrel of oil, a line of pipe must be laid from the initial to the terminating end of the route. It must be of a diameter sufficient to meet the anticipated usual peak capacity and must be wrapped and protected against corrosion, weighted in place at river crossings, and placed in a ditch on a previously secured right of way. Pumping and booster stations must be installed at intervals and gathering lines and intermediate and terminal tank-storage capacity provided. A communication system and access roads are necessary. The system must then be officered and manned and a supporting organization of sales, accounting, maintenance, legal, and stores services provided. These costs—capital investment and the interest thereon—are incurred before the first oil is shipped. The costs of maintaining this plant and organization will continue to accrue whether the line operates at 50 or 100 percent capacity. Much of the expense will continue even if the line is temporarily shut down. Interest charges, general offices, stores, communication, and some operating and maintenance expenses will continue. Clearly this is an example of a carrier with a high percentage of fixed costs. The variable costs would be those of fuel and power, more being required for capacity pumping than for less-than-capacity pumping (but not in proportion), and the increase in maintenance due to increased wear and tear on equipment. Since this is a 24-hour-a-day operation, all other costs would be continuously incurred regardless of quantity of traffic.

Railroads are cited as another example. Before traffic can move between the initial and final terminals, a stable, well-drained subgrade and a cleared, fenced right of way are required. Bridges and tunnels, deep cuts and fills, highway crossings, and grade separations are also required. Rails, ties, and ballast must be laid to form track. Side tracks, sidings, and yards are necessary adjuncts. Stations, engine houses, shops, and fuel, water, sand, and similar facilities are built. A system of train direction with communications and signals is installed to permit safe and efficient movement of trains. Cars and locomotives, equal to the anticipated normal peak traffic must be made available. Again, a supporting organization—operating and maintenance personnel, general offices, stores, traffic (sales), legal, and other services—is necessary whether the line carries 10 trains a day or 30. A major percentage of costs are fixed and continuing without regard to the volume of traffic moving.

Prime examples of fixed-cost operation are found in establishing and maintaining state and Federal highways and Federal waterways. True, the standards of construction and maintenance bear some relation to the volume of traffic anticipated, but fluctuations in that volume find little reflection in the costs of providing a facility that must be ready at all times to bear safely and expeditiously whatever traffic the public chooses to place upon it.

In contrast to the fixed-cost carrier is the one with a major percentage of variable costs and only a few fixed costs. Motor-truck operation may be cited as an example. First and foremost, the truck operator has no investment in or maintenance expense for right of way or pavement. These are provided by the states. He does, of course, contribute to highway costs but principally through gasoline and tire taxes. These costs are incurred only as a vehicle is operated. The trucker needs no wayside fueling or maintenance stations. The local gas stations and garages meet these needs. His unit of operation, the truck, is small, and the number can be readily adjusted to the volume of traffic. Some truckers even rent their vehicles, thereby obtaining the maximum in adaptability to traffic volumes. No signals and no elaborate or expensive systems of communication are required. When communications are used, leased lines or radio are used. Station facilities usually are not elaborate or expensive. The organization supporting such a system is not elaborate either. There are some fixed costs for management, accounting, and solicitation and advertising and some investment in and maintenance of freight stations, garages, and vehicles. With a few companies, these facilities have become rather extensive. Such companies are usually subject therefore to a higher percentage of fixed costs. It has been estimated however that no more than 10 percent of an average trucking company's costs are fixed; the remaining 90 percent are variable.[1]

Single-unit-type carriers usually are in the variable-cost category. Assembled and continuous-flow types almost invariably have a major percentage of fixed costs. Carriers utilizing small-capacity units are more likely to experience variable costs than those with large capacity units, the small capacities being more easily adapted to fluctuations in traffic. Nevertheless, the obligation, or lack of it, to provide the way and structures is usually the deciding factor.

Conveyors and aerial tramways fall into the fixed-cost category. A complete plant must be built and maintained regardless of volume of traffic. Barge, small airline, and bus operators are variable-cost carriers, along with truck operators. Large ship and airline operators form an intermediate group. These last are variable-cost carriers insofar as they have no direct responsibilities for building or maintaining a routeway or extensive terminal facilities. However, the great cost of even one ship or airplane establishes a basic capital and operating-cost burden that is incurred regardless of whether the ship or plane is fully loaded or almost empty.

Table 12-2 is an attempt to summarize this techno-economic characteristic for the several carriers, based on the author's studies and estimates.

[1] C. A. Taft, *Commercial Motor Transportation*, Richard D. Irwin, Inc., Homewood, Illinois, 1955.

Table 12-2. Percentage of Operating Costs That Vary with Traffic

Carrier	Percentage Variable	Percentage Fixed
Railroads	25–50	75–50
Motor freight carriers (trucks)	80–90	20–10
Buses	80–90	20–10
Airlines	10–50	90–50
Pipelines	30–40	70–60
River and canal barges	50–70	50–30
Great Lakes freighters	50–70	50–30
Conveyors	20–30	80–70
Aerial tramways	20–30	80–70

Excess Capacity and Effect on Rates. A concomitant feature of fixed costs is that of surplus or unused capacity. When a carrier is newly formed and for some time thereafter, a fixed-cost carrier is likely to have more capacity available than is actually used. A ship's hold may not always be filled, requiring it to make part of its run in ballast. The pipeline does not always pump to full capacity. The tracks of a railroad will hold more trains, the locomotives can haul more cars in a train, and more tonnage can be placed in an individual car. Also more cars can be moved through the yards.

If costs are fixed, it is quite evident that the more traffic that is handled, the lower will be the unit cost of transport. The lowest unit cost would be reached, at least in regard to the fixed portion of costs, when the maximum capacity of the system had just been attained. It is also evident that fixed costs and excess capacity are found at several levels and stages in a carrier's development. Thus a railroad may eventually have its initial one track filled to capacity. Any increases in volume of traffic would lead not to lower but to higher costs owing to delays and interference of the increased number of trains. A pipeline may reach the stage of having its lines and pumps working at their maximum throughput. When that stage is reached, the railroad may add a system of CTC to its single track or build an additional track, thereby raising its maximum traffic capacity to a new level. Similarly, the pipeline may install heavier pumps or add another line of pipe. Again a new stage or level of capacity and development is reached. It is this sequence of events that has caused some writers, J. M. Clark for example, to say that 90 percent more or less of any carrier's costs are actually variable.[2] Over a long period of time and from this point of view, Clark is correct. However, for the short and intermediate term and for any one level of capacity, that is, where no additional capital costs are involved, the fixed-cost concept holds true.

With no variable costs or expenses (all costs fixed), unit costs would vary directly with the volume of traffic, increasing as traffic declined and decreasing as traffic increased. In this situation, prices on some units might safely be set at less than over-all average costs of operation (but greater than out-of-pocket costs) because the revenue thus obtained would help to cover a portion of fixed costs. There are no carriers that fall completely within the 100 percent fixed-cost category although a pipeline or a conveyor system is close to it.

Where there are no fixed costs (all costs variable), expenses would increase directly with increases in traffic and decrease directly with decreases in traffic. Unit costs would remain approximately constant. Under these circumstances, the rate, that is, the selling price, can never be set lower than the unit cost, at least for an appreciable time, if the carrier is to remain solvent and in business. Truck, bus, and airline operations, the low capacity, unit-type carriers, come closest to this category.

A third possible group is that in which a large portion of the costs are variable but a significant percentage are fixed. In this situation, some rates will be set well above the cost of service for traffic that can afford to pay a high rate, but traffic that cannot be had at the higher rates will be priced at something less. This practice is similar to dumping surplus goods on a foreign market. The earlier-noted lower rates for off-peak loads in power production and for off-season periods at resorts and lower rates given by contract and private truckers for return loads are based on the same principle. All transport agencies are subject more or less to this situation, but railroads, pipelines, conveyors, and large ships are typical of the category.

Another characteristic of transportation, as opposed to a manufacturing industry, is that the product produced—transportation—cannot be stored. The service performed by a vehicle moving over its route is either utilized then in moving payload or is lost forever.

[2] J. M. Clark, *Studies in the Economics of Overhead Costs,* University of Chicago Press, Chicago, Illinois, 1923, p. 268.

Hence it behooves every transport operator to keep his operations as near to capacity as possible.

From a slightly different point of view, one might assume a situation where there is enough traffic to cover the fixed costs of the plant and the direct or out-of-pocket costs of the actual carriage of existing traffic. The carrier would, however, make more money if its full capacity were being utilized. It therefore tries to get enough traffic to fill that capacity. Because the present traffic is already covering the actual costs, the carrier will not feel obliged to charge the same high rates as obtained from the traffic already being carried. Evidently the existing rates have brought in all the traffic that can be attracted by those rates. A lower rate, nevertheless, would be likely to attract a different category of traffic. The carrier would be willing to charge any rate that would cover the out-of-pocket or direct costs and give some small profit. In fact, even if the present traffic and rates are not covering all the fixed costs, a lower rate on *additional* traffic would be acceptable if it brought in traffic that would pay its direct costs and *make some contribution to fixed costs.*

Effects of Cost on Competition. If the ability to establish rates were fully utilized, an excess-capacity carrier would have a system of rates somewhat as follows:

1. High rates on commodities that could afford to pay the high rates and would ship by that type of carrier in any event.

2. A lower band of rates for traffic that could not pay the high rates (or could find a competitive service with lower rates) but would be willing to utilize the carrier in question if lower rates were offered.

3. Successive bands of rates (sometimes becoming numerous to the point of a different rate band for each commodity) attracting traffic at different levels of ability or willingness to pay. The only limitation would be that the rate would have to cover out-of-pocket costs and make some contribution, however small, to fixed costs and/or profits.

A variable-cost carrier is thus placed at a competitive disadvantage. The proportion of fixed costs is so small that there is little leeway in setting prices. As explained earlier, the unit cost (and therefore the unit selling price or rate) remains approximately constant. Unit costs remain about the same regardless of how much traffic is secured because total costs are incurred in direct proportion to the volume of traffic. A fixed-cost carrier with a high excess capacity might possibly set rates so low (still covering costs) as to drive a competitor out of a particular traffic field or even out of business entirely. A strong carrier might deliberately set some rates below cost for a time for the same purpose, a form of "cut-throat competition."

In setting up a private transport system, these same principles should be kept in mind. A fixed-cost carrier might be selected where there is the likelihood of a large volume of traffic to bring about low unit costs. Where the volume of traffic is small, a variable-cost carrier would be more appropriate so that a high overhead would not continue to be incurred when the system was not being fully utilized.

Costs versus Regulation. Guided largely by fear of possible resort to the foregoing cut-throat competition, the regulatory bodies, especially the I.C.C., have tended to restrain the freedom of fixed-cost carriers to keep them from exercising this inherent ability to cut rates. The I.C.C. recognizes that cost of service is a governing factor. However, they define cost of service as the average unit cost for all types and classes of traffic, "on the basis of normal operation considering fully allocated costs." [3] Not only must each ton-mile of traffic bring in a revenue sufficient to cover direct costs, it must also bear a proportionate share of indirect, overhead, or fixed costs. This limits the fixed-cost, excess-capacity carrier's use of a powerful competitive weapon. As might be expected, the policy has been the subject of much heated debate, especially by the railroads, who feel themselves to be the chief sufferers. It is a problem that has not yet been resolved completely by legislation. Economists generally are likely to favor the marginal-cost concept of pricing.

Differential Pricing. Under conditions of true competition, rates tend to approach the actual costs of service. Note in this connection that the foregoing paragraphs have shown how the average cost of service decreases for the fixed-cost carrier as the volume of traffic increases and vice versa. On the one hand, the carrier cannot haul freight at a loss, that is, below the cost of service; on the other hand, the pressure of competition prevents rates that are significantly higher than the costs of service.

Where conditions of true competition do not exist, differential

---

[3] "Surface Transportation," Hearings before a Subcommittee of the Committee on Interstate and Foreign Commerce, House of Representatives, 85th Congress, testimony of Hon. Howard Freas, Commissioner, Interstate Commerce Commissioner, April 1957, p. 65.

pricing is likely to arise. Interference with competition arises in a number of situations.

Monopoly. Where there is a complete or partial monopoly, there is a tendency to take advantage of it by charging rates well above the costs of service—although there is a limit to which this is profitable. Even where competition exists, monopolistic conditions arise. A shipper with a side track on only one railroad is practically subject to that road even though he does have the right to route his freight over a connecting carrier. A railroad can show favoritism by faster movement and prompter furnishing, switching, and spotting of cars. A shipper in a town served only by a truck line is entirely dependent upon that carrier. A truck line with its freight house centrally located in a traffic area enjoys a monopolistic advantage over one with a more remote location. Few if any carriers can be called truly monopolistic today, but most of them have certain localities in which their dominance is almost completely monopolistic.

Concerted action. Traffic pools, price-fixing agreements, and other restraining influences may ensue at times. Generally these practices are restrained under the various anti-trust laws and as a matter of public policy, except when carried out as a permitted feature of government regulation.

Subsidies. Subsidies, usually from public sources, interfere with true competition by neutralizing the cost-of-service advantages or disadvantages. Providing roadways, airways, and shipways, granting land for rights of way, and making deficit payments to airlines and outright grants to ship lines are ways in which subsidies have been granted and have thereby influenced the cost to a carrier of the service it provides. Subsidized roadways, waterways, airways, and airports go a long way toward making the carriers that use these facilities variable- rather than fixed-cost carriers.

Joint costs. The joint costs, already defined, may also affect costs of service and lead to differential pricing. There is always a tendency to have the stronger of the two or more services carry the weaker, sometimes obscuring the actual costs incurred.

Private Operation. From the standpoint of over-all costs, private ownership of transport offers many advantages to an industry equipped to haul its own products. There need be no element of profit included in the costs, the operation is not subject to government regulation, and the size of the operation can be tailored to the needs of the industry served. When a private carrier is organized as a separate company and gives service to more than one unit in a large organization, when it makes a nominal purchase of goods carried, with resale at the time of delivery, or when it hauls its owner's freight from other industries, a question arises as to whether or not it is not actually performing contract or even common-carrier service and therefore subject to regulation. This is an unresolved problem.

Governmental Regulation. Government regulation is directed primarily toward rate making in an effort to prevent cut-throat competition and discrimination between persons, places, or things. Chief among the regulatory bodies is the Interstate Commerce Commission, originally established to regulate the pricing practices of railroads when that industry constituted a near monopoly in transportation. Pipelines, pullman service, express companies, and some interurbans were later brought under its jurisdiction. The Motor Carrier Act of 1935, Part II of the Interstate Commerce Act, placed common and contract motor carriers under I.C.C. control (and private carriers for safety regulation only). In 1940 common and contract carriers by water were included, and in 1942 freight-forwarding agencies. However, owing to excluding features of the law, only about 10 percent of the water carriers are actually subject to regulation.

The Civil Aeronautics Board performs for air transport the same regulatory functions as the I.C.C. performs for other transport.

The I.C.C. and the C.A.B. exercise their control only over interstate transportation. Purely intrastate transport is subject to the individual regulatory commission of each state. Nevertheless, the extensiveness of interstate commerce narrows the field of state exclusiveness even on nominal intrastate movements.

The usual regulatory powers extend to approving or disapproving of maximum rates for all common carriers. Railroads are also subject to specific rate regulation. Contract carriers are generally regulated only as to maximum rates. To facilitate rate control, carriers have their accounting and record-keeping systems prescribed and must report their activities. The issuance of permits to engage in or withdraw from common and contract service are also major functions. The nonuniformity of control over competing forms of transport has given rise to much criticism, primarily from the heavily regulated railroads.

State and Federal commissions have set rates on other than a cost-of-service basis for various reasons: to aid drought-stricken areas, to assist new or critical industries, to foster new types of transportation, or to equalize the competitive position of carriers, commodities, or communities. On the other hand, regulatory bodies generally have not recognized certain cost-of-service features as being permissible. For example, the unit rate for a long haul is required to be the same as for a short haul included in the long haul although the unit cost of making a long haul is less than for the short. There has been considerable I.C.C. reluctance to grant train-load rates as contrasted with car-load rates although again the train-load costs are less.

Composition of Rate. From the cost-of-service standpoint, rates usually contain two principal elements. The first and obvious element is that of line-haul service. This is the cost of providing and maintaining the route and/or equipment and of hauling the goods from one point to another. The second element is the cost of terminal service. This includes costs of freight-house, tank-farm, airport, or transit-shed operation, of classifying and sorting cars in yards, of delivering cars and LCL shipments to final terminal destinations, and of providing passenger-station and ticket-selling facilities. Transfer and placement of cars by other carriers, tug service in berthing ships, and movement of passengers from town to and from airports are supplemental services for which an additional charge is made. Certain other services may be included in the line-haul rate, but reflected in its magnitude, such as icing of refrigerator cars and in-transit privileges.

QUESTIONS FOR STUDY

1. What is the significance of cost of service as a basis for transportation charges as contrasted with other criteria?
2. Distinguish between capital costs and operating expenses; between fixed and variable costs.
3. What factors tend to make a transport agency a "fixed"- or a "variable"-cost carrier?
4. Explain fully the concept of "excess capacity" and relate this to fixed and variable costs.
5. How does the fixed–variable-cost concept introduce hazards in the use of average costs?
6. A railroad moves 20,000 net tons a day over a division at a cost of 200 dollars per mile. What would be the unit cost of the same operation to move 30,000 net tons? 15,000 net tons?

7. A motor freight carrier moves 400 net tons of freight per day over a run at a cost of 4 cents per net ton-mile. What would be the cost per net ton-mile of moving 600 tons over the same territory? 200 net tons?

8. In what situations may a rate be influenced by other than cost-of-service factors?

9. How does the fixed- versus variable-cost characteristic affect the competitive position of each type of carrier?

10. To what extent is a private carrier concerned with the characteristic of fixed–variable costs?

SUGGESTED READINGS

1. J. M. Clark, *Studies in the Economics of Overhead Costs*, University of Chicago Press, Chicago, Illinois, 1923.

2. Kent T. Healy, *The Economics of Transportation in America*, The Ronald Press, New York, 1935, Chapters 10–13, on cost and pricing of transportation.

3. G. M. Wellington, *The Economic Theory of Railway Location*, Sixth Edition, John Wiley and Sons, New York, 1914, Chapter V ff., on operating expenses, pp. 106–185.

4. W. W. Hay, *Railroad Engineering*, John Wiley and Sons, New York, 1953, Chapters 3, 4, and 12.

5. C. A. Taft, *Commercial Motor Transportation*, 1953 edition, Richard D. Irwin, Inc., Homewood, Illinois.

6. *Surface Transportation*, Hearings before a Subcommittee on Interstate and Foreign Commerce, House of Representatives, 85th Congress, April 2, 3, 4, 5, and 11, 1957, Government Printing Office, Washington, D. C.

7. The Interstate Commerce Act, Government Printing Office, Washington, D. C.

8. The Civil Aeronautics Act and the Federal Aviation Act, Government Printing Office, Washington, D. C.

PART IV

Planning for Use and Development

CHAPTER 13

PLANNING

PLANNING REQUISITES

Transportation planning is comprised of a variety of problems and procedures. These will vary with the level at which the planning is conducted and the type of need to be met. It may be the detailed location of a specific route, the selection of for-hire services by an industrial traffic department, or the planning of an entire system of private transportation by an industry. The planning may also be for the establishment of a pattern of Federal interstate highways, waterways, or airways, for the integration of various modes of transport in an urban area, or—on rare occasions—for the over-all needs of the nation among all modes of transport.

Recognition of Need. As a first step, there must be the recognition of a need for new, additional, or improved transport. That need can arise in many ways. The proposal to develop a new timber tract should raise immediately the question of how to transport the timber. Perhaps an existing mode of transport is at hand. Consideration must be given to the capacity and ability of that mode to handle the burden of the new traffic. If existing transport is lacking, is inadequate, or too expensive, the promoters of the enterprise may arrange to develop their own private system. For similar reasons, an industry already utilizing transportation may consider some other means of transport to reduce costs or to provide more convenient, rapid, or dependable movement.

Transportation agencies, themselves, plan to establish new routes and services or to improve those already in existence. Thus a railroad may seek an entrance into a new traffic center, or a highway may be reconstructed with flatter curves and gradients or with wider or additional traffic lanes. Congestion, often accompanied by a high accident or/and delay rate, may indicate the need to improve an existing route or to build a new and supplementary route, perhaps a superhighway type of toll road.

The exploitation of a new oil field calls for pipeline construction. The development of unimproved land areas may require the new construction of several types of transport systems. The planning and revising of city transportation is an ever-changing, never-ending problem.

Not only must the need for new or improved transportation be recognized, but that need must be communicated to others. The traffic manager, chief engineer, or board of directors may have to be convinced in a private industry. Highway departments, legislatures or the Congress, and eventually, a large portion of the electorate may have to be sold on such propositions as subsidies for rapid transit, construction of new highways, of new airfields, or of a St. Lawrence seaway. The engineer thus oftentimes finds himself in the role of promoter. In this he has an opportunity to perform an invaluable public service by providing sound, conservative, well-founded data and opinions regarding the project.

Steps in Planning. Planning and the implementaion of the plans usually follow a general pattern given here in brief outline. Obviously the detail or need for each step will vary with the project.

1. Recognition of need for new or revised transportation
2. Selection of general routes—origin, terminus, and key intermediate points
3. Selection of type of carrier, as to adaptability and economy
4. Selection of final route(s) and traffic allocations
5. Development of plans for financing the project
6. Design and detailed location of the final route
7. Construction (or implementation) of the project

An important aspect of the foregoing procedures is the feedback from one step to another; often all seven steps must be considered at the same time. The breakdown into separate and distinct steps has been made only as an aid to study and analysis. There is a close inter-relation and coordination between all seven steps. The selection of a carrier type, for example, may depend almost entirely on the route to be traversed—or vice versa. The entire project is usually governed by the development of an adequate plan of financing.

The engineer is or should be involved in each of these steps. If he doesn't make the decisions, someone else, not necessarily as well versed in the characteristics of transport, will, sometimes with unhappy results.

Initial planning may indicate the project to be unwarranted or unfeasible. In these events, planning has accomplished a worthwhile purpose in establishing that fact and preventing a wasteful expenditure of funds and effort. If the project does appear feasible, all further planning can be directed toward development and implementation.

Tools and Data Required. In carrying out the foregoing seven steps, certain tools and basic data are needed. Some of these will warrant later elaboration; some have already appeared.

Terminals and intermediate points. The place of origin of the traffic and the key intermediate points—places of junction, transfer, and interchange—as well as the final destination must be known. These are usually but not always self-evident. Marketing ore from a South American country, for example, raises the question of whether European buyers should be supplied directly from the mines or from a stock pile in the United States or at some intermediate point. The decision to utilize a certain port for the water leg of the route makes that port a fixed and key point of reference in all future planning.

Characteristics of alternative systems. The unit costs of construction and operation, rates, technical characteristics, adaptability to the traffic and terrain, etc. for each type of transport that might be utilized must be known. This aids in selecting the type of carrier to use. These characteristics have been developed in Chapters 4 to 12.

Sectional interests and policies. Local interests, policies, and prejudices play a part in carrier and route selection and cannot be ignored. In one community, the merchants will insist that main highways go through the center of town, by their store door. In another community a similar group will want all main-road traffic to by-pass the town to reduce congestion in the shopping district. At the time this is written, the government of South Africa, having a complete monopoly on all transportation, is reluctant to license even a private transport operation, let alone one with common-carrier status. The United States is presently committed to private ownership with government regulation of contract and common-carriers with no economic regulation of private carriers. It also strives to preserve a balance between the several modes of transport. These few examples could be many times multiplied if space permitted.

Standards of design and construction. Certain standards of design and construction must be established, at least tentatively, before an adequate initial appraisal and location can be made. The quantity of traffic to be moved in a given period—a year, a month, a day—establishes one engineering criterion for route design. Maximum permissible gradients, curvatures, sight distances, lifts per lock, number of lanes, tracks, belts, or cables, number of lines of pipe and the pipe diameters, and the number of cars, boats, trucks, or pumping stations are based on route and traffic factors. The horsepower required for tractive, propulsive, or pumping force derives from the foregoing. These are established in the light of traffic, terrain, soils, weather, works of man, etc. Many of these factors have been developed in earlier chapters or will be mentioned in the chapter to follow.

Traffic pattern. These fundamental data include the kinds of traffic, volume of each, origin, destination, and direction of traffic, and the speed and time of movement. The existing pattern and the pattern as anticipated and projected for the future are determined for each route under consideration. Points of origin, interchange, junction, and transfer are noted, and the rate of flow or density over each route and through each key point. The securing, presentation, and interpretation of traffic-pattern data are given more detailed analysis later in this chapter.

Reconnaissance data. A reconnaissance over the area to be traversed by the proposed routes is necessary where new or revised locations are contemplated. Reconnaissance is never a study of a particular route but rather of a land area so that the best position for a route within that area can be determined. The area strip may vary from a mile or so to several miles in width. Early reconnaissance parties seeking a route for the first Pacific railway covered strips of land included within 5 degrees of latitude per party.

In the country, reconnaissance notes will include the general topography with approximate elevations, usually obtained by barometric readings, reference to government or private triangulation points and other markers, all drainage conditions, vegetation, and soil characteristics. Works of man will be specified—land uses, other transport routes, communities, etc. The probable route or routes for further investigation should also be noted. The taking of pictures is helpful in interpreting the notes later on. In cities and built-up areas, works of man will receive much emphasis. Here the reconnaissance should include land use in detail and give estimates of real-estate value. Data on subsurface conditions should be noted where possible. Prospective growth and development of population and industries are especially important in urban areas.

Much reconnaissance data can be obtained from maps, where those are available and drawn with sufficient detail. The United States Coast and Geodetic Survey quadrangles are of this type. Aerial flights are helpful in obtaining a comprehensive picture of a large area, especially if carried out by helicopter, which can hover and permit a more leisurely observation than an airplane. Aerial photographs permit detailed studies of any or all portions of the area as desired in the office. Stereoscopic study of aerial photographs gives the same third-dimensional effect as when actually seen from the air. Contour maps can be prepared from aerial photographs with sufficient accuracy to obtain estimates of earthwork. Even preliminary surveys can be made in the office. However, despite the helpfulness of aerial photographs, it is usually desirable or even necessary to cover a few especially difficult portions of the area on foot, horseback, or at least by car or boat.

Costs of alternative routes. From the reconnaissance, preliminary routes can be selected with sufficient accuracy to make possible a preliminary estimate of cost and economic justification. Such estimates may be made for each possible route and carrier type or combination and will form another criterion for selection.

Costs in place of the route selected. Once a route site has been selected by the foregoing methods, the final location or detailed position on the ground must be made. Again several alternatives will be available because of terrain and topography, drainage conditions, soils encountered, and works of man. The final selection can be determined as before with a tabulation of comparative annual costs, rates of return, or benefit ratios based chiefly upon differences in length, curvatures, and gradients of the several alternatives. Detailed methods for determining these costs are given in Chapter 14.

The application of these and following principles will be seen in the problem example given later in this text. It should be noted here that the several comparisons suggested in the foregoing procedure can be performed with considerable detail in variation by use of electronic computers. Fixed data are established, and then the effects of the several variables or alternatives are determined.

ECONOMIC JUSTIFICATION

Basis of Justification. A primary responsibility of the engineer in the planning stage is to determine whether or not a proposed system is economically justified. The ability to finance the project, to secure risk capital or the commitment of public credit, usually depends upon a favorable answer to this problem. Some kind of initial estimates are therefore required.

A variety of situations are likely to arise under which economic justification and the supporting estimates must be made.

New project. With an entirely new project, the first question to be answered is whether the project has any economic justification for being in the first place. Will it earn a sufficient rate of return or provide a sufficiently adequate and inexpensive service to be worth the money expended? The second question involves the selection between alternate possibilities—between alternative routes where the variables are the effects of terrain, distance, volume of traffic, etc. on the costs of construction and operation. Or the choice may lie between one mode of transportation and another; for example, a conveyor-belt installation as opposed to an aerial tramway. (In this connection, note that comparisons may first have to be made between several alternative conveyor possibilities and several tramway designs in order to select the best of each for final comparison.)

Replacement project. A new service may be proposed to replace one already in use. An industry may contemplate setting up its own trucking system to replace the use of common-carrier trucks or an airline plan to replace its obsolete aircraft with those of more recent design. A new highway location and design may be proposed to replace the one now in use. In these situations, one alternative is always the status quo, continuing with the existing arrangement and the high costs of obsolescence and mounting maintenance. The new proposal must show a definite advantage over the present practice; otherwise there is no point in making the change.

Improvement project. The improvement of all or a part of an existing route or system may be in prospect. A new class of locomotive is planned for a railroad, a ship of larger tonnage for a water route, a second line of pipe for a pipeline, an additional lane for a highway, reduction in gradient, curvature, or distance in the route, or the elimination of grade crossings. Again the comparison is made, not only with new alternatives, but with the existing arrangement unchanged.

Some projects involve equipment only, others routes, and many a combination of both. Certain projects are for direct-revenue purposes, for example, common carriers, others for a reduction in costs of transport. New revenue is secured from entirely new operations, from gaining access to new traffic centers, as with a branch or feeder line, or from attracting new traffic to the line by virtue of better service, lower rates, or more capacity. Savings in cost arise from improving the equipment or the capacity, the gradient or the curvature of a route, by shortening distance, reducing time of movement, or reducing accident and delay hazards. All of these have economic significance.

Guiding Principles. In determining the economic feasibility of a route, the engineer will adhere to certain guiding principles.

1. Transportation projects should not be undertaken unless they show an adequate return on the investment. For commercial ventures—railroads, pipelines, airlines, etc.—the return must be sufficient to provide a reasonable and attractive profit. If the project is a public service—a highway, waterway, airport—the project should show at the least a return on the investment, from economies of the new operation or from tax and toll returns from the traffic using the facility, which is sufficient to attract capital and amortize its costs. (This is not to raise the question of whether or not transport facilities *should* be provided as a public service.) If public funds are used directly, the return should be sufficient to make this use more attractive than for some other purpose, debt retirement, for example.

2. The initial investment must be kept to a minimum consistent with safety and the purposes of the project. The engineer has a duty and responsibility to reduce costs by proper design of location and construction. He must select a route which requires minimum construction costs consistent with adequate revenue and economy. For example, the choice of a ridge location may reduce costs of drainage and bridging. His design will call for a minimum of hand work and permit the utmost utilization of machine work and modern, economical materials. He will endeavor to specify standard methods

and materials, which usually are less expensive than special requirements. Any increase in costs beyond the minimum must be justified as an economical investment in their own right. For example, if present construction calls for a four-lane highway and future plans require one of six lanes, there may be economy over the years in buying right of way for the six lanes at present prices—but this economy must be definitely established.

3. As an expansion of the foregoing, no expenditure should be avoided that will, in itself, prove to be a profitable investment.

4. A modifying principle arises over the availability of funds. No construction should be undertaken that cannot be carried to completion with the funds on hand or available. The use of stage construction and pay-as-you-go plans to implement this principle will be discussed later.

5. A new project must go through a seasoning and development period, especially when dependent upon its own resources for income. Financial planning should take these initial lean years into account. Only that construction absolutely necessary should be carried out at the beginning. Thus a second main track, an additional lock, or multiple lanes of highway may be deferred until the need for these actually arises.

6. Any revision in plans and design must be subjected to the same scrutiny and economic justification as the original design, to assure that it contributes to the economic integrity of the project.

7. Much of the value of any economic study depends upon the accuracy and validity of estimates of future traffic and the revenues or taxes to be derived therefrom. Projections of present growth cannot safely be made too far into the future. A 20-year period is about the limit attempted, and even that is usually made with reservations. The use of stage construction, building only what is needed now, introduces flexibility into the plan and permits later revisions as warranted by future developments.

In summarizing these principles, one can do no better than to quote from that master of the processes of economic planning, A. M. Wellington, who summarized his own statement of principles in these words:

. . . that excepting when and as a specific reason to the contrary appears, the cheapest line is to be built over which it is physically possible to carry the probable traffic with proper safety and speed, using to this end any grades and curves and length of line which must be conducive to this end only—and never abandoning it by increasing the expenditure, unless the investment—not investment as a whole, for the line as a whole, but each particular investment for each particular purpose—will be in one way or another profitable in itself.[1]

In applying the foregoing principles, detailed estimates of cost may be prepared for each alternative. Such effort not being economically necessary at the preliminary stage, a unit-cost approach is usually in order. Unit costs for plant and equipment are frequently set up on a per-1000-ft or a per-mile basis exclusive of grading. Grading costs have to be developed separately because of the widely differing character of terrain. Equipment may or may not be included in the route costs.

Table 13-1 gives current unit costs of constructing a mile of route. Cost of equipment, based upon the quantity of traffic and design of roadway and gradient must, in most cases, be added. Operating costs (see Chapter 12 for some average values) are also determined for the motive power and rolling stock in use. Financial costs—the costs of borrowing—must be included. From these several data, indices or criteria of economic desirability can be developed. Where actual or comparable costs are available, those should be used rather than the average costs given in this text.

The following section presents several methods for making economic comparisons and selections. Each has its special field of applicability, but, in general, the most conservative should be used and vague and speculative estimates of intangibles avoided.

Rate of Return. One of the oldest and soundest criteria of economic feasibility is the rate-of-return method using the basic location formula. This involves a comparison of the rates of return on investments from several alternative systems, routes, locations, or designs using the formula $(R - E)/C = p$, where R = anticipated revenues, E = operating expenses including taxes and depreciation, C = investment in plant and equipment, and p = rate of return. This method has had considerable application in the detailed comparison of alternative railroad locations where the effects of gradients, curvature, and distance for each are under consideration. However, it has application to almost any comparison that may arise in transportation planning. It permits a determination of whether the rate of return is large enough to attract capital, a necessary test for

[1] *The Economic Theory of the Location of Railways,* Sixth Edition, John Wiley and Sons, New York, 1914, p. 18.

Table 13-1. Typical Construction Costs per Route Mile

(Equipment Included except Where Specifically Excluded)

Carrier	Cost per Mile of Route (dollars)
Railroads:	
Track only	90,000–100,000
Track, structures, and equipment	140,000–150,000
Rapid-transit—surface	2–6 million
Rapid-transit—subway	5–12 million
Highways:	
24-ft rural highway (concrete, 2-lane)	100,000–400,000
Freeway (urban area)	4–11 million
Superhighway (expressway, freeway):	(Cost depends on number of structures.)
Maine Turnpike	450,000
Pennsylvania Turnpike	461,000 and 861,000
New Jersey Turnpike	1,900,000
Ohio Turnpike	1,250,000
Pipelines:	
Petroleum and gas	100,000–150,000
Coal (suspension process)	90,000–150,000
Conveyors:	
Belt-type	200,000–1 million
2-way, Great Lakes to Ohio River proposal: 104 miles, 72-in. belt; 104 miles, 54-in. belt; 27 miles, 42-in. belt	2.1 million
Moving sidewalk	1–1.5 million
Aerial tramways	70,000–120,000
Monorail:	300,000–1 million
Alweg System, São Paulo proposal	2,500,000
Houston—experimental	300,000–500,000
Los Angeles—proposed	945,000

projects being financed in the open money market and a conservative guide even for projects financed directly by taxes. The method also permits evaluation of the revenue and the costs of securing that revenue. For example, will enough revenue be secured from a traffic source to justify a longer route and additional operating expense to serve that traffic? It is useful in getting the most done for the least money, that is, maximizing the rate of return and giving priority to those projects yielding the highest rate. This is especially important in the highway field, where one is faced with a multiplicity of projects being urged for performance.

The rate of return should be sufficient at least, even with public projects, to amortize the investment and pay off all borrowed moneys with interest. In addition, a commercial venture must show reasonable promise of profit. It is possible that some or all schemes will be discarded as not yielding an *attractive* rate of return.

A question will arise as to what value can be used for R, the revenue, in a nonrevenue project such as a nontoll highway. Where revenue is constant or where there is no direct revenue, consider the numerator of the formula as the difference in total costs of operation of the old, or the base, project and the new. In this situation, the project, to be justified, must show a reduction in the over-all costs of maintaining the roadway and of vehicle operation over it. Reduced gradients, flatter curves, shorter distances, faster speed—these should add to lower costs for fuel, maintenance, labor, and other pertinent items. The equation now actually shows the rate of return from the savings.

The use of this form of rate of return on investment is seen in the following simple illustration.

Given: a proposal to build a 20-mile branch-line railroad to feed traffic to the main line. Three alternative locations are available: A, B, and C. Their revenues, construction costs, operating expenses, and, as a result of the rate-of-return calculations, rates of return are shown in tabulated form.

Formula Term:	A	B	C
R = revenue	\$ 840,000	\$ 840,000	\$ 840,000
E = expense	720,000	780,000	660,000
C = construction cost	1,600,000	1,520,000	1,880,000
p = rate of return	7.5%	4.0%	9.6%

Sample calculation:

$$(R - E)/C = p; \quad (840{,}000 - 720{,}000)/1{,}600{,}000 = 7.5\%$$

In spite of its higher construction cost, alternative C gives the most favorable rate of return because of lower operating expenses. B

would hardly be acceptable, even if it were the highest, because it barely earns enough for fixed charges, let alone profit.

Another version of the rate of return determines the rate of interest at which two alternatives have equal annual costs. One alternative is taken as the base and the others compared with it. When improvements of existing facilities are contemplated, the status quo or do-nothing alternative must always be considered as a possibility and serves as a base for comparison. Each alternative is compared with that status quo, which will have no construction costs but will have its own operating costs, and the rate of return is computed. Those plans are discarded that do not show a rate of return sufficiently high to attract capital. The rate of return is next computed on the increase in investment between proposals of successively higher costs. Those not showing an attractive rate of return are discarded before computing the rate of return on the next increment. Economically speaking, the desirable alternative is the one having more than the attractive rate of return both on total and incremental investments.[2]

This method does not really avoid the problem of establishing a minimum acceptable rate of return and is not always an easy way to rank investment alternatives. The method has found principal application in highway studies, especially as a basis for making improvements. A straight rate-of-return comparison of alternative investments is the most direct, easily understood, and satisfactory procedure.

Annual costs. With the annual-cost method, the capital or investment costs are reduced to an annual basis and added to the annual operating expenses to obtain total annual costs. The alternative giving the lowest annual cost is, logically, the one selected. This method is adaptable to an industry planning its own transport system or to an evaluation of the effects of improvements on an existing route (in which the existing or status-quo situation is considered as a possible alternative). This method has the serious defect of giving widely differing results for various assumed interest rates and life-of-property elements, values for which engineers are not in full agreement.

---

[2] L. I. Hewes and C. H. Oglesby, *Highway Engineering,* John Wiley and Sons, New York, 1954, pp. 66–67, 70–71.

Problem Example: Using the data of the preceding problem example, the annual cost would be compared in the following manner.

Formula Term:	A	B	C
Operating expenses	$720,000	$780,000	$660,000
Annual capital recovery (expense) *	80,832	76,790	94,978
Total annual cost	$800,832	$856,790	$754,978

* The construction or investment costs of the preceding problem example are reduced to an annual basis by multiplying the investment by the annual-capital-recovery factor (CRF). This procedure is given fuller explanation in the section entitled Capital Recovery. In the foregoing example, Project C, having the lowest annual cost, is preferable.

Benefit-Cost Ratio. The determining factor in benefit-cost studies is the ratio, R_b, of annual benefits, B_a, to the annual costs, C_a. Or, $R_b = (C_{u1} - C_{u2})/(C_{a1} - C_{a2})$ where C_{u1} and C_{u2} are the annual user costs before and after improvement, that is, the benefits, and C_{a1} and C_{a2} are the total annual costs before and after improvement respectively. The total annual costs are computed as for the annual-cost method, using the CRF to include capital costs. A ratio greater than 1.0 indicates that the additional expenditure for the alternative over the base or equivalent cost is justified; a ratio less than 1.0, that the benefits are less than the costs. After taking the original or base condition, further ratios are computed between successively higher increments of investment cost. That alternative of maximum investment cost that reaches a satisfactory cost ratio on both total and incremental investment is the most acceptable.

Argument has arisen as to what benefits should be included. Should only the direct benefits to users of the system be counted or should such secondary benefits as enhanced property values, increased sales, and more industrial starts, be included? While secondary benefits are often quite real, they are difficult to evaluate accurately. The tendency is to overstate their importance, and there are possibilities of inadvertently counting these benefits more than once, that is, accounting for their effect in more than one situation. Conservative opinion holds to restricting estimated benefits to those enjoyed by the users of the system, that is, to the savings in transportation costs arising from reductions in fuel and wages, in road time, in accident costs, etc. User costs are more readily imposed. Secondary benefits will be recognized in more goods or capital available for other services or in lower prices of goods moved over the improved system.

The benefit-cost method has found extensive use in highway, waterway, and other public projects. The results obtained vary with the rate of interest assumed. In stating a ratio, the same interest rate should be stated and used throughout.

Capital Recovery. Not only must the capital investment be recovered by the project but the interest charges as well. On a yearly basis, the annual amount is obtained from the interest formula, $R = P\{(1 + r)^n / [(1 + r)^n - 1]\}$, where R = annual charge for n years to recover investment with interest, n = life of the property (or duration of the obligation), r = the rate of interest, and P = principal or initial investment. The value of $(1 + r)^n / [(1 + r)^n - 1]$ is called the capital-recovery factor, CRP. Computations are facilitated by use of a table in which representative values for the CRF are given for various values of r and n. See Table 13-2. Intermediate values are found by interpolation. The capital-recovery cost per year for the annual-cost problem of the preceding section is

Table 13-2. Capital-Recovery Factors (CRF) for Various Lives and Interest Rates *

Life, Years	0%	2%	3%	4%	5%	6%	8%	10%
5	0.20000	0.21216	0.21835	0.22463	0.23097	0.23740	0.25046	0.26380
10	0.10000	0.11133	0.11723	0.12329	0.12950	0.13587	0.14903	0.16275
15	0.06667	0.07783	0.08377	0.08994	0.09634	0.10296	0.11683	0.13147
20	0.05000	0.06116	0.06722	0.07358	0.08024	0.08718	0.10185	0.11746
25	0.04000	0.05122	0.05743	0.06401	0.07095	0.07823	0.09368	0.11017
30	0.03333	0.04465	0.05102	0.05783	0.06505	0.07265	0.08883	0.10608
35	0.02857	0.04000	0.04654	0.05358	0.06107	0.06897	0.08580	0.10369
40	0.02500	0.03656	0.04326	0.05052	0.05828	0.06646	0.08386	0.10226
50	0.02000	0.03182	0.03887	0.04655	0.05478	0.06344	0.08174	0.10086
60	0.01667	0.02877	0.03613	0.04420	0.05283	0.06188	0.08080	0.10033
80	0.01250	0.02516	0.03311	0.04181	0.05103	0.06057	0.08017	0.10005
100	0.01000	0.02320	0.03165	0.04081	0.05038	0.06018	0.08004	0.10001

* L. I. Hewes and C. H. Oglesby, *Highway Engineering*, John Wiley and Sons, 1954, p. 60, Table 5.

computed as follows—assuming a 40-year life (n) and 4-percent rate of interest:

Alternative A:	investment $\times$ CRF = $1,600,000
	$\times$ 0.05052 = $80,832
Alternative B:	$1,520,000 $\times$ 0.05052 = $76,790
Alternative C:	$1,880,000 $\times$ 0.05052 = $94,978

Capital Costs and Recovery. The degree of accuracy of any method depends in part on the accuracy of the data used. For initial feasibility studies, average construction and equipment costs will serve for the investment. Eventually more accurate estimates will be required. Construction and equipment estimates present about the same problems and degree of accuracy as any other engineering estimate.

Problems arise in converting investment costs to annual costs. If the project has a finite life—as with a conveyor installed to move aggregates for dam construction—the total cost is simply divided by the anticipated duration of the project. Total cost in this case would include interest and any other financing costs. It could also include an estimate of the total operating cost for the life of the operation. If a finite life is not definitely known, one must be assumed. One assumption is to use the life of the financial obligations incurred. For example, if 50-year bonds have been used for financing, the interest and capital cost are spread over 50 years. This method may have advantages in setting up sinking funds to retire the obligations but does not square with the physical and economic facts in trying to establish a fair evaluation of a project.

More often, the economic life span of the plant is estimated. A new problem then arises in that the several elements of plant and equipment have different life spans. Trucks, tractors, and trailers may have a life of 6 to 10 years, airplanes 10 to 15 years, railroad cars and locomotives, ships, and barges 20 to 30 years. Structures are assumed by the A.A.S.H.O. and the A.R.E.A. as having a 40-year life. In that time, they are likely to become obsolete even if not completely worn out. Pavement life varies from 4 to 48 years, with an average life of 18.5 years being adopted by the A.A.S.H.O. Railroad track, through continual piecemeal renewal, has an indefinite life. Lives of 50 to 100 years have been used in economic studies. The Bureau of Public Roads has adopted 100 years as the life for grading in highway. This would also be applicable to railroad and canal grading. Longer economic life is often assumed than the accuracy of predictions concerning wear and obsolescence justify. In computing capital-recovery values, each element is computed separately (or a weighted average is obtained through the use of interest tables). More research is needed to make more accurate evaluations of economic life for different classes of property.

The following problem illustrates the method of accounting for differential life spans.

Class of Property	Investment per Mile	Economic Life	CRF, 4%	Annual Cost
Right of way	$ 3,000	80 yr	0.04181	$ 125
Grading	11,000	60 yr	0.04420	486
Track	72,000	80 yr	0.04181	3,010
Structures	20,000	40 yr	0.05052	1,010
Signals	8,000	30 yr	0.05783	463
Total	$94,000			$5,094

Capital versus Operating Costs. A definite relation exists between construction and operating costs. Construction costs generally occur only once, but their effects continue thereafter in interest and retirement charges, whereas operating expenses continue to accrue for the life of the route, even after construction costs have been amortized. A greater sum spent for construction or equipment can often reduce operating costs. However, undue refinement in the plant produces burdensome capital charges. Just how much additional or incremental construction cost should thus be incurred and the improvement in revenues and operating costs arising therefrom is a relation the engineer must determine, whether by rate of return or some other method. He must view each alternative in the light of the credit-income situation.

Operating Costs. Operating costs may be obtained from records of current and past experience or from generally accepted averages (as in Chapter 12), from national cost statistics published by regulatory agencies, or from the actual costs of a carrier similarly situated.

In assuming costs for a "fixed"-cost carrier, a principle of Chapter 12 should be recalled—only the variable percentage of total costs is used for costs due to incremental increases or decreases in traffic.

Units for measuring operating costs are the ton-mile (gross or revenue) or the 1000-ton-mile and the vehicle mile (or train mile, truck mile, plane mile, ship mile, etc.). Ton-mile costs are usually used in railroad, conveyor, pipeline, and other commercial transportation studies, but vehicle miles are often used in highway comparisons.

METHODS OF FINANCING

Importance. The ability to raise investment capital is a basic requirement for any project. The method of financing may have considerable bearing on the design of plant and equipment, location of routes, and rate of progress of the work. Land grants by Federal and state governments and gifts from local communities influenced the location of many miles of railroad. The lack of large amounts of capital may require a deferred or stage construction program. The use of Federal funds for highway construction and improvement is limited to routes of Federal choosing. In any case, a project should not be undertaken if funds are not available for its completion or if it is not going to be sound enough to attract investment capital.

Two primary types of financing are found in transportation enterprises: private financing and financing with public funds and credit. In any study of financing, the engineer must distinguish in his own mind between what is being done, what can be done, and what should be done.

Savings and Reinvested Income. The most conservative method of financing is to utilize savings. Whether the project is private or public, accumulated surpluses and reserves can be invested in the company's or government's own activities. If the return to be earned in the company's own business isn't attractive enough for reinvested savings or earnings, then there is something wrong with the business, and the wisdom of its continuance is in doubt. Furthermore, outsiders could hardly be expected to hazard their capital in such a venture. However, savings and other accumulations are seldom adequate for large projects, so additional resources must be had by other means.

Stocks and Bonds. Capital investment in the form of stocks and bonds has been a traditional method of financing for railroads, pipelines, and other commercial operations. No return need be paid on stock unless it is earned (and not always then) so that stock sale represents the lesser obligation for the carrier. Nevertheless, stock sale disperses ownership and will not bring the desired capital unless the project has a good credit position.

Bonds are a fixed obligation of the company. The effort to pay fixed charges and avoid bankruptcy often leads to deferred maintenance and accelerated deterioration of the plant and equipment. Service also suffers. There is no income or new capital to replace obsolete or worn out plant or to take advantage of new developments. The burden of paying fixed charges is excessively great for an enterprise attempting to become established.

If a transportation company goes into receivership, the trustees usually concentrate first of all on saving the bond holder's investment by making up deferred maintenance and restoring the physical integrity of the property that has been pledged as security for the bonds. Maintenance engineers may find this a more satisfying situation with ample funds to carry on their work than that of a solvent, economy-minded carrier!

Government Financing. Several transportation services are built and financed by the Federal Government. In other instances aid in various forms has been given. The basis of most government financing is the general credit and taxing power of the government, whether it be Federal, state, or local. Traditionally, the Federal Government has provided waterways—constructed, lighted, policed, and maintained harbors, canals, locks, rivers, and dams—without cost to the user. Airways and navigational aids are also provided by the Federal Government on the same basis. Construction and maintenance costs are financed through the general tax fund by Congressional appropriation.

Other government aid has included land grants to early railroads as an encouragement to build into undeveloped territory, direct subsidy payments to airlines (during their development stages, sometimes rather prolonged) and to the merchant marine, and loans and guarantees for loans, especially to the railroad industry in more recent times. Airports have been built for airlines, but for these, landing fees and hangar etc. rentals are charged.

Except on Federal lands and reservations today and two noteworthy attempts in its early history, the Federal Government has not taken direct part in road building and maintenance. Since 1916, however, an increasingly large share of the construction and maintenance expense of the state roads has been met by Federal contributions. As noted in an earlier chapter, the current program of Federal interstate highway construction, although built under state supervision, is financed by Federal funds obtained by Federal taxes collected on the sales of fuel, oil, and tires. The program is one of user charges on a pay-as-you-go basis.

In addition to Federal grants for national roads, states obtain highway funds from property taxes and general appropriations, but principally from state fuel taxes, motor-vehicle-registration fees, license fees, and from the revenues of toll roads, bridges, and tunnels. Towns and cities receive state aid in maintaining those streets that form part of a state or Federal route but may also impose local fuel and registration taxes, draw on the general fund, make special assessments, and utilize returns from parking meters and traffic fines.

Government Bonds. The tax returns for any one period are seldom sufficient to permit the heavy construction that may be desired in that period (although some states have tried to operate their highway program on a pay-as-you-go basis). Money must be borrowed, usually in the form of state, county, or municipal bonds. Bonds are also issued by authorities or agencies that are created by and are instruments of the state. These bonds have as security both the general credit of the state and the taxes and other fees collected from highway users. The rates of interest are usually lower than commercial bonds, and their life may be as much as 75 years, but usually 30 to 40 years. Some issues fall due in a complete block at maturity. Others are designed for retirement in smaller blocks and over the life of the issue. Difficulties arise and programs are delayed when the bond issues required may exceed the statutory debt limit of the state or encounter other legal difficulties. Some states have made use, then, of the bond-issuing powers and credit of the counties by having the counties issue bonds and build roads as county roads. These may later be absorbed into the state system.

Several kinds of bonds may be utilized, the choice depending on the interest rates that must be paid, the sources and extent of amortization funds, and the condition of the market.

Bonds with general-tax support. The credit of the state is behind these bonds but no specific taxes or revenue are earmarked for their retirement.

Bonds with vehicle-tax support. All or a certain percentage of taxes from license fees, fuel taxes, and tire taxes, from the state as a whole or from a specific section or portion of highway being financed, are set aside to support these bonds.

Revenue bonds. Revenue bonds have gained much favor as a means of financing toll roads, bridges, and tunnels. The tolls received for use of the facility are pledged to the payment of the principal and interest until the bonds are retired. After that the facility may be thrown open to the public at no charge or at reduced rates sufficient only to cover annual maintenance charges. Such a charge should also include contribution to a sinking fund so that the highway can be rebuilt when worn out. Toll roads provide an ideal example of user-benefit payments.

Toll roads of superhighway type are generally feasible only in congested, highly populated areas, where sufficient traffic will be found to provide adequate revenues. If a new highway cannot attract enough toll-paying traffic to pay its way, the question might well be raised as to whether the road should be built at all, or at least as to whether a lower standard of design and construction should not be used.

It should be noted that revenue bonds are applicable to other forms of government financing of transportation such as airways and waterways. The one new requisite would be for the imposition of a user charge or toll over those routes.

Alternative Programs. A necessary phase of the financing problem, whether for private or government enterprises, is deciding whether to proceed on a pay-as-you-go basis or by borrowing money, that is, issuing bonds. The pay-as-you-go plan is based on deferring portions of the program for new construction or rehabilitation and doing each year only that amount of work for which funds are available from income or taxes. This means that the full advantages of a completed program must also be deferred for many years.

The alternative, borrowing money by issuing bonds, makes enough cash available and credit available in the present to complete the entire project. The advantages and possible savings are realized at once. The disadvantages lie in the heavy interest burden that the project must bear, especially in the initial years when, as a developing enterprise, it may be least able to do so.

There are offsetting features to the interest charges of borrowing. If, for example, a railroad, highway, or canal is to be rebuilt on a pay-as-you-go basis, then the old and unimproved portions must continue to be maintained and operated to bear the present and future traffic until those portions have also been improved. The fact that the route is being rebuilt indicates it to be inadequate, worn out, or obsolete.

In any case, its upkeep probably involves excessive maintenance charges and equally excessive transportation costs through traffic delays, accidents, and administration. These excess costs must be balanced against the interest charges on bonds and mortgages to determine which will furnish the capital at the lowest over-all economic cost. This is simply to repeat that the status quo is always an alternative which must be considered. The possibility of increased revenues arising from the improvements should also be included as an offsetting factor to the interest charges.

The decision will be influenced by the proposed duration of the bonds versus the duration of the pay-as-you-go plan. Average excess operating costs will be greater over a 20-year pay-as-you-go plan than over a 10-year plan. Total interest charges on 20-year bonds will be less than on 40-year bonds. Obviously, comparisons must be made both ways and in the light of anticipated annual funds from income or taxes.

An important problem in this analysis is the engineering-economic determination of what the excess construction and operating expenses will be with the pay-as-you-go plans of different durations. Piecemeal construction will usually be more expensive than would building a completed project at one time. Nice engineering judgment supported by as much historical cost data as possible must be the answer. Sometimes a combination of two plans may be desirable.

Another pay-as-you-go problem confronting the engineer is that of fitting the operation of the new portion of the route and operation to that of the old. A ship-to-shore telephone installation will not be fully efficient and reliance for communication cannot be placed on it until all ships and dispatchers of the line are so equipped. A section of high-capacity, high-speed expressway pouring its traffic into narrow congested obsolete streets or roadways may create impossible traffic situations. Instrument-landing installations at airports will not bring about the desired improvement in safety and capacity until all aircraft are equipped with corresponding devices. Cab signals on a railroad cannot replace wayside signals until all locomotives and signal locations on a territory are completely equipped. This is not to imply, however, that stage construction (next section) is impossible or undesirable. The difference lies in the deliberate designing and planning to build completely, for stage construction, only that which is needed immediately, or a completed section of the whole. Pay-as-you-go involves the hazards of being forced to halt a project at an inconvenient spot and condition if funds for the year prove insufficient or the estimates of revenues or taxes have been overly optimistic. Pay-as-you-go, combined with careful stage-construction planning, has much to recommend it.

Stage Construction. Stage construction is similar in many respects to a pay-as-you-go plan. The method is applicable both to new construction and to rehabilitation. The initial program calls for doing only what is presently needed and to the minimum standards for the present needs. Improvements and additions will be made as required—when the increased traffic that demands the improvements will cover the costs, or the bonds for the initial work have been retired. A two-lane highway may be adequate at the moment. Five years hence a third lane will be added, and 10 years from now the fourth lane. Similarly additional main tracks for a railroad may be added. Railroads and highways are sometimes laid out with sharp curves and heavy grades for initial construction economy. Grades and curvatures are reduced at a later date. It is possible to fall into serious error at this point. A railroad laid out with many heavy grades may have to be entirely relocated in the future to achieve operating economy. If, however, good construction and location principles are followed, the grade will be held as low as possible to some one spot and then the elevation will be overcome, all at one time. The initial construction may call for a heavy ruling grade at this location. Later the grade can be reduced by relocation of the ruling grade only or by drilling a tunnel. At a third and much later stage, a much longer and lower tunnel will be drilled to lower the ruling grade still more. In these several operations, the rest of the line will not need to be touched, having already been given proper location.

Railroads are frequently built initially with lightweight rail. As traffic increases, the light rail is replaced with rail of a heavier section in the normal maintenance cycle. The revenue and income to provide the heavier rail are thus earned by the increasing traffic that has brought about a need for heavier rail. One is the logical economic outgrowth of the other.

It should be recognized that some types of new construction do not lend themselves to pay-as-you-go construction and hardly to stage construction. An aerial tramway must be built complete from end to end. Similarly a pipeline must be complete before any oil can be pumped. True, additional lines of pipe can be laid later and the first pumping equipment can be replaced with heavier, more powerful pumps and prime movers. Nevertheless, the initial plant must be a fully equipped operating unit at the outset over the mileage being served. This is in contrast to a railroad or highway that can be built between two communities, later to advance to and add the traffic of a third, still later a fourth, and so on. If a cableway or conveyor is to be extended (and of course it can be), a definite length must be established so that a cable or belt of proper length can be secured and a prime mover of suitable capacity provided. A railroad can, if necessary, be extended rail length by rail length, a highway panel by panel, but a cable or belt cannot be so readily spliced for extension.

The over-all economic advantages of stage construction is determined by comparing its costs with those of immediate construction to ultimate standards and requirements, a method very similar to the tests described for pay-as-you-go plans. Another factor to consider is the possible changes in traffic patterns and technology that may come later on and that should not be held back by a large investment in fixed plant from an earlier day. These are decisions that can hardly be made without close study.

ALLOCATION OF COST

Principle of User Payment. Common carriers, contract carriers, and toll roads, bridges, and canals collect user payments for their service and from those payments meet the costs of operation and financing. Where toll roads, bridges, tunnels, and canals are built by public agencies, there is sometimes a question as to whether the tolls are adequate for full-cost recovery, but the question is largely one of degree, not of principle.

The engineer is more likely to become involved in cost allocations and recovery in connection with publicly owned highways, waterways, and airports. If there is no charge for use of the facility, as is the case with United States inland rivers and canals, the general taxpayer must bear the cost. Costs cannot be avoided. Although support of waterways by the general taxpayer has long been traditional, many engineers and economists do not accept that as a sound method of allocation. The St. Lawrence Seaway and the Panama Canal exact tolls (fees for the former are claimed by some to be inadequate), establishing a pattern for other waterways. Justification for free waterways lies in the concepts of public benefits conferred—the public good—and national defense. These factors are also present for railroads, highways, and airports—and have been urged as a basis for public support of the last two.

As earlier pointed out, conservative opinion holds, however, that only user benefits should be considered in making economic justifications and that costs, therefore, should be allocated only among the users. Such user-cost allocations are in keeping with a national system of competitive transport and offer a rough test of demand for the service. On this basis, user costs are collected from highway users in the form of fuel, vehicle, and accessories taxes, and from airlines and private air operators in the form of landing fees and rental for hangar, ticket sales, office, and other space occupied. Whether or not all costs are thus recovered or whether some remainder must be borne by the general taxpayer is a matter of debate. The majority opinion seems to hold that most but not all of the costs are user borne. The problem here is again largely one of degree.

Differential Users. A more serious problem, involving engineering solutions, arises in allocating costs among the several classes of users of a facility. In an earlier chapter, it was pointed out that charges exacted by common and contract carriers are based primarily on costs of service. Those costs were known to vary for different classes of services, operations, and vehicles. Similarly, costs and the tolls or taxes in payment of costs for highways, waterways, and airports should be based on costs incurred in providing the various types of service for which there is a demand. Service, in these instances, usually refers to the load and size capacities of the facilities required by the users.

The engineering solution to the problem is not in any case easy, especially in the case of highways. A series of full-scale tests conducted by the Highway Research Board for the Bureau of Public Roads and interested state groups have been conducted or are under way in Maryland, Idaho, and Illinois to determine the effects on various types of test pavements of different axle combinations and loads.[3] The Maryland tests and those conducted by the Western Association of State Highway Officials came to the same general conclusions.[4] Failure to the pavement was, in general, the result of pavement cracking as a result of first being undermined by pumping

[3] *Road Test One—Md.,* Highway Research Board, Special Report 4, 1952.
[4] *The WASHO Road Test, Part 2,* Highway Research Board, Special Report 22, 1955.

and compression of the subgrade under repetitive load applications. A further general conclusion was that even the permitted minimum single-axle load of 18,000 lb will cause damage and that a pavement designed for 18,000 lb will suffer even greater damage under heavier loads than those for which it was designed. Tandem loads should not exceed single-axle loads by more than one and one half times to avoid excess damage.

It would seem then that some method should be devised, not only to exact payments, but to allocate the costs equitably so that those vehicles causing the most user wear and tear, or for which maximum design is required, should bear a greater share of costs proportionately than the lighter vehicles, which do little damage or would be sustained on lighter construction.

While the determination of needs and costs of each class of vehicle, therefore, is primarily an engineering problem, it is made complicated by political factors and the belief in some quarters that providing a road for private passenger vehicles is a government function, which should be supported, at least in part, by more than proportionate charges to commercial vehicles. In any case, the engineer's problem is still to determine the true costs of each kind of road, letting adjustment factors if any be imposed upon those costs.

Methods of Collection. Unfortunately there is still no real agreement as to what actual costs for each type of traffic are. Attempts have been made to establish rough criteria in different methods used or proposed for collecting highway taxes. (Note that railroads face a somewhat similar problem in distinguishing between costs of freight and passenger traffic.)

Incremental or differential cost theory. This method assumes joint use of highways by passenger vehicles, buses, and trucks with basic costs being based on passenger-vehicle requirements. The additional costs required to adapt the highway design to light trucks and buses would be allocated on an equal basis to these vehicles, and the further costs necessary to make the highway suitable to heavy classes of vehicles would in turn be allocated to the class of vehicle requiring the improvement. The additional costs incurred for heavier vehicles appear in the form of thicker and/or reinforced pavements, stronger subgrades, additional uphill lanes on grades, etc.

Ton-mile theory. A few states have assessed taxes on the theory that wear and tear on pavements is a joint result of the weight and the distance carried over the pavement. Problems have arisen through opposition from trucking operators, difficulties in obtaining accurate ton-mile records, and inequalities that arise from not taking low mileage into consideration in the large vehicular registration fees that are often combined with the ton-mile method.

Unit cost. It is assumed that vehicular operating costs increase with the weight but, as seen in Chapter 12, decrease on a per-ton basis as the load increases. This provides a lower tax than the ton-mile method. A practical objection is again the difficulty of securing adequate cost records.

Differential benefits. Under this theory, it is proposed to set a tax on the savings brought to different classes of operators by reductions in time, distance, gradient, curvature, etc. These again may be difficult to determine accurately. There has been little experience with this method.

Federal Allocations. The Federal system of interstate highways is being financed on a pay-as-you-go basis (more or less) by taxes imposed on fuel and accessories. A general tax of 1 cent per gallon on gasoline fuel (increased to 2 cents in October 1959) serves as a use tax on all gasoline-fueled vehicles including private passenger cars. A 2-cent tax on diesel fuel recognizes the higher pavement requirements for the heavier, diesel-fueled trucks and buses. Tires are taxed at 8 cents a pound—heavier vehicles require heavier, larger tires and again pay more tax; inner tubes 9 cents a pound, and tread rubber 3 cents a pound. There is also a tax of $1.50 per year on each 1000 lb of taxable gross weight (unloaded weight of tractor and trailer plus weight of maximum load customarily carried) for any vehicle of more than 26,000 lb.[5]

Whether or not these tax rates suffice to cover the portion of interstate highway design required by heavy trucking is hotly debated in some quarters, but at least the principle of differential user cost has been applied, regardless of its accuracy in application.

Even where user costs are more or less properly allocated to classes of vehicles by foregoing methods, some of the vehicles, both truck and passenger, may never, or at least infrequently, travel over the highway for which they are taxed. Little can be done in a practical way about this, short of establishing toll gates at frequent intervals and collecting directly from the users. The "injustice" in the present situation may average out in a crude way. The taxes collected today

[5] Title II—Highway Revenue Act of 1956, Public Law 627, 84th Congress, H.R. 10660, pp. 14–17.

from A may go to help B; tomorrow B's taxes will be used to improve the roads used by A.

Application to Other Routes. These concepts of allocation can be modified to use by other carriers as well. The axle load effects of different truck weights find a direct parallel in the loads and impact effects of various weights, wheel arrangements, and types of aircraft on airport runways. Space occupied and special services rendered can of course be charged at conventional rates. User charges for Federal airways could be allocated on a seat-weight-mileage basis or on differential operating costs. The same methods can be applied to waterways with fuel taxes and locking tolls being assessed. Canals and rivers might also base charges on the tonnage of the craft using the waterways with a mileage factor included. Panama and Suez canal tolls are on a tonnage basis, using volumetric equivalents.

In any case, the engineer has a primary responsibility to determine the differential costs of providing service for various types of automobiles, trucks, buses, aircraft, ships, tows, etc. There is much research and analysis required to achieve data that will be generally acceptable.

Urban Transit. A somewhat different approach may be required as a practical matter for a service that is deemed necessary but does not, from its inherent nature, always prove self-sustaining. The outstanding example is that of rapid-transit-commuting service whether rendered by bus, subway, elevated, or railroad. A commuting carrier hauls peak loads from the suburbs to the central business district between 7 and 9 in the morning and home again in the evening between 4 and 6. Peak load capacity for track and vehicles must be maintained but is used only 20 to 24 hours a week with decreasing use during off-peak hours. If commuting fares are adjusted to cover costs, patronage declines and the carrier continues to operate at a loss. This problem has many facets, not the least of which is the psychological reluctance of many people to use public transit at all, but especially during the off-peak hours.

While some systems are claiming to make expenses or even show a profit by rigid adherence to economy and service, a majority of such operations have financial difficulties. The New York and Chicago transit systems are city owned and, despite high fares, incur deficits to be met by the taxpayer. Tax relief has been granted the Long Island Railroad. The City of Boston and the State of Massachusetts have granted subsidies to the Old Colony Railroad. The problem, still unsolved, is further aggravated by the building of expressways with government credit thereby draining away some but not all of the public-transit patronage. In the instance of line-haul railroads performing commuting service, the losses suffered on commuting traffic may constitute a burden on and be subsidized by the rates charged intercity traffic.

There may be disagreement as to whether a proper combination of good service, pricing, management, and financing might not enable a rapid-transit system to show a profit or at least earn its costs. Recognizing that such a formula has not been developed for general application and that some form of public support—subsidy, tax relief, or deficit payment—must be met from general taxes, the problem of cost allocation again arises in a slightly different form.

Users of public transport usually come from the suburbs, but subways and bus lines may be owned by the city and never receive a cent of tax support from the riders or their suburban communities. If a lines does extend through several communities, taxes may or may not be collected from the communities in proportion to the use made or benefits conferred.

Solutions to the problem have been several.

To extend the city limits, placing the entire urban or metropolitan area under one municipal and taxing agency. This is cumbersome and has objections from other than transportation standpoints.

To let the county assume responsibility. This is not practicable where county and population areas do not coincide.

To let the state assume responsibility. This possibility is receiving increasing attention but has limitations, especially when several states are involved; for example, Wisconsin-Illinois-Indiana around Chicago, Illinois-Missouri around St. Louis, and New York, Connecticut, and New Jersey around New York City. Further, state control may end in state aid with costs allocated on state residents far removed from the metropolitan area in question.

To establish a transport authority with taxing powers similar to the Port of New York Authority. This would have to have the consent of the several states or communities involved. It offers possibilities.

Form a confederation of communities in which each retains its municipal identity but acts in concert with its neighbors in transport planning, operation, and financing. This plan has been used successfully in the Toronto area.

In any solution, there still remains the problem of cost allocations and determinations. This is a problem requiring additional research and study.

QUESTIONS FOR STUDY

1. Name, state one or more examples of, and give the significance of each step in the planning process.

2. What is the purpose of reconnaissance and how is the locality reconnoitered related to the final route location? What modern aids are available to assist reconnaissance?

3. What is meant in this text by economic justification and in what situations and by what means is it determined?

4. Give examples for each of the guiding principles in determining the economic feasibility of a route.

5. Given: Route A has a possible revenue of 5 cents per net ton-mile, operating expenses of 4 cents per net ton-mile, construction costs of 150,000 dollars per mile, available net tonnage of 1,800,000 annually; alternative Route B has a possible revenue of 5 cents per net ton-mile, operating expenses of 3.6 cents per net ton-mile, construction costs of 180,000 dollars per mile, and available net tonnage of 2,000,000 annually. Both routes are 500 miles long. The local attractive rate of interest is 5 percent. Determine which of these routes is preferable using the rate of return on investment (basic-location formula).

6. Using the data of Question 5, determine which route is preferable using the annual-cost method.

7. Using the data of Question 5, determine which route is preferable using the benefit-cost method.

8. Given: right of way at 4000 dollars per mile, grading at 9000 dollars per mile, pavement at 40,000 dollars per mile, structures at 50,000 dollars per mile, and interest at 4½ percent, determine the average annual cost of the investment.

9. Compare "pay-as-you-go" plans and stage construction as to the meaning of each, basis of justification, and engineering problems involved with each.

10. What are the operational characteristics of mass transit systems that may require a different approach to economic justification and financing? What solutions are offered and how would you evaluate each?

SUGGESTED READINGS

1. A. M. Wellington, *The Economic Theory of the Location of Railways,* Sixth Edition, John Wiley and Sons, New York, 1914, Preface and Chapter 1.

2. Clarence E. Bullinger, *Engineering Economic Analysis,* Second Edition, McGraw-Hill Book Company, New York, 1950, especially "Part I—The Economic Analysis."

3. Sigvald Johannesson, *Highway Economics,* First Edition, McGraw-Hill Book Company, New York, 1931.

4. E. L. Grant and W. G. Ireson, *Principles of Engineering Economy,* Fourth Edition, Ronald Press, New York, 1960.

5. "Highway Benefits and the Cost Allocation Problem," by Richard M. Zettel, Research Economist, Institute of Transportation and Traffic Engineering, University of California, Berkeley, a paper presented to the Forty-Third Annual Meeting of the American Association of State Highway Officials.

6. L. I. Hewes and C. H. Oglesby, *Highway Engineering,* John Wiley and Sons, New York, 1954, Chapter 4, "Highway Economy" and Chapter 5, "Highway Finance."

7. "Money for Roads: How Would You Finance Our Needed Highways?," a symposium, *Engineering New-Record,* December 27, 1955, pp. 30–56.

8. "Is Subsidy Necessary for Adequate Mass Transit?," address by Charles E. De Leuw, President, De Leuw, Cather & Company, Chicago, before the 1955 Convention of the American Society of Civil Engineers.

CHAPTER 14

PLANNING—CONTINUED

TRAFFIC PATTERNS

Need for and Substance of Traffic Data. Securing an adequate traffic pattern, including kind, volume, density, origin, and destination of traffic, is a necessary element in transportation planning. The need and the traffic pattern may be simple, definite, and clearly indicated. An oil field is opened with an estimated daily or annual production that is to be refined at the nearby refinery owned by the producer. A pipeline of the size to handle that volume is projected from the field to the refinery by the most direct route. This procedure involves few planning problems. When, however, the production is tied in to future as well as present demand, when the alternative between pipeline, rail, barge, or a combination of these is involved, and when the location of a new refinery with respect to producing and consuming areas enters the picture, the problem can become quite complicated. Complex situations as in the foregoing, when projecting a new railroad or highway, or attacking problems of urban transit, require much ingenious and detailed effort to secure the variety and extent of necessary data. Many data-securing procedures are available, the use of which will vary with local conditions and the complexity of a particular problem.

In planning for and obtaining traffic data, the following questions should guide the planner in his efforts.

1. What traffic is involved? Is it persons, freight, or both? Is it perishable, bulk, liquid, granular, package, fragile, dangerous, or does it include all types?

2. In what volumes is it moving? If several types are included, the volumes of each will be required. What will the future volume or demand be?

3. Where does the traffic originate? What are the sources and generators of the traffic? Does it come from residential areas? From the central business district? From other carriers? From a mining, farming, or oil-producing area?

4. Where is the traffic going? What are the nominal and final destinations?

5. By what routes and systems is it moving? By rail, highway, airline, private car or truck, common or contract carrier? Is it following a direct, circuitous, trunk-line, alternate, or bypass route?

6. What is its present speed of movement? At what speed should it move?

Answers to these questions will require such data as population and industrial trends, riding habits, vehicular registration, fuel consumption, and actual volumes of traffic now being generated and carried so as to project transport needs into the future. The peak demands and densities of present and future traffic are also determined. The routes over which traffic now moves are inventoried to give lock sizes and capacities, number of tracks and traffic capacities, widths and capacities of existing streets and highways, landing and take-off capacities of airports, and grades, distances, and curvatures where these apply—all depending on the mode of transport presently or to be involved. Delays, congestion, and accident rates of existing facilities should also be obtained.

Published Data. Published data, to the extent it is available, should be used to shorten the time and cost of securing a traffic pattern.

Interstate Commerce Reports. The I.C.C. compiles and publishes certain freight and passenger statistics for all interstate common and contract carriers except airlines. Principally these statistics give totals of traffic by commodities or passenger originated, interchanged, and terminated. Such data are of little help in developing a traffic pattern. The exclusion of much private and exempt carriage leaves a big gap in most figures. Their compilations of water-borne traffic are of help only in obtaining revenue tons moving on the major navigational areas—the Atlantic and Gulf Coasts, the Great Lakes, the Mississippi River and its tributaries, the Pacific Coast, and the intercoastal area. These are published in *Selected Financial and Operating Statistics from Annual Reports of Carriers by Inland and Coastal Waterways and Maritime Carriers,* I.C.C. Bureau of Statistics.

The *One-Percent Samples of Waybills,* which the I.C.C.'s Bureau of Statistics compiles and issues, are of some value in obtaining volumes of rail traffic between states or areas by commodities.[1] In order to obtain a representative sample, all rail carriers are required to file with the I.C.C. copies of waybills having serial numbers of 1 or ending with the digits 01. A continuous study is made of traffic flow of the I.C.C.'s 216 commodity classifications. A series of regular releases, as well as special statements, have been developed. Among other data, the releases show:

1. Quarterly comparisons of traffic and revenue by commodity classes
2. Quarterly and seasonal comparisons of carloads, tons per car, length of haul, and revenue per hundredweight by commodity classes
3. Distribution of freight traffic and revenue averages by commodity classes
4. Tons of freight originated and tons terminated by states and by commodity classes
5. State-to-state distribution of carloads for each commodity class by type of car

The Bureau has made a few similar studies for motor freight carriers. Eventually, it is hoped, such data will be made available for other modes of transport as well.

Federal Aviation Administration. The F.A.A. compiles general statistics for all United States civil aviation, including statistical totals of passengers and cargo carried and miles flown of each. No breakdown is made of commodities or routes, so the information is of no use in preparing traffic patterns. One-percent samples could be taken of both ticket sales and freight waybills, but the writer knows of none publicly available at the time this is being written. Such data may eventually be compiled.

U. S. Army Corps of Engineers. The Corps of Engineers of the U. S. Army compiles and issues a series of transportation reports giving considerable data on water carriers and routes, but tonnage data is generally limited.

Series 1—Transportation on the Great Lakes, 1937 revision, gives history, development, and details of channels, routes, ports, and port

[1] *Waybill Statistics—Their History and Uses,* I.C.C. Bureau of Transport Economics and Statistics, Statement No. 543, File No. 40-A-3, February 1954, pp. 15–44, 45–50.

facilities for the Great Lakes. The movement of principal commodities from port to port is shown in great detail both in tabular form and graphically in flow diagrams. The coverage is excellent but is, unfortunately, out of date for most purposes.

Series 2—Transportation in the Mississippi and Ohio Valleys, 1929 revision. This report gives the same detail for the territory named as the Series 1 report. Again the data is out of date for most purposes.

Series 3—Transportation Lines on the Great Lakes System. This series is issued annually and comprises three tables:

Table I lists lines, owners, addresses, and services—whether common, contract, or exempt.

Table II describes the vessels of each transportation line, giving net register tonnage, register and over-all lengths, register and over-all breadth, draft (loaded and light), horsepower, carrying capacity in short tons (and number of passengers if any), height of superstructure, cargo-handling facilities, local operating base, and year built or rebuilt.

Table III gives description of operation, waterways upon which operated, locations between which service is conducted, type of service, schedules, navigation season, and principal commodities carried; also connections with railroads that share in joint rates. Single-port servicing facilities such as towing, lightering, lifting, marine construction and repairs, coal and oil bunkering, supplying water, etc. are not included. This data is contained in the Port Series reports.

Series 4—Transportation Lines on the Mississippi River System and the Gulf Intracoastal Waterways gives the same annual information for 877 (in 1955) lines in the territory named as does Series 3.

Series 5—Transportation Lines on the Atlantic, Gulf, and Pacific Coasts give similar information for 1636 (1955) lines as does Series 3 for the territory involved.

Data on ports is available in the Corps of Engineers Port Series. Series 3 and 4 describes ports on the Atlantic, Pacific, and Gulf coasts and at the Panama Canal. A great variety of information is contained in these reports, including description of harbor and port facilities, channel depths, tides, weather, fire protection, administration, charges for towing, pilotage, running lines, dockage, handling, loading and unloading, wharfage, storage, grain elevators, labor agreements and rates in effect, rail, motor, and airline connections and facilities, and, of much importance to the traffic pattern, tonnage of imports and exports by principal commodities. Lake Series Nos. 1 to 9 do the same thing for ports on the Great Lakes.

The Engineers also keep locking records of vessels and traffic moving through locks on the rivers and lakes. Of these, the Soo Locks' figures are the most revealing but give only a limited indication of traffic over the several lake routes. These data are not generally available to the public.

State highway departments. The Federal Highway Act of 1936 authorized the states to speed 1½ percent of the annual Federal contributions to highways to make planning surveys and other studies. These surveys, now well under way, provide a wealth of data, including mileages by road types and conditions, grades, curvatures, visibility, structures, adjacent land use, and adjoining buildings. Bus, truck, and school-bus routes and traffic volumes over routes are shown. Motor-vehicle registration for the state and its subdivisions are given. Traffic counts and origin and destination studies for special areas have been made. State road maps are kept up to date thereby. Details of what is available in a particular state can be obtained from the state's highway department.

Two important reports based on these studies have been issued: (a) *Toll Roads and Free Roads* (*1939*) and (b) *Interregional Highways* (*1944*). These are obtainable through the Bureau of Public Roads. Highway deficiencies and needs were explored in these reports and improvements recommended. The recommendations included relief from traffic congestion on principal approaches to areas of large population and improvement of the standards of design, construction, and maintenance for rural highways, both main roads and farm-to-market roads. The recently approved program for improvement and construction of a system of inter-regional Federal roads is the outcome of the 1944 study and recommendations.

Bureau of Public Roads. The B.P.R. issues an annual report, *Highway Statistics*. Among the data presented are:

1. Motor-fuel consumption by user type and the tax and revenue therefrom

2. Motor-vehicle registration by types; trucks by weights and capacities; rates and registration revenues

3. Vehicle and traffic characteristics; operation of trucks and combinations, vehicle miles of travel on rural roads; motor vehicle travel in the United States each year; speed trends on main and rural highways by vehicle types

4. Taxes
5. Highway finance
6. Mileage of public roads and streets by states and types of roads
7. Federal-aid systems
8. Road-life studies to determine the economic life of existing and proposed roads

Other governmental agencies. The foregoing and other governmental agencies issue reports and special studies from time to time. Such a study was the series of reports prepared by Federal Coordinator of Transportation Joseph B. Eastman during the 1933–1934 depression years. A more recent study of traffic patterns is found in *Transportation of Oil,* issued in 1951 by the Petroleum Administration for Defense, Supply and Transportation Division, Department of the Interior. It provides data on the use of petroleum tank trucks, railway tank cars, pipelines, barges, ocean tankers, and storage. Traffic-flow statistics and diagrams are presented and origin and destination data. Capacity requirements of the several modes of transport for various routes and areas are also given.

Trade associations and companies. Trade associations—Association of American Railroads, American Trucking Association, National Association of Motor Bus Operators, Air Transport Association, and others, publish statistical summaries, of which some can be of aid in establishing traffic patterns. The National Tank Truck Carriers, for example, have made shipping-record studies similar to the I.C.C.'s one-percent waybill studies.[2]

Individual companies have also made studies. The Erie Railroad has followed the I.C.C.'s lead in making waybill-sample analyses of its own traffic.[3] Most railroads, in one form or another, compile and make limited issue of a freight car received and forwarded or passing report. The daily passing report is prepared by many large railroad yards and junction points, giving a complete report on all cars received and forwarded by that yard during the past 24-hour period. Information contained in a typical passing report is obtained from the car waybill and shows car initial and number, waybill date and number, origin, destination, route, shipper, consignee,

---

[2] "Discussion of the Use of Traffic Flow Data-Carriers," C. Austin Sutherland, Managing Director, National Tank Truck Carriers, in *Traffic and Transportation Flow Analysis,* compiled and edited by Beatrice Aitchison and G. Lloyd Wilson, 1953, pp. 26–29.

[3] *Ibid.,* "Utilization of Transportation Flow Data by Carriers," E. S. Root, Chief of Research, Erie Railroad, pp. 21–25.

commodity, departure time, train symbol or schedule, and engine number. The passing report is used as a record of activity at each yard and interchange point and enables cars to be traced and located. Copies are sent once or twice daily to principal freight-association offices and agents, both on- and off-line offices. Passing reports are not generally available and are not of use to the public, but individual railroads can make good use of these in developing their own traffic patterns.

Dispatchers' records. A useful source of data for the actual movement of transport units is the records of dispatchers. Train dispatchers, truck and bus, airline, and pipeline dispatchers keep logs showing the time of departure, movement, type, tonnage, origin, and destination of the trains, trucks, buses, aircraft, or shipments of liquid. These again are not generally available to the public but are invaluable to the carrier's own studies.

Accident reports. Accident reports maintained by police and highway departments, the I.C.C., the C.A.B., and the U. S. Coast Guard are often of aid in establishing those aspects of traffic flow and density.

Special studies. Special surveys of rider habits and other traffic-pattern data have been made from time to time by research institutes, universities, and consultants. Many cities have on record elaborate traffic surveys prepared by firms of consulting engineers. These may be useful in advancing the same study to later years, revising the transport arrangement, or in planning for additional facilities for the city of the original report or a satellite community. Analogies may also be drawn when similar conditions exist elsewhere.

Field Surveys. Published data are seldom sufficient or fully applicable to a particular situation. Additional information must be secured by actual survey to determine the traffic flow, the volume of traffic over various routes, and the origin and destination of that traffic. The survey may take any or all of several forms, depending on the types of problems and carriers involved.

Waybill sampling. The I.C.C.'s one-percent waybill-sampling procedure can be extended to any particular company or carrier by making a sampling survey of waybills, other shipping papers, or passing reports. The principal problems usually encountered are (a) obtaining access to the shipping papers (by anyone outside the company) and (b) obtaining a representative sample. In regard to the first problem, it may be necessary on occasions to ask the carriers to furnish the desired information. In order to inspire the maximum cooperation, the carrier should be shown that the information requested is entirely pertinent and necessary to a satisfactory solution of the problem at hand. The problems of sampling are thoroughly discussed in the symposium *Traffic and Transportation Flow Analysis,* previously cited as a reference, especially pages 2 to 12. Volumes of traffic, by commodities, over various routes, and points of origin and destination can thus be secured.

Traffic counts. An obvious method of obtaining traffic-flow data is to count the actual number of persons, vehicles, trains, aircraft, or ships arriving at, departing from, or passing a given point. Such counts can be made manually, with hand-operated counters or tally sheets, or by use of automatic counters.

The counting of highway traffic has been most highly developed. One device uses a photo-electric detector "eye" on which a beam of light from the opposite side of the roadway or lane impinges. Cars passing between the two interrupt the light beam received by the detector, the interruption being recorded as a vehicle. Continuous counts with permanent installations can thus be made at points of critical interest on highways and can similarly be used to count traffic moving through locks or other narrow channels or over a railroad track where a simple enumeration is required. Television is already in use to record cars of a train entering or leaving a yard and may have further application in this connection. The device has limited use where several streams of traffic pass at the same time.

Portable highway-traffic counters make use of pneumatic tubes laid across a traffic lane and connected to a recording device. The actual record is that of the number of axles passing over the cable. Correlation factors found by manual check counts relate the number of vehicles with more than two axles to the total vehicle count.

Cordon counts and screen lines. The total volume of traffic entering or leaving an area, city, or region may be obtained by surrounding the area with interviewers and checkers, obtaining through questions and observation the number, kind, purpose, origin, destination, mode of travel, etc. of all traffic entering or leaving the area. Practically, such cordon stations may often be limited to a few key points—junctions, yards, and interchange points for a railroad situation; airports and railroad and bus passenger stations for passengers in and out of a city; principal streets or highways at the edge of the area for vehicular traffic; the entrance or exit of bridges and tunnels bearing vehicular traffic. Every person on foot and every driver of a vehicle (or every fifth or tenth person or vehicle, depending on the size of sample required) may be interviewed. The weighing stations set up by highway patrols to check the weights of commercial vehicles (and the records thereof) may also serve as check points.

Similarly, screen lines or stations may be thrown across any series of routes to count the volume of traffic moving between two points across the line. Thus the flow between two areas in a city or between two adjacent route sections, communities, states, or regions may be obtained. Adjustments may have to be made for traffic originating and terminating *between* two screen-line stations.

In this connection, it is often easier (and more detailed information is obtained) if a large area under study is broken into smaller areas and the traffic flow between each of the smaller or subareas obtained. A city can be divided into grid squares, neighborhoods, or into quadrants or sectors. Counties or states or regional groupings may serve when larger areas are in question.

Questionnaires. While the foregoing cordon and screen-line methods imply a certain amount of questionnaire activity, the use of this device is more fully realized in door-to-door studies or in surveys conducted by mail. Questionnaire sheets or cards are prepared on which can be recorded complete information concerning the travel habits and requirements for each individual in a family, usually for a 1-day period. See Figure 14-1. Each trip made (or to be made) during the 24-hour period is entered on a separate line showing origin, destination, route, purpose, and by whom made, as well as the mode of travel; whether by private automobile, rapid-transit train, bus, taxi, or other means. Interviewers call at every house in a block (or every fifth or tenth house depending again on size of sample desired) and fill out the questionnaire form by personal questioning. The questionnaire forms may also be sent by mail or handed to persons at stations and other check points. The response by mail is seldom as complete or satisfactory as by interview.

Questionnaire answers are either filled in directly on punch cards or transferred to punch cards from the original sheets for sorting and tabulating by machine. A great many sortings and comparisons can thus be made quickly. Hand sorting is slow and can be used only where the replies are few in number. Desired tabulations will indicate the number of trips to and from each area and will classify them by destinations and origins as well as by mode of conveyance.

FORM BHR 150A

ILLINOIS DIVISION OF HIGHWAYS

CHAMPAIGN-URBANA AREA TRAFFIC SURVEY

DWELLING UNIT SUMMARY

INTERVIEW ADDRESS

IDENTIFICATION

STREET ADDRESS

CARD

DISTANCE FROM CBD

SOCIO-ECONOMIC TYPE

SAMPLE NO.

ZONE

DATE OF TRAVEL

A. HOW MANY PASSENGER CARS ARE OWNED BY PERSONS LIVING AT THIS ADDRESS?

B. MAKE AND YEAR OF EACH CAR

M YEAR M YEAR M YEAR

C. HOW MANY PERSONS LIVE HERE?

D. HOW MANY ARE 5 YEARS OF AGE OR OLDER?

M YEAR M YEAR M YEAR

E. HOW LONG HAVE YOU LIVED AT THIS ADDRESS?

F. HOUSEHOLD INFORMATION:

PERSON NO.	RACE SEX	PERSON IDENTIFICATION	AGE	CODE	OCCUPATION AND INDUSTRY	TRIPS YES NO
01						
02						
03						
04						
05						
06						
07						
08						
09						
10						

G. TOTAL NUMBER OF TRIPS REPORTED AT THIS ADDRESS

1. NUMBER OF PERSONS (5 YEARS OF AGE OR OLDER) MAKING TRIPS

2. NUMBER OF PERSONS (5 YEARS OF AGE OR OLDER) MAKING NO TRIPS

3. NUMBER OF PERSONS (5 YEARS OF AGE OR OLDER) WITH TRIPS UNKNOWN

H. COMMENTS AND REASON IF COMPLETE INFORMATION WAS NOT OBTAINABLE

I. FACTOR

ADMINISTRATIVE RECORD

INTERVIEWER

CALLS

DATE   TIME

(1)

(2)

(3)

(4)

REPORT SUBMITTED INCOMPLETE

DATE

REASON

SUPERVISOR'S COMMENT

REMARKS:

REPORT COMPLETED _____ (DATE)

INTERVIEWS CHECKED _____ (INITIAL)

CODED BY _____ (INITIAL)

CODING CHECKED BY _____ (INITIAL)

INTERNAL TRIP REPORT

SHEET ......OF.....

CARD [2] DISTANCE FROM CBD [ ][ ][ ] SOCIO-ECONOMIC TYPE [ ] SAMPLE NO. [ ][ ][ ][ ] ZONE NO. [ ][ ][ ] DAY OF TRAVEL [ ]

1	2	3	3 a	3 b	4	5	6	7	8	9	10	11
OCCUPATION AND INDUSTRY	PERSON NO.	TRIP No.	SEX RACE	AGE	WHERE DID THIS TRIP BEGIN?	WHERE DID THIS TRIP END?	TIME OF TRIP WITHIN SURVEY AREA	PURPOSE OF TRIP FROM | TO	No. IN CAR	SCREEN LINE	MODE OF TRAVEL	KIND OF PARKING
			1 2 3 4 5 6				A.M. P.M.	1 WORK .... 1 2 BUSINESS ...... 2 3 MED.-DEN ..... 3 4 SCHOOL .... 4 5 SOCIAL-REC. ... 5 6 CH. TRAVEL MODE 6 7 EAT MEAL ...... 7 8 SHOPPING ...... 8 0 HOME 0			1 AUTO DRIVER 2 AUTO PASS. 3 STREETCAR-BUS 4 TAXI PASS. 5 TRUCK PASS.	1 STREET FREE 2 STREET METER 3 LOT FREE 4 LOT PAID 5 GARAGE FREE 6 GARAGE PAID 7 SERVICE OR REP. 8 RES. PROPERTY 9 CRUISED 0 NOT PARKED
			1 2 3 4 5 6				A.M. P.M.	1 WORK .... 1 2 BUSINESS ...... 2 3 MED.-DEN ..... 3 4 SCHOOL .... 4 5 SOCIAL-REC. ... 5 6 CH. TRAVEL MODE 6 7 EAT MEAL ...... 7 8 SHOPPING ...... 8 0 HOME 0			1 AUTO DRIVER 2 AUTO PASS. 3 STREETCAR-BUS 4 TAXI PASS. 5 TRUCK PASS.	1 STREET FREE 2 STREET METER 3 LOT FREE 4 LOT PAID 5 GARAGE FREE 6 GARAGE PAID 7 SERVICE OR REP. 8 RES. PROPERTY 9 CRUISED 0 NOT PARKED
			1 2 3 4 5 6				A.M. P.M.	1 WORK .... 1 2 BUSINESS ...... 2 3 MED.-DEN ..... 3 4 SCHOOL .... 4 5 SOCIAL-REC. ... 5 6 CH. TRAVEL MODE 6 7 EAT MEAL ...... 7 8 SHOPPING ...... 8 0 HOME 0			1 AUTO DRIVER 2 AUTO PASS. 3 STREETCAR-BUS 4 TAXI PASS. 5 TRUCK PASS.	1 STREET FREE 2 STREET METER 3 LOT FREE 4 LOT PAID 5 GARAGE FREE 6 GARAGE PAID 7 SERVICE OR REP. 8 RES. PROPERTY 9 CRUISED 0 NOT PARKED
			1 2 3 4 5 6				A.M. P.M.	1 WORK .... 1 2 BUSINESS ...... 2 3 MED.-DEN ..... 3 4 SCHOOL .... 4 5 SOCIAL-REC. ... 5 6 CH. TRAVEL MODE 6 7 EAT MEAL ...... 7 8 SHOPPING ...... 8 0 HOME 0			1 AUTO DRIVER 2 AUTO PASS. 3 STREETCAR-BUS 4 TAXI PASS. 5 TRUCK PASS.	1 STREET FREE 2 STREET METER 3 LOT FREE 4 LOT PAID 5 GARAGE FREE 6 GARAGE PAID 7 SERVICE OR REP. 8 RES. PROPERTY 9 CRUISED 0 NOT PARKED
			1 2 3 4 5 6				A.M. P.M.	1 WORK .... 1 2 BUSINESS ...... 2 3 MED.-DEN ..... 3 4 SCHOOL .... 4 5 SOCIAL-REC. ... 5 6 CH. TRAVEL MODE 6 7 EAT MEAL ...... 7 8 SHOPPING ...... 8 0 HOME 0			1 AUTO DRIVER 2 AUTO PASS. 3 STREETCAR-BUS 4 TAXI PASS. 5 TRUCK PASS.	1 STREET FREE 2 STREET METER 3 LOT FREE 4 LOT PAID 5 GARAGE FREE 6 GARAGE PAID 7 SERVICE OR REP. 8 RES. PROPERTY 9 CRUISED 0 NOT PARKED

FIGURE 14-1. Questionnaire form for traffic-habits study. (Courtesy of Illinois Division of Highways, Springfield.)

The purposes and the time of day for each grouping will also be helpful.

The foregoing use of questionnaires has been explained in terms of passenger travel. Similar questionnaire studies can be made of the origin, destination, volume, and mode of conveyance for freight sent and received by industries and commercial houses. Chambers of commerce may already be compiling such data or will assist in obtaining industry's cooperation in obtaining the data.

Statistical Estimates. While field counts of vehicle volume and questionnaire and screen-line counts and interviews are usually a necessity in determining existing traffic flow and patterns, engineers are conducting research on the possibilities of a statistical representation of traffic generation from a given type of generator. Tabulations have been prepared showing the average residential-area trip generation in cities of varying sizes based on automobiles per dwelling unit, persons per dwelling unit, trips per dwelling unit, trips per capita, and automobile trips per capita. Other tabulations show the percentage of trips made by various modes of travel—automobile, taxi, mass transit—and the purposes of trips for cities of various sizes.[4] Similar data have been developed for the relation between types of transport and length of trip. Employment, retail sales, and floor space are additional criteria used to determine the extent of traffic generation.

Such data are useful in making preliminary estimates of traffic generation and in checking predictions for the future.

A somewhat different approach is found in determining a positive correlation between the amount, kind, and density of land use and traffic generation. Here the goal, the land use proposed for the future being known, is to predict the traffic (trip) generation on the basis of the traffic-producing characteristics of each type of land use; whether residential, commercial, industrial, recreational, or what. The problem has been to discover indicators of land use from which satisfactory correlation between trips generated and the use of the land can be obtained. Various methods of approaching the problem have been developed. The reader is referred to the suggested readings at the end of this chapter for more details on individual methods. Whatever method is used, the accuracy is primarily dependent upon

[4] T. J. Frater and T. M. Matson, "Traffic Engineering," in R. W. Abbett's *American Civil Engineering Practice,* Vol. I, John Wiley and Sons, New York, 1956, pp. 3-16, 3-17.

the forecast of the future land use and the intensity of that use. As cities of medium to large size will encompass many zones or neighborhoods, the burden of repetitive computations by any of the several methods can be reduced by resort to electronic computers.

One such land-use study, for example, made as a part of the Chicago Area Transportation Study, shows the relationship between land use and other factors and mass-transit usage within the Chicago study area.[5] An equation was developed during this study that permits an estimate of the percentage of mass-transit trips in a zone when residential density and automobile ownership are known. Thus in the 426 analysis zones under study, when mean car ownership per zone was 298.4507 and mean residential density was 121.8309, the mean percentage that mass-transit trips were of all trips to and from each zone was 16.2840. The equation derived for this purpose and giving a suitable correlation is

$$Y_{178} = 19.7331 + 0.0610X_7 - 0.0365X_8$$

where Y_{178} = percentage mass-transit trips are of total trips from a zone, X_7 = net residential density, and X_8 = cars per 1000 people. The process used could be adapted to developing a similar equation for other communities, when X_7 and X_8 are known.

A more subjective approach is that of selecting an industrial or commercial site deemed, subjectively, to be of average activity, calling that 100 percent intensity, and rating the activity of other zones above or below the one selected as the "norm." An intensity factor is thus obtained that is used to multiply the commercial or industrial acreage to obtain the "effective acreage" devoted to these uses in each zone. The effective acreage is then multiplied by the trip attraction per effective industrial acre to obtain traffic generation. In New Haven, Connecticut, the following generation factors were developed.[6]

Trip Production

1. Three trip ends per passenger car in zone of registration
2. Four trip ends per truck in proportion with effective industrial and commercial acreage

[5] Robert H. Sharkey, "Mass Transit Usage," *C.A.T.A. News,* Vol. 3, No. 1, The Chicago Area Transportation Study, January 9, 1959.

[6] W. R. McGrath, "Land Use Planning Related to Traffic Generation and Estimation," *Proceedings, Institute of Traffic Engineers,* Institute of Traffic Engineers, Washington, D. C., 1958, p. 72.

Trip Attractions

1. 100 trips per effective industrial acre
2. 200 trips per effective commercial acre
3. One-half trip per vehicle per passenger car in zone of registration

Having determined traffic generation, the problem of zone-to-zone movements is encountered. A growth factor may be computed for each zone by which the present zone-to-zone movements are multiplied and adjusted to conform to trip ends estimated in each zone. Much time can be saved in complex studies involving many zones by using electronic computers.

Dr. Carroll of the Chicago Area Study is developing a method of predicting zone-to-zone movements by means of a mathematical model. Trips from a particular zone are distributed depending on the number of opportunities for satisfying the trip desires at greater than minimum travel time. This again calls for electronic solution.[7]

Presentation of Data. Regardless of how secured, traffic-flow data and patterns must be presented in such a way as to allow rapid and accurate analysis and comprehension. Tabular presentations, while useful as supporting evidence, are usually only supplementary to graphical presentations.

Flow diagrams show the volume of a single portion or all of the traffic moving over different routes. The width of line is indicative of the volume on a particular portion of route. See Figures 14-2 and 14-3. Flow diagrams may also show the distribution of traffic to various destinations and by carrier types. See Figures 14-2 and 14-4.

The volume of traffic moving across screen lines between two areas may also be indicated. Such screen lines may be set across a series of roughly parallel routes between two localities or on a series of more or less concentric circles to show changes in traffic volume at intermediate points. The lines separating the subareas suggested in the discussion of cordon counts and screen lines may thus be used to obtain and present data on movements between neighborhoods or other subareas. When set on concentric circles, the data show the variation in traffic volume as the traffic recedes from or approaches a central point of origin—a port, an industrial area, a central business district. The graphical presentation may be in the form of arrows indicating both direction and volume of flow. The arrows may be

[7] Glenn E. Brokke, "Factors Associated with Traffic Growth," paper presented at the 46th Annual Illinois Highway Engineering Conference, University of Illinois, February 24, 1960.

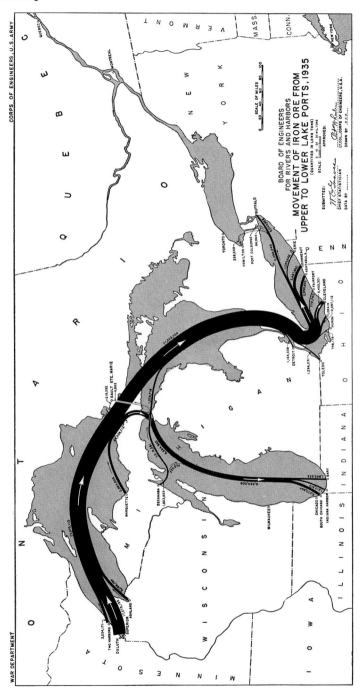

FIGURE 14-2. Volume of ore traffic moving over Great Lakes routes. (Courtesy of the Corps of Engineers, U. S. Army.)

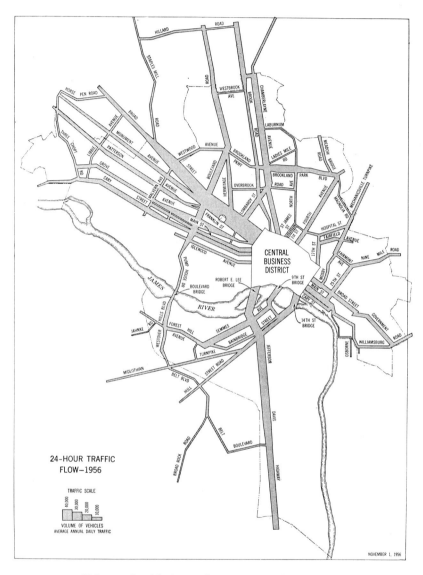

FIGURE 14-3. Volume of vehicular traffic on various city streets. (Courtesy of Harland Bartholomew and Associates, St. Louis.)

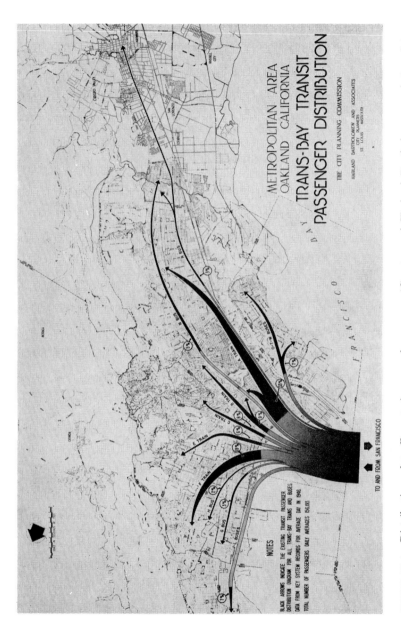

FIGURE 14-4. Distribution of traffic entering an urban area. (Courtesy of Harland Bartholomew and Associates, St. Louis.)

further shaded and scaled to show existing as contrasted with required capacity of routes at these points. See Figure 14-5.

Origin and destination or desire-line diagrams present the travel and shipping needs or "desires" for passenger- and freight-generating areas, giving the straight line or direct flow between any two points regardless of route. See Figure 14-6. Again the width of line can be indicative, to scale, of the volume of traffic having common origins and destinations.

In preparing such diagrams, it is again helpful to divide large areas into subareas. All trips or shipments from a particular subarea to the same destination are represented, either by individual lines for each trip or shipment, or by a line the thickness of which represents to scale the number of trips or shipments. This line (or lines) is drawn from the origin subarea to the destination subarea. If each individual trip and each individual destination are spotted for the two subareas, the representative line of scaled width may be drawn from the center of gravity of the origin dots to the center of gravity of the destination dots. Other destinations are similarly treated and the process is then repeated for other subareas.

Desire-line diagrams point out the several traffic generating areas and sectors. Traffic generators include residential, recreational, and industrial areas, shopping centers, central business districts, ports, railroad yards, freight stations, airports, mining and oil fields, and other sources of raw and manufactured goods.

Analysis and Planning. The analysis involving traffic patterns then includes the following.

1. A determination of the volumes and types of traffic moving over the various routes and by the several modes of transport. (The reader shouldn't forget that in simple or obvious problems, only one or two routes or modes may be involved.) This is accomplished by securing and presenting graphically traffic-flow data.

2. Determining where the traffic is originating and where it is terminating. This too is known from the traffic-flow, screen-line, and desire-line diagrams.

3. Comparing and adjusting the traffic volumes and origin-destination desires to future demand, traffic assignment. Here are encountered problems of forecasting future volume and demand by correlating past and present demand and volume for areas and zones or subzones to such indices as past and present population, land use, vehicle registration, fuel consumption, car loadings, industrial pro-

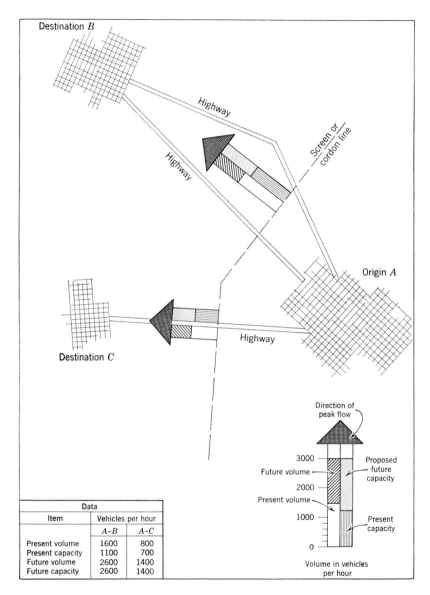

FIGURE 14-5. Graphical presentation at screen lines. (After W. S. Pollard, Jr., and Harland Bartholomew and Associates, St. Louis.)

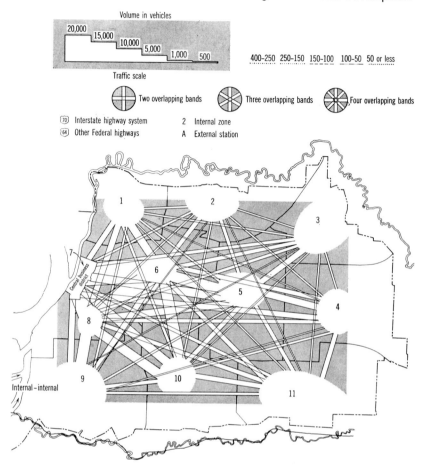

FIGURE 14-6. Desire-line diagram (showing internal flow only). (Courtesy of Harland Bartholomew and Associates, St. Louis.)

duction, and other economic factors. Similarly, future demand for transportation is correlated to statistical projections of population, vehicular registration and fuel consumption, and industrial production. In highway or city-street planning, for example, the relations between population, vehicular fuel consumption, and vehicle registration are particularly significant. See Figure 14-7. Population figures give the potential number of vehicular users of the future, registration projections give the number in that population that will actually own automobiles, and fuel-consumption figures will indicate the use

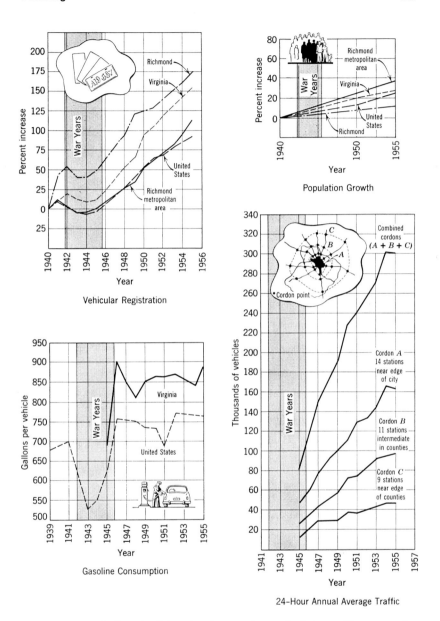

FIGURE 14-7. Indices to determine transport growth factor. (Courtesy of Harland Bartholomew and Associates, St. Louis.)

made, that is, number of trips, with those automobiles. A railroad serving a port area would consider the future trends in port traffic and note past, present, and future trends in distribution of that traffic between its own lines and competing carriers and to various locations on the lines of each. A coastal tank-ship line would develop past, present, and future relations between its traffic and the production—past, present, and future—of the oil field(s) served, the division of traffic from that field between tanker, barge line, pipeline, and railroads, sales from the refineries served, and the over-all market demand and conditions affecting petroleum utilization.

The reader should refer to the many texts on economic forecasting for details on the techniques to be employed. The primary factor to determine is a growth factor by which present traffic volume and capacity demand can be multiplied to give a reasonable estimate of volume and capacity demand 10, 15, or 20 years in the future. For automotive traffic, the growth factor may be taken as the product of the ratio of present-to-future population *times* the ratio of present motor-fuel sales to future sales *times* the ratio of present vehicular registration per capita to future vehicular registration per capita.

Recognition must also be given to other factors that might affect future demand. A proposed change in land use might cause considerable variation in the origin and destination characteristics and desires of urban traffic. The depletion of a source of raw materials— oil field, timber reserve, mineral deposits, etc.—will dry up one source, while the development of new fields and resources will create demand in other directions. Changes in consumer habits or in technology may in turn affect the traffic potential for industrial or commercial movement. Often a full economic survey is necessary to determine these matters. Usually projections of flow and demand are not attempted beyond a 20-year period.

4. Present capacity is compared with present and future demand and revisions of existing routes and plant are proposed to make the two compatible. Especial care must be given at this point to eliminate bottle necks and to assure adequate route capacity at all points for the local variations in traffic flow; the next chapter gives more detail.

The solution may simply be one of enlarging present capacity over the years by appropriate stage construction; by adding additional tracks or traffic lanes, buying more trucks, planes, or buses, or enlarging a lock. However, new routes may be necessary to meet changes in traffic desires caused by changes in land use, in consumer habits, or by technological change. New, more direct routes are possible solutions. The analysis must also consider revising allocations of traffic over several routes or to more than one mode of carriage, selecting those with the most favorable techno-economic characteristics.

The methods of collecting and presenting traffic-pattern data are varied and limited only by the inventiveness of the investigators. Nevertheless these functions are largely routine. Analysis of the data, on the contrary, calls into use all the selective factors heretofore mentioned. Many questions must be answered, of which the following may be considered as a summary and a check list.

1. Are the present facilities adequate for the volume of traffic present or anticipated? If not, why not and to what extent?

2. Does traffic move in the most direct line to its destination? Does it move in the shortest time?

3. At what points is there interference between lines of flow?

4. Is traffic routed into an area with inadequate facilities to handle it or take it away once it gets there?

5. Is traffic routed through a congested area when it could be routed around it?

6. What duplication of facilities exists? To what extent is that duplication necessary?

Other questions will arise in regard to specific local problems. The final question that must be answered in each instance is: How can that particular condition be corrected?

The reader is again reminded that the foregoing is inclusive of all types of problems and that much can be omitted or determined merely by inspection in the simpler, more obvious types of problems, that is, giving service to a new source of raw materials, to a new industrial plant, or to a new residential area. More elaborate and complicated problems as in the over-all transport planning for a large industrial complex are likely to involve a great many of the procedures just described. The most complex problems of traffic flow and distribution today are found mainly in highway and city traffic, further complicated by the growing trends toward regional and metropolitan development. This is largely because it is only recently that attempts have been made to correct existing poor conditions in these areas. One can find interesting speculation on the complexity of the problems in redesigning the existing rail facilities in a large city, for which there is usually much room for improvement. Such studies have been made in regard to passenger facilities in the in-stance of the Cincinnati Union Station terminal construction, unifica-tion of the passenger facilities in New Orleans, and the proposed passenger-station unification in Chicago. No major attempt at revising an entire city's freight facilities has, to the author's knowl-edge, been made in recent years.

QUESTIONS FOR STUDY

1. What is meant by the term "traffic pattern," what are the elements which compose it, and what is the significance of each?
2. What use could a railroad make of a passing report in planning to expand its facilities?
3. What are the five questions that a traffic-pattern analysis must answer and what is the significance of each? Give one or more examples of the problems encountered for each.
4. What is meant by a "one-percent waybill sample" and how can it be ob-tained and used?
5. Assume a small city of about 20,000 population, approximately square in shape, oriented directly with the compass, the CBD near the middle, and an industrial area in the southeast corner. The city has the following traffic distribution approaching from the west:

To the central business district and terminating there	2000 vehicles
To the industrial area and terminating there	400 vehicles
To the rest of the city and terminating there	100 vehicles
Traffic going to the CBD but then continuing to the east	1500 vehicles
Traffic that goes beyond the city with no need to stop in the city	200 vehicles

Prepare a traffic-flow diagram for the foregoing situation and data.

6. A community has been divided into five approximately equal neighborhoods or zones, and the following are the daily number of trips between each zone, half in each direction. Assume a sketch of the city with the neighbor-hoods arranged aphabetically, more or less like sectors of a circle, in a clock-wise direction. Draw a desire-line diagram.

A to B	300	trips per day
B to C	200	trips per day
A to C	400	trips per day
C to D	200	trips per day
A to D	500	trips per day
D to E	50	trips per day
A to E	200	trips per day
B to D	80	trips per day
C to E	300	trips per day

7. What elements would be considered in determining an increased demand factor for a railroad branch line serving a port area? Outline the procedure to be followed in determining that increase factor.

8. The ratio of estimated 1980 population to 1960 population is 1.90 and the ratio of 1980 vehicular registration per capita to that of 1960 is 1.7. The ratio of 1980 motor-fuel sales (usage) to 1960 sales is 1.25. What is the combined increase factor?

9. What significance would you attach to *time* as contrasted with *distance* in the planning of a route or its revision?

10. What is the significance of "disposition of traffic at destination" upon the rest of the route-design procedures?

SUGGESTED READINGS

1. *Discussion of the Use of Traffic Flow Data—Carriers,* compiled and edited by Beatrice Aitchison and G. Lloyd Wilson, 1953.

2. William S. Pollard, Jr., "Urban Area Street and Highway Planning Techniques," *Proceedings of the Third Annual Highway Short Course,* Bulletin No. 26, February 1958, Engineering Experiment Station, University of Arkansas, Fayetteville, Arkansas.

3. "Transportation on the Great Lakes," *Transport Series No. 1,* Corps of Engineers, U. S. Army, Washington, D. C.

4. T. M. Matson, W. S. Smith, and F. W. Hurd, *Traffic Engineering,* McGraw-Hill Book Company, New York, 1955.

5. T. J. Frater and T. M. Matson, "Vehicle Volumes," in Abbett, *American Civil Engineering Practice,* Volume I, John Wiley and Sons, New York, 1956, pp. 3-06 to 3-09.

6. C. W. Churchman, R. L. Ackoff, and E. L. Arnoff, *Introduction to Operations Research,* John Wiley and Sons, New York, 1957.

7. Reports of various consulting firms planning transport facilities.

CHAPTER 15

ROUTE DESIGN AND LOCATION

EFFECT OF TRAFFIC PATTERNS

Primary Location. The tools for planning the mode, services, and primary location of a transportation route have already been considered. The primary location, that is, initial and final terminals and key traffic centers between, depend upon the purpose of the route, potential traffic of various types, competition, and market. These in turn are modified by economic-geographic factors. A detailed location follows by developing a satisfactory relation between the primary location requirements, the traffic pattern, and the factors of economic-engineering location. Once a solution has been tentatively determined, for more elaborate studies at least, flow-line and desire diagrams can be redrawn to show the new proposals and to check their effect and suitability. The final allocations of traffic as to routes and modes having been made, the physical plant—routes and equipment—to meet the projected and allocated demands are then designed and located.

Traffic Allocations. The traffic demand, developed through methods of the preceding chapter, also bear an important relation to location. An early question is that of traffic allocation. Is an existing route to be improved or rehabilitated to meet the full present and future demand or can some of the traffic be allocated to an existing alternate route? If existing facilities are not suitable even with improvement (or if none presently exist), a new route will have to be designed and located. New-route construction may also prove more economical than revisions of existing routes (recall the comparison with the status quo, etc.). Regardless of this choice, the present and future demand in the final plan must be equaled by the present and future capacities of the several routes to which the traffic is allocated.

The desire-line diagram is of help in locating routes and allocating traffic. The thickness or density of lines is indicative of transport needs between two points. Where the lines are dense or heavy, a way must be provided of a capacity equivalent to that demand. Desire lines are not to be thought of, however, as actual routes. The traffic represented may presently or later be spread over several routes (including different modes of transport), some of which may involve a degree of circuity. Only occasionally does a heavy origin-destination (O-D) line coincide exactly with the final location of a major route.

In allocating and routing traffic, a certain volume can be allocated to existing facilities in a present or improved state. If this is not sufficient, additional tracks or highway lanes, etc., are considered. In the case of urban traffic, the change from a major street to an express-way type of facility may be necessary. If the expressway is not adequate for the demand from a certain area (or adequate only under conditions of exorbitant land use and cost), a rapid-transit line may be proposed instead of, or supplementary to, the expressway. The reserving of a center mall suitable for eventual use as a rail-transit right of way, an express bus lane, or even additional general traffic lanes adds flexibility to planning at this point—and permits the advantages of stage construction.

Rail and expressway facilities are not readily shifted once they are in place. It is therefore necessary that great care be exercised to assure that such routes are placed where ready access can be had by the greatest number for many years to come. Bus, truck, private car, and feeder and taxi airlines are flexible in regard to physical shifting of route and can be relied on to accommodate detailed shifts in transport demand. Railroads, rapid-transit lines, and expressways must be located with long-term land-use factors in mind.

One phase of the problem involves assignment of traffic to different modes of transport; how much should go to rail, how much to high-way, how much to air, water, pipeline? The selection of mode be-tween cities, as earlier discussed, will probably be based in part on technological suitability to the type of traffic to be moved, in part by factors of cost and/or rates. Where private companies are com-peting for traffic, the assignments will therefore depend largely on the competitive success of each individual company. For this reason, traffic assignment between railroads for example has been an entirely different problem from that for street and highway traffic. Should all the nation's railways ever be united into one gigantic system by government ownership, a corresponding problem would develop. The problem is with us today from the standpoint of conserving our national resources and effort.

Assignment of street and highway traffic is probably the most complex example of the problem to be encountered and has received much study and research effort.

The problem is simple enough in theory. Having available the trip desires (present and future) from one zone to all other zones (from the O-D studies and projections), each trip is routed over the shortest route, including turning time at intersections, to its destination. The total number of trips allocated to each route or section is accumulated by sections and determines the capacity that must be provided. A portion of that capacity (in terms of trip desires) may be allocated to a rapid-transit line. A commonly used basis of projection is to assume that every trip will follow the fastest route, that is, have the minimum travel time or follow the minimum path.

In going from one zone to adjacent zones, the minimum path is probably self-evident, but in going to zones not adjacent, some many zones removed, the problem becomes complicated because a variety of alternate routes are available. A further complication lies in the increase in time via any route as the volume of traffic assigned thereto increases (because of traffic interference). A multiplicity of possible minimum paths, depending upon the volume of traffic assigned to each section of a route, thus occurs. The planner usually has had to rely on his own judgment (as would the driver of a car making a trip); otherwise he is faced with a task of many months' or even years' duration. Computer methods of solution are being developed to reduce the great amount of detailed analysis thus involved.

Dr. Carroll of the Chicago Area Transportation Study has developed a procedure based on work by E. F. Moore for finding the shortest path through a maze.[1] Variations in the basic plan permit assigning all trips between zones without regard to direction. The second method assigns all zone-to-zone trips by direction. Programs have been written for an IBM 704 with 32,000 words of memory. A system with less than 900 *nodes*, that is, any specific point used for identification purposes such as a zone centroid or a route intersection, can use a computer with a 8000-word memory. A loaded section is

---

[1] Glenn E. Brokke, "Factors Associated with Traffic Growth," paper presented at the 46th Annual Illinois Highway Engineering Conference, University of Illinois, February 24, 1960.

totaled both as to vehicle-miles and vehicle-hours, computed separately for arterial systems, expressways, and freeways.

A method of "corridor analysis" being used and further refined by Mr. W. S. Pollard, Jr., offers considerable promise in a more realistic assignment of future traffic desires to existing as well as to proposed routes. Traffic flow is analyzed along and across parallel strips of one half to three quarters of a mile in width, the boundaries of the strips being taken between major streets.

Level of Demand. Another question to answer is what level of demand is to be satisfied. If one designs for the average hourly (or daily) demand, the facilities will likely be inadequate for peak periods. If demand for the maximum peak period is used, there will be unused capacity the rest of the day (or year). This essentially is the problem that plagues commuting and rapid-transit lines where the peak capacity for only 20 out of 168 hours each week must be met, with a greatly reduced load factor for the remainder of the time.

Some practical adjustment is necessary. In highway and street-traffic studies, the thirtieth highest traffic hour of the year is found to give a reasonable design value. Anything less than this will be inadequate and cause frequent congestion. Peaks beyond the thirtieth highest hour will occur so infrequently and be of such relatively short duration that no great inconvenience will occur.

Certain facilities—pipelines, conveyor belts, aerial tramways—may be built for a continuous fixed flow. These are likely to have in addition a 15- to 20-percent overload capacity. It has already been pointed out that even the minimum of rail facilities usually possess a high overload or surplus capacity and when that has been reached and another capacity level attained (by means of adding another track or installing CTC) a further large surplus of capacity is attained. It isn't always that easy, however, in the case of very dense traffic, and especially with rapid-transit lines and commuting lines where peaks occurring only briefly must be met as a matter of maintaining legally adequate service. Even here, however, some leeway is possible. The daily average peak with a 15- to 20-percent overload capacity gives a more reasonable basis for planning than a peak occurring say once or twice a year during a holiday rush. Consideration might well be given to the applicability of the thirtieth-highest-hour criterion used for street traffic or some modification of it. More study is probably warranted on this point.

Time as a Factor. The time factor is always important, especially in urban transport. A longer route may be advantageous when it avoids difficult or congested areas, thereby permitting a shorter elapsed time for a trip. This is part of the philosophy of bypass route design.

The financial equivalent of time saving is rather difficult to determine and should be introduced with caution if at all. For street and highway passenger traffic, the prevailing average wage rate may be applied to the time saved for the driver and his adult passengers. Wage rates also apply to the time saved for drivers, pilots, and crew members of trucks, aircraft, buses, etc. when they are paid on a strictly hourly basis. When payment is on a "day," trip, or other fixed rate, only the overtime which may be saved can properly be considered. Capital costs on equipment may be included because a shorter elapsed time can mean a quicker turn-around, more effective utilization of equipment, and less investment therein. Offsetting costs are those of fuel and other operating costs for the greater distance. Care must be exercised not to count a cost or saving twice, that is, as a time and distance factor both.

If a low over-all trip time is what is desired (the usual situation for urban travel), a circuitous route that avoids congested areas may afford the shortest travel time. Bypass and belt-line railroads and expressways, which circumvent crowded localities, thus provide a rapid service and a saving in land and construction costs. The costs of trying to force a rail line or a freeway through a congested downtown district would be enormous, often to the point of practical impossibility. Short cuts have been provided as in the tube systems under Manhattan Island and the New York Central's approach under Park Avenue. Neither of these projects was cheap!

The traffic studies will indicate what percentage of traffic approaching a town or city has no need or desire to pass through the built-up area before continuing the trip. In general, the larger the city, the greater the percentage of traffic approaching the city that desires to enter the built-up area, particularly the CBD. Traffic desires between periphery points and satellite communities will also be a part of the traffic survey. With these two sets of data, the need and capacity for a bypass or belt route can be determined. A similar approach will indicate what percentage of traffic coming by rail from a given direction is destined to points beyond the city and therefore likely to find belt-line routing advantageous.

In planning a railroad bypass belt line, economy may suggest having several railroads utilize one set of tracks or one route. This should not be permitted in a literal sense since a derailment or other difficulty on the one line could tie up all of the railroads using it. An alternate or detour route should always be available and not too circuitous.

Detailed location. Once the primary location has been determined, the actual detailed location with reference to features of terrain is undertaken. Planning tools used in fixing primary location, especially those of economic justification, are also applied to detailed location. Points to be served between principal terminals and requiring diversions from the primary route to tap intermediate traffic sources and interchange points are thus determined and justified.

The engineer defines location as fixing the horizontal and vertical position of a route, that is, the grades and alignment. Between any two points, a route may be given an infinite number of detailed locations. However, terrain and works of man usually reduce the practical number to a relatively few alternatives, often no more than two to six.

Economic-engineering location is the selecting of a route for which the revenues, construction costs, and operating expenses will be proportioned to yield the maximum rate of return and greatest over-all economic efficiency. This is simply to apply again the principles of Chapters 13 and 14 in more detail and to the final location of route—the mode, traffic allocations, and primary location having already been determined. Again the basic location formula $(R - E)$ $/C = p$ is used, this time to give a measure of the detailed effects of distance, curvature, gradient, works of man, etc., and their relations to propulsive-power characteristics. These effects will be considered later in the chapter after a brief review of the primary features of geometric design—alignment and profile.

GEOMETRIC DESIGN

Route Elements. Location has been defined as the horizontal and vertical position of a route. The horizontal position is the trace of the route on the ground; it is the plan view one would see looking down from an airplane. The basic element in the horizontal position is the tangent or straight-line location. From time to time the tangents must make angular changes in direction to conform to topography or to reach a given destination. In the case of aerial tramways and conveyors, the angular change is just that, made at the point at which the tangents intersect and called an angle station. Pipelines may be similarly laid out although some form of transition curve or bend is generally used. Railroads, highways, and, to a lesser extent, canals cannot tolerate abrupt changes in direction. Intersecting tangents are connected by some form of curve, usually an arc of a circle. Airplane runways almost never have an angular change of direction in any given path.

The vertical position of a route refers to its profile—its grades, its rise and fall with or opposing the natural contours of the terrain. Again there are a series of intersecting tangents or grade lines. Railroads, highways, aerial tramways, belt conveyors, airport runways, and pipelines break the abrupt change in grade at the intersection of two grade lines with a vertical curve, usually a parabola. Canals normally have little or no change in grade between any pair of locks and no breaks in grade.

Alignment. Horizontal curves are arcs of simple circles. The sharpness of curvature is the degree of curve, D, but the amount of curvature is measured by the central angle, I, equal to the deflection angle of the two intersecting tangents measured at their point of intersection, the PI. See Figure 15-1. In a preliminary survey, only the tangents are intersected, but in the final survey, the curves are staked.

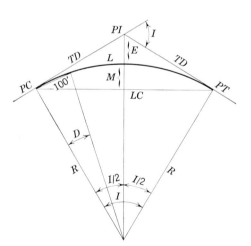

FIGURE 15-1. Functions of a simple curve.

Tangent distance = $TD = R \tan I/2$
Long chord = $LC = 2R \sin I/2$
Midordinate = $M = R$ vers $I/2$
External distance = $E = R$ exsec $I/2$
Length of curve = $L = I/D \times 100$

The equal distances from the *PI* to the *PC* and *PT* (point of curve and point of tangent respectively) are the tangent distances. By simple trigonometry, the tangent distance, $TD = R \tan I/2$, where R is the radius of the curve in feet. See Figure 15-1.

The degree of curve is the amount of central angle subtended by a chord of 100 ft or, according to another definition, an arc of 100.007 ft. A relation between degree and radius is established by equating the circumference of the curve in feet to the circumference in unit of arc (or chord) subtended by D degrees, or $2\pi R = (360/D)$ (100.007). Hence, approximately, $D = 5730/R$ or, conversely, $R = 5730/D$. If the 100-ft-chord definition is used, $R = 50/(\sin D/2)$.

The length of curve L is therefore equal to I/D in engineering stations of 100 ft each, or $L = I/D \times 100$, in feet.

Simple curves of different degrees and radii may adjoin to form compound curves where terrain or other obstructions are severely restrictive. Compound designs are undesirable (and even dangerous, especially in highway design) and should be used only where all other measures fail.

In order to provide for railroads and highways a smooth and gradual transition from tangent to full curvature, a connecting spiral curve, a form of the cubic parabola, is introduced between the simple curve and tangent near each end of the simple curve (the simple curve must be shifted inward a small amount to provide room for the spiral). The spiral also serves to introduce widening of highway pavements on curves and to facilitate steering of motor vehicles. A more important function is to introduce superelevation into a curve at a rate varying directly with the curvature. Superelevation is the difference in cross elevation between the inside and outside rails of a track or edges of a highway slab to compensate for centrifugal forces acting on the vehicles. For a standard-gage railroad, superelevation, $e = 0.0007DV^2$ in. For highway slabs, $e = 0.0000117DV^2$ ft per foot of slab width. In both expressions, D is the degree of curve and V is the vehicle speed in miles per hour.

Spirals and superelevation are used only with railroad and highway alignments and find no counterpart in other transport routes. Any manual or textbook on curves or route surveying will give necessary theory and practice for curve and spiral design and installation.

Profiles. The profile of a line is its position in the verticle plane. It is also composed of tangents (grades) and connecting curves.

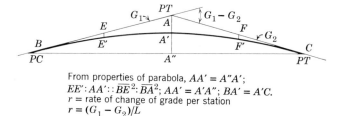

From properties of parabola, $AA' = A''A'$;
$EE'::AA'::\overline{BE}^2:\overline{BA}^2$; $AA' = A'A''$; $BA' = A'C$.
r = rate of change of grade per station
$r = (G_1 - G_2)/L$

FIGURE 15-2. Properties of a parabolic curve.

In the United States, grades are usually measured in percent, the rise in feet per 100 ft. This has previously been explained in Chapter 6.

Vertical curves form a transition from one grade to another, easing the sharp break at the point of intersection or vertex. A parabola having among others the following properties is commonly used. See Figure 15-2:

1. A line drawn to the intersection of the two tangents from the midpoint of the long chord bisects the curve and is bisected by the curve.

2. The offsets from the grade line to the curve vary as the square of the distance along the tangent (grade line).

The length of the curve is a function of the rate of change in grade per station in easing from one grade tangent to the adjoining tangent. Expressed mathematically, $L = (G_1 - G_2)/r$, where r = rate of change in feet per 100-ft station, G_1 and G_2 are the two intersection grades used with proper signs indicating whether the grade is ascending ($+$) or descending ($-$), and L is the length of curve in stations. To provide for smooth slack action in the train, the American Railway Engineering Association recommends a value of $r = 0.05$ ft per 100-ft station in sags and not more than 0.10 ft per 100-ft station on summits. For secondary, low-speed tracks, the values may be twice the foregoing.[2] These values also permit adequate sight distances for the engineman in going over the crests of hills.

Sight distance is an important factor for safety in highway design. A curve long enough to produce 1000 ft of sight distance is generally recommended for high-speed modern highways. Adequate sight distance is based on an assumed average height of the driver's eye

[2] *Manual of the Engineering and Maintenance Section, A.A.R.*, 1953 edition, American Railway Engineering Association, Chicago, Illinois, p. 5-3-13.

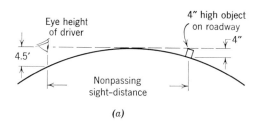

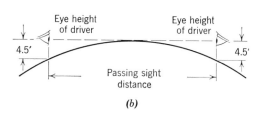

FIGURE 15-3. Sight distance over crests: (*a*) sight distance adequate to see an object 4 in. high at far range of vision; (*b*) sight distance adequate to permit opposing vehicles to see each other.

above the pavement of 4.5 ft (it may be as much as 6 ft for large trucks) and should permit him to see an object 4 in. high at the far range of vision. See Figure 15-3. Hewes and Oglesby give the following equations as presenting a suitable sight distance.[3] These are similar to the recommendations of the A.A.S.H.O. If A = the algebraic difference in grades in percentage $\div$ 100, S = sight distance in feet, and L = length of vertical curve in feet, then when S is greater than L, $S = (7.28/A) + L/2$. When S is less than L, $S = 3.82\sqrt{L/A}$. If a sight distance sufficient for passing on the crest is desired, the same reference gives the following equations with the same symbols: when $S > L$, $S = (18/A) + L/2$ and when $S < L$, $S = 6\sqrt{L/A}$. Such a length of flat vertical curve can only be obtained in many instances by heavy and expensive excavation.

Aerial-tramway design is based on a parabola of the form $x = 2c/y^2$, which is a smooth curve representing approximately the funicular polygon formed by weights hung equidistantly along the chord between two supporting points. For uniformly spaced loads, the cable deflection at any point is practically the same as for a uniformly loaded cable with a weight per foot taken as equal to the weight per foot of the cable alone plus that of one load divided by the load spacing in feet. Using this approximation and taking moments about

[3] I. L. Hewes and C. H. Oglesby, *Highway Engineering,* 1954 edition, John Wiley and Sons, New York, p. 178.

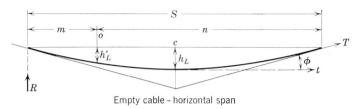

Empty cable - horizontal span

FIGURE 15-4. Aerial-tramway cable deflection.

the midpoint c of a level span between two supports, Figure 15-4, equations for the deflection, based on the loaded side, may be obtained:

$$h_L = s^2(L/d + r)/8t$$

and

$$h_L' = (L/d + r)mn/2t$$

where h_L = the midpoint deflection, h_L' = deflection of the cable at any point, s = span in feet between the two towers, L = weight of the loaded cars spaced d feet apart, r = weight per foot of the cable, and m and n are the respective horizontal distances to the point where the deflection is being found, and t is the midpoint tension in pounds. Cable deflection in aerial-tramway design must be checked to insure that the cars and cable clear all ground obstructions including works of man, trees, rock out-juttings, and drifted snow.

To permit the track cable to lie snugly in the saddle without an excessive angle between tangents at the crest, the deflection angle over the tower saddle is held to 2 degrees, 52 minutes, using more than one tower if necessary with the total angle divided between them (although German practice has used a total crest angle at a tower as high as 15 degrees). Heights of towers are determined by fitting a simple circular curve best suited to the profile between the two tangents. For a complete discussion of geometric design for aerial tramways, the reader is referred to "Aerial Tramways and Cableways" by Edward B. Durham in Peele's *Mining Engineers' Handbook*, Volume II, Third Edition, John Wiley and Sons, New York, 1952, pp. 1–51, from which the foregoing equations are derived.

FACTORS IN ENGINEERING LOCATION

For surface transportation, factors affecting construction and operating-cost differences are grades (or elevation), curvature, distance, and land and its acquisition. The over-all difference in elevation between control points rather than the rate of grade is important for pipelines and canals. Other topographical features and works of man may also have important effects. These problems have no direct counterpart in airways or in lake- and ocean-borne operations.

Distance. Other conditions being equal, a route should be as short as possible. In general, fixed costs are not affected by small changes in distance, but direct costs of construction will usually vary with distance. Consideration of costs due to distance should therefore be based primarily on variable or direct costs of construction and operation. For the latter, fuel, direct maintenance, and sometimes wages are the principal factors. Small or moderate increases in distance are of little consequence when a serious grade or curvature can thereby be improved or avoided or an additional source of traffic gained. In rail operation, the total operating cost does not vary in proportion but is only partly variable with a change in distance. Thus added costs are only approximately 30 percent of average costs per 1000 gross-ton-miles for changes in distance of less than 1 mile, 35 percent for 1 to 10 miles, and 48 percent for changes over 10 miles.[4]

Small changes in distance on highways can have an appreciable effect, especially when a heavy traffic flow is anticipated or experienced, because highway vehicles are variable-cost carriers. A 3-mile reduction in distance over which operate 2600 vehicles per day at an average cost of 4 cents per ton-mile would afford an annual saving per ton equal to $3 \times 0.04 \times 2600 \times 365 = \$113,880$. As with the railroad example cited above, not all of this would be an actual saving as the average 4-cent figure contains some elements of fixed cost that would be present regardless of distance. Nevertheless, for a route with a fair percentage of passenger traffic, savings in distance can be as important a cost factor as grade reduction. The many other factors that enter into highway location often make distance a matter of secondary consideration. Directness of route is, however, one of the characteristics that have recommended superhighways to the motorist, more from the standpoint of time saved, however, than from that of operating economy.

Distance is also important to pipelines. Flow resistance per mile accounts for a major portion of required pumping pressures except

[4] *Proceedings of the A.R.E.A.*, Vol. 39, 1938, pp. 518–531, American Railway Engineering Association, Chicago 5, Illinois.

where excessive differences exist between the elevations of any two or more pumping stations. Since there is little restriction due to terrain on a pipeline location, the shortest route is usually the cheapest. Furthermore pipeline traffic is all one-way and there is no need to deviate from a straight route in order to secure a return load. There is, however, need for an economic balance in the distribution of pumping stations. Stations of low pumping pressure are relatively inexpensive but must be close together. Stations of higher pumping pressures are more expensive but can be placed farther apart, a certain economy thereby being achieved. An economic balance must therefore be determined between pumping pressures and number of stations.

Canal costs are divided between route costs and locking costs. The latter depend on the differences in elevations rather than on route gradients (which should be level or nearly so), leaving distance as a vital route-cost factor. Where a lower elevation difference, leading to fewer lockings or smaller over-all lifts, can be had by increasing distance, the costs of the two alternatives must be compared to determine the one giving greater over-all construction and operating economy.

Curvature. Topography seldom permits an ideal straight line between two points. Curvature does not add materially either to highway construction costs or operating costs of highway motor vehicles. Some additional labor and material may be expended in widening and superelevating curves; also in painting center lines for safety. There is also excess wear on tires and pavement due to tangential forces and side thrust but these are negligible if modern safety requirements are maintained. Today's practice is to flatten curves to the point where the effects of curvature are nominal. The theoretical layout of curves is a problem in geometric design. In highways, space must be provided for horizontal sight distance, pavement widening, and spiral approaches.

The adverse effects of curvature on railway operating expenses (and construction costs to a lesser degree) are much more pronounced because of flange wear on rails and wheels, side thrust on the track structure, and consequent excess labor and material in maintaining gage, line, and surface. The total amount of curvature, the sum of the central angles of all curves in a route, is more important than the number of curves or degrees of curve. The same resistance is considered as being encountered in running through 528 degrees of central angle as is encountered by a train in running over 1 mile of tangent track (assuming an average value of 8 lb per ton for train resistance on tangent level track in still air for high modern train speeds). The costs of curvature can thereby be computed since it has been determined that the 528 degrees of equivalent curve mile will incur additional operating expenses equal to 30 percent of the average cost per 1000 gross-ton equivalent miles.

Curvature has a limiting effect on speed both for highways and railroads. This too is a matter of geometric design. In general, railroad curves for high-speed traffic—70 to 100 mph—are held to 1 to 2 degrees and 2 to 3 degrees for moderate speeds of 45 to 69 mph. If sharper curves are required by terrain or construction costs, speed must be reduced accordingly. Minor-branch and slow-speed lines usually do not exceed 8 to 12 degrees. Industrial switching tracks may go as high as 30 to 40 degrees (but curvatures above 20 degrees are not recommended). Diesel-electric road and general-purpose locomotives are usually limited to curves not exceeding 20 to 22 degrees.

Curves of principal highways should not exceed 3 degrees, while superhighways and expressways will hold to the same standards as high-speed railroads. Secondary roads may safely go to 10 degrees. Sharper curves are limited to temporary and low-class roads and to city streets. Where curvature restricts sight distance, the capacity of a highway is thereby reduced.

Curvature should be avoided in pipelines but presents no special problems. Bends of 20 to 30 degrees from the tangent are acceptable, but more sweeping changes in direction are preferred. The added flow resistance of such curves is considered only where precise calculations are required.

Curvature is not a major problem in canals and canalized rivers except as it limits the size of vessels going around a bend and creates problems in maneuvering. The limiting length of vessels can best be determined by laying out curves and vessels to scale on paper with templates. There should be room for the passing of two large ships, barges, or tows plus a factor of safety and an allowance for increases in size of future equipment. Sharp curvatures are avoided wherever possible. Guiding a long tow around a sharp bend is always difficult, and sometimes disastrous when a heavy current is running.

As pointed out earlier, curvature is normally not encountered with conveyors. The changes in direction are made at the ends of the belt flights. Aerial tramways either change direction abruptly at an angle station with appropriate towers and guide rails transferring from one cable to another or direction changes are made by introducing long curves so slight as to be almost imperceptible.

Grades and Elevation. The principles governing resistance to propulsion imposed by grades and differences in elevation have already been presented in Chapter 6. That chapter should be reviewed in studying these economic aspects of route location. In Chapter 6, it was shown that a resistance of approximately 20 lb per ton of vehicle and cargo weight per percent of grade must be overcome by all land-based vehicles—railroad, highway, monorail, aerial tramway, airway (during take-off), and conveyor equipment.

For rail and highway operation, grades affect costs in two ways: (a) by adding to the costs (and road time) of operating any given train or motor vehicle (fuel, maintenance, wages, etc.) and (b) by limiting the size of load in any one train or motor vehicle and thereby determining how many trains or motor vehicles with all their attributable costs will be required.

The latter effect is by far the more important. For example, the locating engineer must select a ruling grade for railroads that will permit the maximum load per train (for the type of locomotive in use), and therefore the least number of trains, and the minimum of expense. His selection will probably involve a comparative study of several alternative routes and/or grades. In general, the more money invested in construction costs, the flatter will be the ruling grade that can be obtained and the lower the operating costs. The engineer must decide how much money to spend and which grade and route is the most economical to build and operate. He must apply one or more of the cost-study methods given in earlier chapters, preferably the rate of return through use of the basic-location formula. In addition to selecting an economical ruling grade, he must also keep the minor grades, those less than the ruling grade, within economic limits. Since the ruling-grade location may be combined with a sequence of minor grades, these aspects of elevation form two individual elements in considering the over-all capital or annual costs or rate of return for a route alternative.

The ruling- and minor-grade concepts must be kept in mind in highway location as well, especially when heavy truck traffic is anticipated. Probably these effects should be given more consideration than they usually receive where truck traffic is a major percentage of the total. However, as discussed in Chapter 6, the limiting-grade concept is equally or even more important, at least for conventional two-lane highways. The limiting grade reduces vehicle speed and, if speed is reduced below 25 to 30 mph, limits the number of vehicles that can negotiate that grade in a given time. The capacity of a highway is thereby limited. Heavy grades materially reduce the speed of trucks and buses, adding to the number of vehicle units required to move a given volume of traffic and to the costs of fuel and wages. With both railroads and highways, the length and total mileage of excessive grades are matters of concern. One long steep ruling grade may not be too serious, but a succession of such grades or of grades less than but approaching the ruling grade in magnitude can have a severely adverse effect on road times and operating costs.

It is true today that in highway location especially, works of man often have as important an effect on grades as does terrain. The necessity to provide grade separations, for example, in building a superhighway or other limited-access road may well establish the grade line without reference to other factors.

The material in Chapter 6 on momentum and floating grades should be reviewed in developing detailed aspects of costs of gradients.

The locating engineer must display much ingenuity and adopt many expedients to keep his grades as light as possible. In rugged, difficult terrain, light grades are usually had only at the cost of heavy excavation, bridging, tunneling, or development. These are all expensive. Cheaper but far less desirable from an operating standpoint are switchbacks (not unusual on mountain highways) and inclined planes. Several Alpine railways are so designed that a dual-drive locomotive can be used that operates by adhesion to the rails on normal grades but engages a driving cogwheel in a rack laid between the rails when grades of excessive rise (4 percent or more) are encountered. Cableways are also extensively used in that mountainous land.

Development consists of adding distance to the length of line to reduce the rate of grade. Thus a mountain route may head up a main valley but, to add distance and thereby reduce the gradient, it will follow a long loop along both sides of one or more side valleys, perhaps looping over or under itself. Where side valleys fail to provide sufficient added distance, spiral tunnels looping into and upward through adjacent mountain walls have provided the necessary (but costly) additional footage. The Alpine railways again provide spectacular examples of this device as does also the Canadian Pacific in crossing the Rockies. The added distance and curvature of development increase construction and operating costs as well as the time required to negotiate the route. The advantage lies in fewer and heavier trains—or in being able to operate any trains at all.

In locating canals and canalized rivers, problems in grades as such are replaced by problems in differences in elevation. Canal gradients are theoretically flat and the slack-water pools of canalized rivers are nearly so. Differences in elevation are overcome by locks (or by inclined planes in primitive setups). The engineer's problems then become those of (*a*) determining whether excess distance is more economical than excessive locking and (*b*) deciding whether lifts shall be made in many small locks or in a few high locks. The stream and terrain pattern will, in many instances, decide these questions.

Airways laid out for high elevation and stratosphere flying can usually be designed with a maximum disregard for terrain—although rough weather usually associated with mountain ranges may cause diversions in an otherwise straight route to avoid bad weather. Airways for low-altitude flying must seek out passes through mountain barriers and, where contact flying prevails, will generally follow, where feasible, easily distinguishable features of terrain. Runways should be level or slightly sloped downward to avoid grade being added to the normal take-off "drag" on an aircraft.

Good pipeline location keeps the net rise between two pumping stations at a minimum. The cargo must be lifted through that height as well as transported longitudinally. However, as long as the line stays below the predetermined hydraulic gradient, grades as such are of minor importance, except as ease of construction is affected. Abrupt changes in elevation, even within the limits of the hydraulic gradient, should be avoided, especially close to the pumping station, for smoothness of pumping and flow, and to avoid "pockets." The initial terminal should be lower than the gathering lines so that gravity can aid in feeding petroleum to the pumping station.

Here again the locating engineer has a decision to make about the economies of building to a low elevation (with low-pumping-pressure units) or building to higher and cheaper (construction costs) elevations with higher pressured and more expensive pumping units (or more units of the same pressure but spaced closer together). However, the higher pumping pressures may require expensive line construction to withstand that pressure.

Other Factors Affecting Location. Other factors than the fore-going also have important effects on location. Some of the most important of these are herewith briefly mentioned.

Topography. Topography affects gradients, alignment, and distance. In addition, location of mountain passes, favorable sites for river crossings and for tunnels, harbors, and entrances to metropolitan areas as well as for space to build or provide access to terminal facilities are often critical. The lee side of a ridge gives protection from rain, snow, ice, and wind. Areas of frequent snow slides and avalanches should be avoided. Ridge routes provide better drainage and require less bridging but pose problems in reaching and serving valley communities. Valley routes usually require less excavation but require heavy bridging and are subject to drainage problems and floods. In penetrating a mountain barrier, it is usually preferable to proceed as far as possible into the foothills and ranges with a minimum grade and overcome the bulk of the interposed elevation at one point rather than trying to pick it up a little at a time. This will permit territories of easy gradients plus one territory of heavy gradients rather than having the entire route a series of heavy grades.

Soils. The soils encountered should be firm enough to serve as a subgrade or base for the roadbeds of railroads and highways. Materials suitable for subgrade construction should be accessible to the route location. Canals require impervious soils that will not allow too much seepage loss from channels and dams and firm materials for lock and dam foundations. Rock excavations are usually more expensive than earth. Acidic soils cause pipeline corrosion and are avoided when other factors permit. Since ideal soils for any purpose seldom if ever occur in nature, the engineer is faced with the problem of adapting the soils encountered to his needs and taking measures to overcome their unfavorable characteristics. In extreme cases, the soil encountered is removed and better materials are hauled in, or the location is changed to reach firmer or otherwise more favorable ground. The exploration, adaptation, and correction of soils and soil conditions are primarily problems for the soils engineer and are treated in detail in works on that subject.

Water. Water when under control is a desirable adjunct for most routes. Steam railroads must have an extensive supply for locomotive boilers. Even diesel-electric locomotives must have some water for radiator cooling and for heating units. Water is required for power plants of railroads, pipelines, tramways, conveyors, and locks. Personnel and passengers must be supplied with potable water. A large and constant supply of water is mandatory for canals. Finding adequate sources of water supply is often a prime duty of the canal's locating engineer. If the canal parallels a water course, natural supply can be used with the water course sometimes forming a part of the route. Water shortage must be protected against by artificial storage in lakes and reservoirs.

Miscellaneous problems. Works of man offer problems in connecting to or crossing other routes, bypassing communities, gaining access to terminal and urban areas, and securing land at economical prices. This last is an especially difficult problem in trying to construct a route through or close to an urban area. Advance announcement of the project causes a steep rise in land values and prices. Ease of access to the proposed route for initial construction and later maintenance must be considered, especially for pipelines. Pipelines are often located parallel to a railroad or highway to avoid costs of constructing access roads. Crossings of canals, railroads, highways, and rivers should be avoided if possible or suitable sites selected. Pumping-station locations for pipelines should be selected with reference to fuel, power, water, and accessibility to communities for the station personnel and for ease of delivering supplies and of making repairs to station equipment.

Airport location presents special problems. Runways, often 2 miles or more in length, must be extended in several directions so aircraft can always land and take off into the wind. Space in a locality convenient to the community served, to utilities, and to other types of transport must be selected. In addition, the engineer must note the type of land coverage, drainage and excavation requirements, and soils conditions. Obstructions to the approach zones and glide paths are noted and should be avoided for at least a 3-mile radius, and weather conditions and visibility—fog, smoke, smog, prevailing winds, etc.—given careful consideration. The loud, high-pitched, and often annoying sounds of jet aircraft during warming-up and take-off have made the location of jet airfields in relation to residential areas a matter of importance. In this connection, the regional concepts of land-use development may find jet air service concentrated at centrally located regional airports with the various surrounding communities served by feeder lines, preferably using helicopter or other forms of vertical take-off craft.

Location Procedures. Field work and layout of routes are basically the same for all types of transport. Known terminal and intermediate points are first established, then a reconnaissance survey is made of a strip of land equal in width to about one third to one half the distance between any two fixed or control points. Reconnaissance in earlier days was made on foot or horseback or by small boat or canoe. These modes of travel can be supplemented today by motor car, airplane, and the use of maps and aerial photographs. These last can be used to delimit still further the width of the strip of land under study. Aerial photographs are especially useful in permitting an unhurried study and determination of critical locations where additional observations, perhaps on foot, in the field are required. The Map Information Office of the United States Geological Survey, Washington, D. C., makes available its U.S.G.S. maps, control data, and aerial photographs as well as furnishing lists of similar materials available from other government agencies. Stereoscopic procedures enable a finding of elevations, contours, and earthwork estimates. Much of the reconnaissance can thus be performed in the office. Whether in office or field, the reconnaissance must secure information on all pertinent details of terrain, vegetation, climate, topography, works of man, and any other factors that might affect the choice of routes. After the reconnaissance and paper survey, one or more partial or complete preliminary lines are set in the field. Tangents are run to their points of intersection but curves are not staked. Topography is noted in sufficient detail to permit comparison of the construction and operating costs of alternative locations. The effects of gradient, curvature, and distance on operation and on the construction costs of earthwork, bridging, tunneling, etc. for each possible route are compared. Such comparisons are facilitated by the use of electronic computers. Several routes have thus been given detailed comparison in a fraction of the time that would have otherwise been required. Note that preliminary surveys can sometimes be avoided if adequate aerial mapping is available.

Once a selection of route has been made, the final location is staked complete with curves and offsets where those are needed. Complete topography (cross sections) is taken.

Construction surveys include a reestablishment of the final location and the setting of offset, grade, and slope stakes to mark the vertical and horizontal limits of cuts and fills. The possibility of improving the economic factors by minor revisions of the line should not be overlooked at any stage of survey.

Since gradients and alignments are not as critical in pipeline work as in railroads or highways, the final location is often set approximately on strip maps prepared from aerial photographs with minor changes being made in the field construction survey. Actual ground survey of the route can thus be as little as a day or two in advance of construction if necessary.

In locating an aerial tramway, the engineer does not have to seek the lightest grades on the ground. The big advantage of the tramway is its application to rugged terrain. The route may be traced from crest to crest with wide differences in elevation between adjoining crests and towers. This advantage does not, however, relieve the engineer of seeking the best route possible under the conditions presented. The necessity of running the cables in tangent lines with a minimum number of angle stations imposes further limitations on location that will tax the engineer's skill in adaptation. He will endeavor to have the loaded side on a general downgrade, insofar as conditions permit, to save on power costs.

Conveyors must also follow generally a straight-line location for the extent of each flight. Close attention to maintaining light gradients should govern location to assure minimum operating costs, especially those for fuel or power.

QUESTIONS FOR STUDY

1. Of what importance is the traffic pattern in determining the location of a route?

2. Define the "level of demand" problem and its solution for various types of carriers.

3. In what ways does the factor of time determine route location?

4. What relations exist between economic location and engineering location?

5. Given: a railroad route that changes direction at an intersection of two tangents by a deflection of 24 degrees. If the superelevation is held to a 3-in. maximum, what length of simple curve must be used to connect the two tangents while permitting a maximum authorized speed of 60 mph?

6. Given: an ascending 1.8-percent highway grade intersects a descending 1.2-percent grade at a crest. What rate of change of grade per 100-ft station will give a sight distance of 1000 ft, assuming the length of curve to be greater than the sight distance?

7. Compare the operating costs of two proposed rail routes, each carrying 18,000 gross tons per day, one route containing 7890 degrees of central angle, the other containing 6300 degrees of central angle. Assume operating costs per 1000 gross-ton-miles to be 4 dollars.

8. Explain the difference in the cost effects of ruling grades as contrasted to the cost effects of distance, curvature, and minor grades.

9. What is meant by development in route location and how can it be accomplished?

10. What are other factors besides traffic pattern, distance, and elevation (gradients) that are likely to influence location?

SUGGESTED READINGS

1. A. M. Wellington, *The Economic Theory of the Location of Railways,* 1906 edition, John Wiley and Sons, New York.

2. "Economics of Railway Location and Operation," *Manual of the A.R.E.A.,* 1953 edition, American Railway Engineering Association, Chicago, Illinois, Chapter 16.

3. W. W. Hay, *Railroad Engineering,* Volume I, John Wiley and Sons, New York, 1953, Part I.

4. L. I. Hewes and C. H. Oglesby, *Highway Engineering,* John Wiley and Sons, New York, 1954, Chapters 6 and 7—"Highway Surveys and Plans" and "Highway Design."

5. Sam Osofsky, "Electronic Computers Save Time on Traverses and Earthwork," *Civil Engineering,* November 1956, pp. 464–468, A.S.C.E., New York.

6. William T. Pryor, "Aerial Survey Methods Solve Highway Location Problems in Tropics," *Civil Engineering,* October 1949, pp. 40–44, 81, A.S.C.E., New York.

7. Highway and Bridge Surveys, Journal of the Surveying and Mapping Division, Proceedings of the A.S.C.E.:
Reconnaissance, Paper 1593, April 1958.
Introduction to Bridge Surveys and Reconnaissance, Paper 1713, July 1958.
Preliminary Surveys, Paper 1697, July 1958.
Location Surveys, Paper 1698, July 1958.
Preliminary Bridge Surveys, Paper 1842, November 1958.

8. Controlled Access, a panel discussion, Sixth Annual Highway Conference, 1957, American Association of State Highway Officials, Washington, D. C.

9. *A Policy on Arterial Highways in Urban Areas,* American Association of State Highway Officials, Washington, D. C., 1957.

10. *A Policy on Geometric Design of Rural Highways,* American Association of State Highway Officials, Washington, D. C., 1954.

11. George E. MacDonald, "Surveys and Maps for Pipelines," Surveying and Mapping Division, *A.S.C.E. Proceedings,* Separate No. 393, January 1954, A.S.C.E., New York.

12. Brigadier General (retired) D. H. Timothy, C.E., "Major Pipe Line Crossings of the Mississippi River," *The Military Engineer,* April 1952, pp. 38–40.

13. *C.A.T.S. Research News,* a fortnightly publication of the Chicago Area Transportation Study, especially Robert H. Sharkey, "The Effects of Land Use and Other Variables on Mass Transit Usage in the CATS AREA," Vol. 3, No. 1, January 9, 1959, pp. 3–10.

14. *Research Letter,* published by the Pittsburgh Area Transportation Study, especially Louis B. Keefer, Study Director, "Traffic Assignment—What It Is," Vol. II, No. 2, February 1960, pp. 1–7.

15. Arthur T. Row, "Land Use Planning Related to Traffic Generation and Estimation," *Proceedings of the Institute of Traffic Engineers,* I.T.E., Washington 6, D. C., 1958, pp. 62–65.

16. William R. McGrath, "Land Use Planning Related to Traffic Generation and Estimation," *Proceedings of the Institute of Traffic Engineers,* I.T.E., Washington 6, D. C., 1958, pp. 66–78.

17. *Traffic Assignment by Mechanical Methods,* Highway Research Board Bulletin 130 (papers presented by the Thirty-Fifth Annual Meeting, January 17–20, 1956), Washington, D. C., 1956.

APPENDIX I

TYPICAL TRANSPORT UNITS

FIGURE AI-1. Diesel-electric locomotive. (Courtesy of ALCO Products, Inc., New York.)

TYPICAL RAILROAD TRANSPORT UNIT

Type: **Diesel-Electric Locomotive**
Service: Freight and passenger
Model: DL 600
Builder: American Locomotive Company
Classification: C-C
Over-all length: 66 ft, 5 in. (inside knuckles)
Over-all width: 10 ft, 1⅝ in.
Over-all height: 14 ft, 8¾ in.
Distance between center pins: 43 ft, 6 in.
Center-to-center measurement of trucks: 39 ft, 10 in.
Motors: Six GE 252 (2S-3p, 6p—automatic transition)

455

Driving wheels: 6 pairs, 40-in. wheels
Weight on drivers:
  Minimum: 325,000 lb
  Maximum: 390,000 lb
Fuel capacity: 2400 gal
Maximum curvature: 21 degrees, coupled; 25 degrees, single unit without train
Tractive effort—continuous:
  65-mph gearing: 29,500 lb
  75-mph gearing: 69,800 lb
  80-mph gearing: 65,200 lb
Short-time tractive effort—for 4 minutes: 107,400 lb
Starting tractive effort at 25-percent adhesion: 97,500 lb
Prime mover: ALCO 244 V-Type, 16-cylinder, supercharged
  Horsepower: 2250 (manufacturer's rating)
Brakes: clasp type; dynamic braking capacity, 3400 hp

FIGURE AI-2. Highway tractor. (Courtesy of Truck and Coach Division, General Motors Corporation, Detroit.)

TYPICAL HIGHWAY TRANSPORT UNIT

Type: **Highway-Motor-Carrier Tractor**
Model: DLR-8000
Service: Hauling highway-motor-freight trailers
Builder: Truck and Coach Division, General Motors Corporation

Prime Mover:
Engine: GM 6-71 S. E. diesel, 6-cylinder, 2-cycle, 4½-in. bore,
5-in. stroke, 425.6-cu-in. displacement, 17-to-1 compression ratio
Horsepower: 189 maximum gross brake at 1800 rpm
              175 maximum net break at 1800 rpm
Torque: 577-lb-ft maximum gross at 1200 rpm
         533-lb-ft maximum net at 1200 rpm
Transmission: 5-speed synchromesh overdrive
Differential: 4:33–5.91:1
Tires: 11–22.5 in. and 12–22.5 in. front and dual rear
Dimensions—tractor:
Wheelbase: 108 in.
Bumper to end of frame: 181 in.
Width: 96 in.
Height: 111 in.
Capacities:
Curb weight—tractor: 10,450 lb
GVW: 30,000 lb
Gross combined weight: 60,000 lb
Axle loads: 9000 lb front and 21,000 lb rear
Speeds:
Maximum road speed (GCW): 51.5 mph
Maximum geared speed: 52.7 mph
Maximum grade (GCW): 15.3 percent at 4.3 mph

TYPICAL GREAT LAKES TRANSPORT UNIT

Type: **Great Lakes Bulk-Cargo Carrier**
Name: *Arthur M. Anderson*
Owned by: Pittsburgh Steamship Division, United States Steel
          Corporation
Built: 1952
Trade: Iron ore—Duluth to Chicago and Lake Erie ports
Motive power:
Steam turbine: 2-water-tube, oil-fired boilers, 7000 s hp normal
                rating, 7700 maximum
Propeller: rpm—108 normal, 111.5 maximum
Dimensions:
Length over all   647 ft, 0 in.
Length between perpendiculars   629 ft, 3 in.
Length on keel   620 ft, 0 in.

FIGURE AI-3. Great Lakes bulk-cargo carrier. (Courtesy of Pittsburgh Steamship Division, United States Steel Corporation, Cleveland.)

Breadth, molded	70 ft, 0 in.
Depth, molded	36 ft, 0 in.
Designed summer draft	25 ft, 0 in.
Block ratio (approximate)	0.92

Tonnage:

Empty plus fuel: 8847 long tons (approximate)

Cargo: 19,700 long tons (approximate)

Hatches:

Number: 19

Center-to-center spacings: 24 ft, 0 in.

TYPICAL RIVER TRANSPORT UNIT

Type: **Towboat** (Pusher)

Name: *A. D. Haynes II*

Service: Inland-river "towing" for Mississippi Valley Barge Line

Builder: Dravo Corporation

Prime mover:

Engines: diesel-electric Nordbergs

Horsepower: 4200 at 514 rpm

Propellers: 2 stainless-steel, 10-ft diameter with Kort nozzles

Dimensions:

Length: 200 ft

FIGURE AI-4. River towboat. (Courtesy of Dravo Corporation, Pittsburgh.)

Depth: 12 ft
Width: 45 ft
Draft: 9 ft (approximate)

TYPICAL AERIAL TRANSPORT UNIT

Type: **Jet Air Transport**
Model: DC-8
Builder: Douglas Aircraft
Operator: United Air Lines
Prime Movers:
    Engines: 4 Pratt and Whitney J-57
    Combined thrust: 40,000 lb
Cruising speed: 550–575 mph at 25,000–30,000 ft
Landing stall speed: 116 mph
Dimensions:
    Length: 150 ft, 6 in.
    Wing span: 139 ft, 9 in.
    Height: 42 ft, 4 in.
Tires:
    Main: dual tandem 15.50–18
    Nose: dual 11.00–14

FIGURE AI-5. Transport airplane. (Courtesy of United Air Lines, Chicago.)

Weight:
  Empty: 115,839 lb
  Loaded: 265,000 lb
Wing loading: 96.2 psf
Wing area: 2258 sq ft
Aileron area: 158 sq ft
Flap area: 454 sq ft
Fin area: 225 sq ft
Rudder area: 127 sq ft
Stabilizer area: 392 sq ft
Elevator area: 167 sq ft
Rate of climb at maximum gross weight: 1670 fpm (at sea level)
Service ceiling with maximum load: 35,500 ft
Range with maximum pay load: 4660 miles
Range with maximum fuel load: 6050 miles

II

PROBLEM EXAMPLES

The multiplicity of situations and individual problems that are involved in transportation planning make the presentation of a problem example that includes all elements of planning difficult. The two problems that follow contain a goodly number of the planning processes and will present patterns that can be applied to other situations. They are not, however, a comprehensive statement of the contents of this book. The reader is warned not to be misled by the oversimplification.

PROBLEM EXAMPLE ONE

This example gives some of the problems and procedures in planning a new transport route in an undeveloped country.

The Need for Transportation. A large ore-producing organization wishes to add 500,000 tons annually to its output by opening a new mine in a remote and inaccessible part of an undeveloped country. The mine property is located in a valley surrounded by rugged mountain ranges rising precipitously to elevations of 6000 ft. The mine capacity is estimated at 500,000 tons annually for a 20-year period.

The undeveloped character of the land in which the mine is located and the type of ore determine that this product must be transported to overseas markets via ocean shipping.

Terminal Points. The mine location has established the originating terminus of the route. Three ocean ports are available. Port X is so far away that simple inspection rules it out. Port Y is just beginning to develop but is found to have ample room for expansion and a good harbor. Port Z is more fully developed but is becoming congested, with little room for expansion, and has adverse tidal currents that lead to frequent ship delays. Port Z also involves 50 additional route miles of distance. Port Y, a location called Welcome Bay, is therefore selected as the ocean terminus. (*Note:* this problem will not be concerned with transportation problems beyond Welcome Bay.)

Selection of Carrier. Ore, a granular-mass commodity, is most efficiently moved by rail, water, or conveyor transportation. A rail route is available part of the distance, but the best mode and route giving access to the rail line are not readily ascertainable. Consideration is given to highway trucking, a conveyor, an aerial tramway, a suspension-flow pipeline, or a combination of these to reach the existing rail line.

The pipeline and conveyor systems are ruled out because the transport used must permit inbound movements of fuel and supplies to the mine. Also, the region is too arid to provide the water necessary for a pipeline flow. A selection among the other possibilities can be made only on the basis of field-reconnaissance data.

The Reconnaissance. Maps of the area show no topographic detail. A field reconnaissance by car, rail, helicopter, and on foot is conducted that involves a study of terrain, drainage, elevation, and other pertinent features of the intervening land between the mine and the railroad. A map of the area is developed from this reconnaissance. See Figure AII-1. On the basis of the reconnaissance, three principal routes and modes are selected for further consideration.

Route A. A 30-mile highway haul over existing 8-percent mountain grades to a lightly constructed and little-used rail line owned by the mining company, and thence by rail (on a ruling grade of 2-percent) 200 miles to Welcome Bay. The existing portion of the route would require new and heavier rail, strengthened bridges, new ties and ballast, and additional cars and locomotives. The estimated cost of rail rehabilitation is 50,000 dollars per mile. The cost of improving the "highway" by resurfacing, bank and cut widening, and improving drainage is estimated at 30,000 dollars per mile. The total length of the route is 230 miles.

Route B. Ten miles of aerial tramway across a mountain range and 20 miles of new railroad construction through rolling country to the same railroad with the same 2-percent ruling grade as in Route A but at a point only 160 miles from Welcome Bay. The total length of Route B is 190 miles.

Route C. An aerial tramway 140 miles long over rough mountainous terrain direct to Welcome Bay.

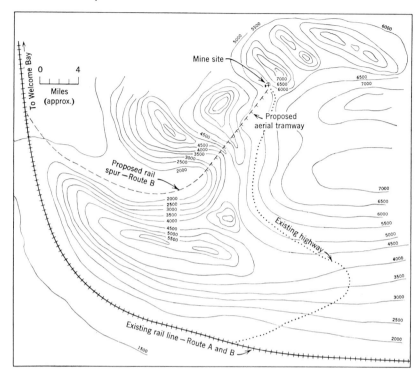

FIGURE AII-1. Portion of reconnaissance map for proposed new transportation route.

Preliminary Analysis of Cost. The following data are next computed in order to have a preliminary estimate of cost for economic justification.

Common data:

Tonnage—annual mine production = 500,000 tons
daily mine production (310 days per year) = 1612 tons
Cost of mine and mine equipment = $20,000,000
Estimated daily cost of mine operation = $3.50 per ton
Estimated sales price of ore at Welcome Bay = $20 per ton

Route A

Truck Requirements

A truck is considered that weighs 18 tons empty and has a 260-hp (net) engine operating at 1500 rpm, with gear ratios of 6:1, 4:1, 3:1, 1.7:1 and 1:1 for the transmission and 6.5:1 and 5.9:1 for the differential. Because of steep, 8-percent, ascents and descents, this vehicle is assumed to operate in fourth gear (4:1), leaving the lower gear combinations for emergency situations. Driveline mechanical losses are 10 percent. Tires are 48 x 12 in.

Torque $= T = \text{hp}/0.00019N = (260/0.00019) \times 1500$
$= 912$ lb-ft

Tractive effort $= TE = T \times G_1 \times G_2 \times e \times r/12$ (as explained in Chapter 5)

$= 912 \times 4.0 \times 5.9 \times 0.9 \times 24/12$

$= 9730$ lb $TE = 375 \times \text{hp}/V$

$V = 375 \times 260/9730$
$= 10$ mph

$$\text{Road resistance} = R_r = \left(17.9 + \frac{1.39V - 10.2}{W}\right) r_r + \frac{CAV^2}{W} W$$

where $r_r =$ ratio of the fair-road-surface resistance, 40 lb per ton, to resistance for good surface conditions $= 2$

$W =$ empty weight of truck unit $= 18$ tons

$A =$ cross-sectional area $= 90$ sq ft

$$R_r = \left[\left(17.9 + \frac{1.39 \times 10 - 10.2}{18}\right) 2\right.$$

$$\left. + \frac{0.002 \times 90 \times 100}{18}\right] 18$$

$= 670$ lb   (in unit terms, $R_r = 670/18 = 37.2$ lb per ton)

Total empty-truck resistance on 8-percent grade $= 670 + 8 \times 20 \times 18 = 3550$ lb

Net tractive resistance $= DBP = 9730 - 3550 = 6180$ lb

Pay load $= 6180/(37.2 + 8 \times 20) = 31.5$ tons   (Use 30 tons.)

Truck loads per day required $= 1612/30 = 54$

Running time per trip $=$ round-trip distance$/V$
$= 60/10 = 6$ hours   (The truck can probably run faster on the return trip because of a lighter load, but many return trips will be under load, bringing in sup-

plies, so, as a factor of safety, the same speed is assumed throughout.)

Loading, unloading, and delay time = 1 hour

Total round-trip time = 7 hours

Round trips per truck per day = 24/7 = 3.4

Number of trucks required (truck loads per day/trips per truck) 1.10—to include 10 percent standby and in-shop equip-ment— = (54/3.4)1.10 = 18 trucks

Two other types of trucks are available and offer the following operating and cost situation, which would be computed in the same way as for the 18-ton truck:

Truck No.	Pay Load	Price of Truck (dollars)	Cruis-ing Speed (mph)	Loads per Day	Round-Trip Time (hours)	Round Trips (24 hr per truck)	Vehicles Required	Purchase Cost (dollars)
1	20	20,000	12	81	6	4.0	23	460,000
2	30	30,000	10	54	7	3.4	18	540,000
3	40	40,000	8	40	8½	2.8	16	640,000

Truck No.	Annual-Capital-Recovery Factor [a]	Total Annual Cost (dollars)	Truck miles per Year [b]	Operating Cost per Vehicle Mile (cents)	Annual Operating Cost (dollars)	Total Annual Cost (dollars)
1	0.12950	59,570	1,656,000	32	529,920	589,490
2	0.12950	69,693	1,011,840	36	364,262	433,955
3	0.12950	82,880	806,400	48	374,976	457,856

[a] Based on a 10-year life for the trucks at 5 percent. See Table 13-2.
[b] Round trips per day × length of round trip × No. of vehicles × 310 days.

This tabulation of comparative annual costs shows that truck No. 2, the 30-ton-pay-load truck in the computation example, gives the lowest total annual cost and will therefore be selected for use in the rest of this problem.

Rail-Equipment Requirements

This part of the study is based on a 2-percent ruling grade, an average train resistance of 6 lb per ton, 60-ton cars (40-ton pay load), and an 1800-hp 100-ton diesel-electric locomotive.

Locomotive resistance = R_{loco} = tractive resistance and grade
resistance × locomotive weight
= $(6 + 2 \times 20)100 = 4600$ lb

Drawbar pull (DBP) at 10 mph and 25-percent adhesion
$$= \text{tractive effort} - \text{resistance}$$
$$= (308 \times 1800/10) - 4600 = 50{,}840 \text{ lb}$$
Car resistance $= (6 + 2 \times 20)60 = 2760$ lb
Cars per train $= 50{,}840/2760 = 18$
Net tons per train $= 40 \times 18 = 720$ tons
Number of trainloads per day $= 1612/720 = 2.2$
Total turn-around time (average speed of 10 mph) is computed
    from the following items:
    Round-trip running time $= 400$ miles$/10 = 40$ hours
    Delays en route $= 4$ hours
    Terminal time (loading, unloading, inspection, etc.)
        $= 16$ hours
Total elapsed round-trip (turn-around) time $= 60$ hours
Equipment for the foregoing:
    6 complete sets of trains (cars and locomotives) plus one
    standby (or in-shop) set $= 7$ trains
    Cars $7 \times 18 = 126$
    Locomotives $= 7$
    Purchase price:
        Cars $= 126$ at \$6000 $=$ \$756,000
        Locomotives $= 7$ at \$300,000 $=$ \$2,100,000

        Total equipment $=$ \$2,856,000

Route B

Aerial-Tramway Requirements

Tons per hour (24-hour operation) $= 1612/24 = 67$ tons
    (Use 70 tons per hour.)
Maximum average cost $= \$120{,}000$ per route mile
    (Taken because of the rugged terrain, and because \$50,000 is
    needed for a power plant to operate the 10-mile aerial-tramway
    route in one section)
Operating costs $= 8\cancel{c}$ per ton-mile

Railroad Requirements

(As in Route A, 2.2- 18-car trainloads per day will be necessary
    to move the 1612-ton daily output of the mine.)
Round-trip running time $= 360$ miles$/10 =$ 36 hours
Delays en route $=$ 4 hours
Terminal time (loading, unloading, inspection, etc.) $= 16$ hours

Total elapsed round-trip time $=$ 56 hours

Equipment for the foregoing = (56/48) (2.2) = 5 sets
5 complete sets of trains (cars and locomotives plus one set of
standby equipment) = 6 trains
Cars = 6 × 18 = 108
Locomotives = 6
Purchase price:

Cars = 108 × $6000 = $648,000
Locomotives = 6 × $300,000 = $1,800,000

Total equipment = $2,448,000

Traffic capacity of rail line. The existing rail line is already carrying 4 trains per day (2 each way). The addition of 4.4 trains (2.2

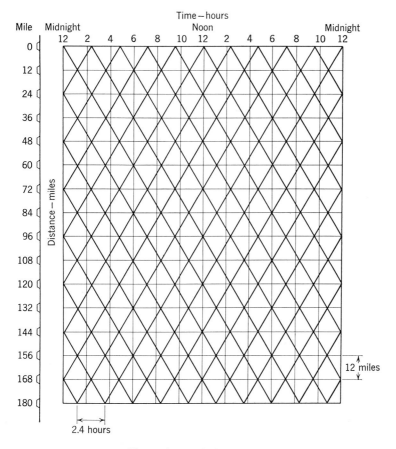

FIGURE AII-2. Theoretical train-hour graphical schedule.

each way) makes 6.6 trains total. Sidings are spaced approximately 12 miles apart (1.2 hours apart if trains run at 10 mph). As the spacing between trains on a single-track line (disregarding fleet movements) must be twice the siding spacing in hours, Figure AII-2, 10 trains can be started in each direction in a 24-hour period, a total of 20 trains per day. Even though theoretical, this can be seen by inspection to be adequate for the proposed 7 trains per day. The 7 trains are well below the possible 20 to 30 trains that a single-track line can handle in 24 hours. A closer siding spacing would, however, reduce delays. It can be assumed that the cost of rehabilitation per mile will include intermediate sidings at several locations.

Using the formulas of Chapter 8, train hours = TH = number of sidings $\times$ 24. If the sidings are spaced 12 miles apart, the 180-mile distance includes 15 sidings, each 1 mile long. The total theoretical train hours will be $15 \times 24 = 360TH$. As each train is running at 10 mph, a running time of 18 hours per train, the total number of trains will be $360/18 = 20$ trains.

Comparative Cost Analysis. A tabulation of route and equipment (construction and purchase) costs and of operating costs for the several routes is as follows:

Route costs

Route	Improve Present Highway	Construct New Railroad	Rehabilitate Present Railroad	Construct New Cableway	Total Route Construction
A	(30 miles @ $30,000) $90,000	—	(200 miles @ $50,000) $10,000,000	—	$10,900,000
B	—	(20 miles @ $80,000) $1,600,000	(160 miles @ $50,000) $8,000,000	(10 miles @ $120,000) $1,200,000	$10,800,000
C	—	—	—	(140 miles @ $120,000) $16,800,000	$16,800,000

Equipment costs

Route	Highway Trucks	Railroad Locomotives	Cars	Aerial-Tramway Power Plants	Total Equipment Cost
A	(18 trucks @ $30,000) $540,000	$2,600,000	$756,000	—	$3,396,000
B	—	$1,600,000	$648,000	$50,000	$2,498,000
C	—	—	—	14 × $50,000 = $7,000,000	$7,000,000

Operating costs

Route	16 Trucks @ 36¢ per Vehicle Mile	Trains @ $7.00 per Train Mile	Aerial Tramway @ 8¢ per Ton-Mile	Total Operating Costs
A	$364,262	(272,800 train miles) $1,909,600	—	$2,273,862
B	—	—	$400,000	$2,118,640
C	—	—	$5,600,000	$5,600,000

In computing the rate of return, only the effects of transportation are needed at this stage. The evaluation of the mine property is not a part of the problem. The ore, on being transported to tidewater, has a sales-price value of $20.00 per ton. Thus the original revenue will be 500,000 $\times$ $20.00, or $10,000,000. Using this foregoing figure in the location formula $(R - E)/c = p$, the tabulated results are the following:

Rate of return

Route	Revenue	Operating Costs	Capital Costs, R & E (Route Costs)	Equipment Costs	Total R & E	Rate of Return
A	$10,000,000	$2,273,862	$10,900,000	$3,396,000	$14,296,000	54.1%
B	$10,000,000	$2,118,640	$10,800,000	$2,498,000	$13,298,000	59.2%
C	$10,000,000	$5,600,000	$16,800,000	$7,000,000	$23,800,000	18.5%

Route C, the all-cableway route, is definitely out of the picture at this point. Route B, combined rail and aerial tramway, has a slight edge over the truck operation. It would probably be wise to give more extensive study to each to determine if a better operating grade or shorter route could be had for the truck, tramway, or railroad route.

Economic Justification. Assuming that Route B continues to be best after further study, the next step is economic justification. Here the justification for the route is dependent upon the justification for its purpose. If the mine plus transportation is not justified, then there is no need to consider the transport problem at all.

Assuming the mine to have a total capital cost of $20,000,000 and its annual total operating costs to be $3.50 per ton, the rate of return on the entire project (and its calculation) is given herewith [the value added by transportation would be the value of the mine per ton at tidewater ($20) less the operating costs at the mine ($20 − $3.50 = $16.50) less capital costs of the mine operation]:

Revenue:		$10,000,000
Operating costs: Mine ($3.50 per ton)	$1,750,000	
Transportation	$2,118,640	
Total	$3,868,640	$3,868,640
Capital costs: Mine	$20,000,000	
Transportation	$13,298,000	
Total	$33,298,000	$33,298,000

Rate of return = ($10,000,000 − $3,868,640)/$133,298,000 = 18.4%

The entire project, including Route B, is thus seen to give a justifiable rate of return even if a 10-percent allowance for contingencies is made throughout. There is no need to test Routes A and C as those have already been eliminated in the rate-of-return comparison. The revenue and the mine costs are the same in all three alternatives.

In making the final location for the route, considerations of detailed gradient, curvature, and distance factors over the general route selected will govern its final design. The same tabulation procedure, this time determining detailed costs instead of general costs, will again be carried out. As suggested in a preceding paragraph, a detailed survey might well be made for Route A as well as for Route B. However, another comparison needs to be made here, quickly. Can the possible saving deriving from a detailed study of a Route A revision offset the added cost of making the study?

One other possible alternative situation should be considered at this point. The railroad might have had different ownership and offered to build and operate the 20-mile rail spur and 10-mile aerial tramway in return for a guaranteed rate to Welcome Bay of $5.00 per ton. In this analysis the rate of return is based on the saving. The R term in the rate-of-return equation now becomes the cost of railroad freight rates, or $5.00 × 500,000 tons = $2,500,000 per year. The E term is the expense of operating Route B, and C is the cost of constructing and equipping Route B. Then ($2,500,000 − 2,118,640)/13,298,000 = 2.9 percent. Under these circumstances it would be hard to justify financially the investment in a private transportation system. The mining company should be able to earn more than a 2.9-percent return on this money by putting it in some other enterprise. Nevertheless, a desire to control the ore movement to the coast or doubt regarding the railroad's ability to maintain their agreement might carry sufficient weight to warrant a private transport system even with the foregoing rate of return.

PROBLEM EXAMPLE TWO

This second problem example includes processes common to solutions for highway and urban-transport planning.

To bring these situations within reasonable scope, simplifications have been secured by stressing certain features of the study and omitting the many ramifications and multiple requirements encountered in most actual situations. The reader should not be misled by its apparent simplicity. Problems of zone-to-zone movement and of "scientific" traffic assignment have been disregarded. The number of alternative routes from zone to zone has been kept to a minimum.

Growth-Use Factor. Computation of use and growth factors for determining future transportation requirements is made as follows.

Given: vehicular registration, gasoline consumption, population growth, and 24-hour traffic volumes for the city (and county) of Metropolis for a 15-year period.

Compute: the over-all use factor for the year 1980, and determine the traffic volume to be planned for in that year.

Comment: note that, as a simplification, local figures only are given. In an actual situation, corresponding data for the state and the nation should be secured and given parallel plotting to check the local trends. If there is much variance, the sources of variance should, if possible, be determined and an estimate made of the continuing or diminishing significance of this variance in the future, and the local trends adjusted accordingly.

An average or straight-line extrapolation of the data into trend lines is sufficient for this problem but in actual situations, at least for large cities, more sophisticated statistical methods of "trending" may be required.

As a further simplification, the use factor hereby determined may be considered as applying to the entire community of Metropolis. In general situations, a local growth-use factor should be developed for each section or neighborhood in the community because rates of growth and development will seldom be uniform. An established, built-up residential neighborhood, for example, may have a much lower use-growth factor than a newly developing or proposed future

Traffic-Generation Trends

City of Metropolis

Year	Increase in Vehicular Registration, percentage	Gasoline Consumption, gal per vehicle per year	Population Growth, percentage (1940—0%)	24-Hour Traffic Volume, thousands of vehicles
1945	0	630	32	30
1947	28	750	42	41
1949	63	740	53	50
1951	94	690	67	62
1953	108	765	78	75
1955	140	760	88	85
1957	152	770	98	93
1959	180	775	108	98
1960	185	780	113	102

Additional data includes:
  1960 population = 141,000 persons
  1960 vehicular registration = 71,398 vehicles

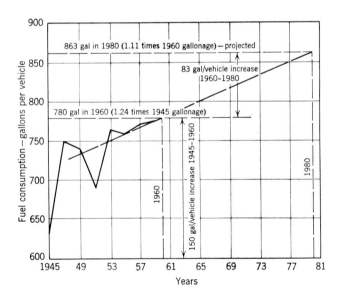

FIGURE AII-3. Gasoline consumption.

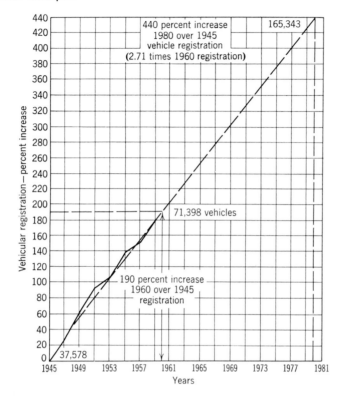

FIGURE AII-4. Vehicular registration.

neighborhood. Industrial areas may be assumed to have the same rate of traffic growth as the rest of the city.

Solution. The statistical data for gasoline consumption, vehicular registration, and population growth are plotted and straight-time extrapolations projected to 1980 in Figures AII-3, AII-4, and AII-5.

The 24-hour traffic volumes for the 1945–1960 period are also plotted. See Figure AII-6.

An initial check is made on the relation between present traffic volume, vehicle registration, vehicle usage, and population. From the 24-hour-traffic-volume plot, Figure AII-6, come the following data.

$$1960 \text{ volume} = 102,000 \text{ vehicles}$$
$$1945 \text{ volume} = \underline{30,000} \text{ vehicles}$$

$$24\text{-hour traffic volume} = 72,000 \quad \text{vehicles, increase}$$

This represents a 240-percent increase in 15 years, 2.4 times 1945 usage.
    For the same period:
    1960 vehicular registration = 190 percent over 1945, 1.9 times
    that of 1945

$$\begin{aligned}
\text{1960 gasoline consumption per vehicle} &= 780 \text{ gal} \\
\text{1945 gasoline consumption per vehicle} &= 630 \text{ gal} \\
\hline
\text{15-year gasoline-consumption per-vehicle increase} &= 150 \text{ gal}
\end{aligned}$$

This is a 124-percent increase or 1.24 times 1945 consumption.
    The combined 15-year use factor = vehicle-registration-increase
factor $\times$ gasoline-consumption-increase factor = $1.90 \times 1.24 = 2.36$.

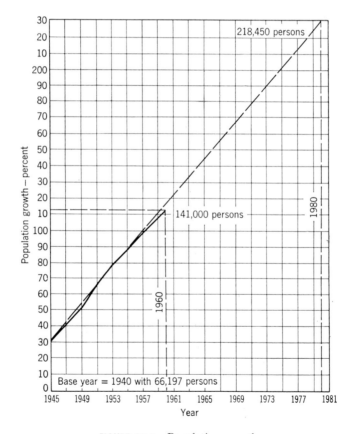

FIGURE AII-5. Population growth.

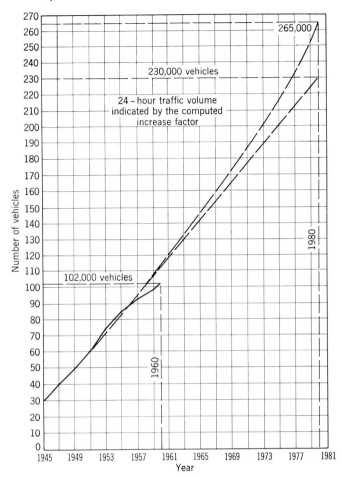

FIGURE AII-6. Twenty-four-hour traffic volume.

This is a close check on the 2.40 increase factor in the 24-hour traffic volume for the same period.

One cannot depend on a simple graphical projection of traffic volume alone to determine 1980 traffic volume. The effects of anticipated population growth, vehicular registration, and vehicular usage (gasoline consumption) must be combined to guide the traffic-flow projection.

$$\text{increase factor} = F_i = F_p \times F_v \times F_u$$

where F_i = increase factor for 1980 traffic volume over 1960

F_p = increase factor for 1980 population over 1960

F_v = increase factor for 1980 vehicle registration per capita over 1960

F_u = increase factor for 1980 gasoline consumption (usage) over 1960

Future traffic flow is obtained by multiplying the ratio of estimated 1980 vehicular registration per capita (1.50) by the estimated-increase-in-population factor (1.60) and multiplying this in turn by the increase-in-gasoline-consumption-per-vehicle (usage) factor

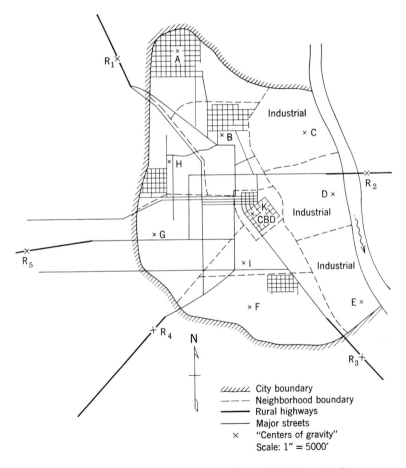

FIGURE AII-7. Neighborhood-zonal map of "Metropolis."

(1.21), or $1.50 \times 1.60 \times 1.21 = 2.60 =$ increase factor. The projection is revised accordingly.

Origin-Destination (O-D) Data. In this second problem the effects of traffic patterns on route location are to be considered. The origin-destination data that follow have been obtained by personal interviews and post-card-questionnaire surveys. This data should be used in conjunction with Figure AII-1 to develop a line diagram or picturization of the O-D study.

Individual lines could be drawn from each resident or block to represent the trip data. The procedure in this problem (and often in practice) is simplified by orienting all trips in a neighborhood or zone with regard to the "center of gravity" of the population or "trip generation."

The "center of gravity" of trip origins and destinations for each

Origin-Destination Data

Trips per Day—Both Directions

Between	1960	1980	Between	1960	1980
R_1–K	2,000	6,800	R_3–K	800	2,720
R_1–R_2	1,000	3,400	R_5–K	200	680
R_1–R_3	5,800	19,720	R_5–R_4	200	680
R_1–R_4	5,600	19,040	R_4–R_2	1,000	3,400
R_1–R_5	6,400	21,760	R_3–R_4	1,200	4,080
R_2–K	1,000	3,400	R_3–R_2	1,000	3,400
			R_3–R_5	1,200	4,080
A–K	7,000	18,200	A–B	500	1,300
B–K	10,000	30,000	A–C	1,700	4,400
C–K	5,200	13,600	A–D	1,300	3,300
D–K	4,000	11,000	A–E	200	1,500
E–K	10,000	27,000	A–F	1,300	3,400
F–K	15,000	37,000	B–C	1,500	5,900
I–K	2,000	5,000	B–D	1,300	3,200
G–K	10,000	5,000	B–E	1,250	2,500
H–K	9,000	23,000	1–D	400	1,300
A–H	1,000	3,500	F–E	4,600	12,500
A–G	700	1,840	F–G	200	400
			C–D	2,000	5,600
			D–E	3,000	7,800

neighborhood is shown by the letter X. See Figure AII-7. In drawing the O-D or desire lines, let the width of line indicate the number of trips according to some scale. For example, a line $\frac{1}{16}$ in. wide might represent 5000 trips.

Data given are for the present (1960) situation. It is necessary to prepare O-D data for the year 1980 by use of the growth-use factor (assume a uniform rate of growth).

Required: an O-D diagram for (*a*) the present (1960) situation; (*b*) the future (1980) situation.

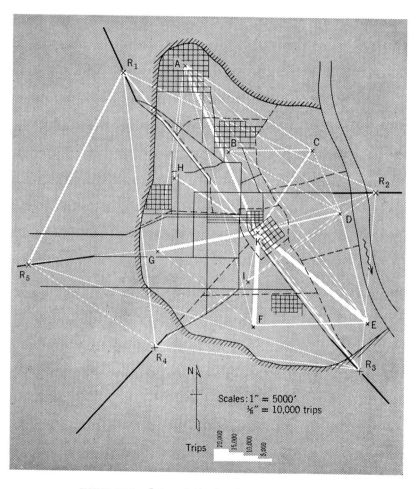

FIGURE AII-8. Interneighborhood trip desires—1960.

Note: all data for internal-internal trips and for internal-external, external-external, etc. have been placed on the same sheet. In practice these would probably first be shown separately and then made into a composite diagram.

The first step in this process is to multiply 1960 trip desires by the increase factor, 2.6, to obtain 1980 trip-desire data; see the foregoing tabulation. It is emphasized that a common increase factor has been used throughout as a simplification. Increase factors for each of the several zones or neighborhoods should be used in practice.

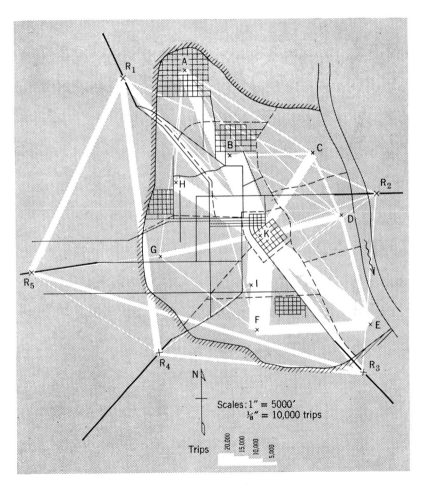

FIGURE AII-9. Interneighborhood trip desires—1980.

These 1960–1980 trip desires are shown graphically in Figures AII-8 and AII-9. Note that these diagrams do not represent existing routes. Traffic between R_1 and R_2, for example, presently must go through the central business district, K, as must traffic between R_1 and R_3, R_1 and R_4, etc.

Route Layout. Using data from and guided by the origin-destination study, a layout of routes can next be prepared. There are countless possible solutions to the detailed street layout. However, there are certain general requirements indicated by the O-D study that must be met. The solution given here is one that presents a reasonably satisfactory means of handling present and future traffic. In arriving at a detailed design, several alternatives might well be considered, to the final selection of which peak-hour capacities, relative costs, rates of return, and ease of financing would contribute.

The two diagrams for 1960 and 1980 trip desires, Figures AII-8 and AII-9, are similar in travel desires, differing only in magnitude. Working with the 1980 diagram, therefore, two general classifications of traffic (and routes) are at once indicated: traffic to and from the central business district (Area K) and traffic going from one main highway to another and passing through the city, but only because no other route is available. A third and lesser traffic is that between zones or neighborhoods and not concerned with the central business district.

A properly located belt line, encircling the city, will carry traffic from rural highway R_1 to rural highway R_2. It will also carry traffic moving between zones (or neighborhoods) A and C, A and D, and C and D, if proper access is provided. A continuation of the belt to R_3 will move traffic from D to E and from R_2 to R_3. The highway flow of traffic from R_1 to R_3 can also follow this route, thereby bypassing the central business district. A more logical routing would be via a continuation of the belt line on the westerly side of Metropolis, which would also serve to carry traffic from R_1 to R_4, R_1 to R_5, and R_5 to R_4. Much of this route will lie close to or just outside the city limits. The belt line may also be used to handle traffic moving between A and G and between A and H by keeping it east of the city line and utilizing existing north-south rights of way.

The belt route can also handle the traffic moving between E and F if given properly located interchanges, and can possibly utilize the existing east-west right of way in the southern part of Zone F.

A central collector-distributor is desirable around the central business district to give local distribution and pickup to inbound and outbound CBD traffic. This in turn would be connected to major streets serving the principal traffic-generating zones E, R, G, H, A, and B.

Major streets give access to the several traffic-generating areas. In B, for example, two routes are located to the east and west of the traffic center of gravity, ✕, permitting local street access to these principal routes from both sides of ✕.

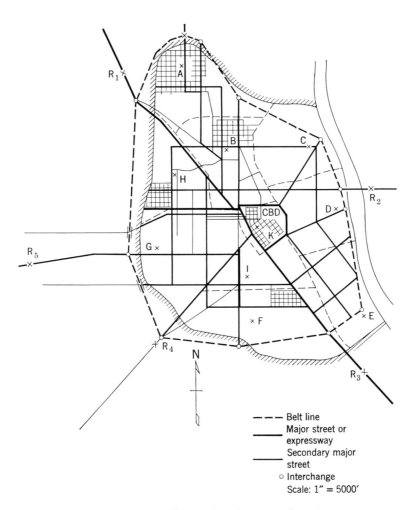

FIGURE AII-10. Proposed major street layout.

The street system proposed, Figure AII-10, offers the following features:

1. Principal streets are spaced approximately one half mile apart, providing movement from the traffic-generating centers to and from main arterials and/or the central business district.
2. A central collector-distributor around the central business district gives local pickup and distribution.
3. An outer belt line gives quick movement to nonadjacent interzonal traffic and allows through-highway movements to bypass the central business district.

Movements presented on the O-D diagram are thus provided with routes that, it is repeated, do not necessarily coincide with actual lines of the diagram or with existing streets.

The next problem is that of determining the capacity to be provided and its allocation to existing or proposed roadways.

Route Capacity. The route layout of Figure AII-10 does not indicate the required capacity of the proposed routes, nor does it indicate whether that capacity is to be provided by one street or by more than one. Capacity is usually expressed as the maximum hourly capacity required or to be provided.

One solution is based on the thirtieth-highest-hour concept, that is, the concept that capacity designed should not exceed that of the thirtieth highest hour of the year. Any design beyond the thirtieth highest is uneconomical, and the number of times the thirtieth highest hour is exceeded is relatively inconsequential. Anything less than the thirtieth hour would be inadequate. For a highway experiencing average traffic fluctuations, the thirtieth highest hour is equivalent to *approximately* 15.5 percent of the average *daily* or 24-hour traffic. For the inner distributor loop, it might be about 8 percent; for the belt highway, 12–14 percent. The factor of directional split also has major importance. By determining the daily traffic over the major routes and taking the proper percent thereof, a capacity is obtained, which is then translated into the required number of lanes. Those lanes may be planned in one street or distributed over several. More precise and detailed street design is possible if data on traffic flow are obtained at individual points. Thus, in Figure AII-11, maximum one-way flow is determined on existing streets by a series of traffic counts taken at observation stations along (in this problem) four sets of more or less concentrically located screen lines or cordons:

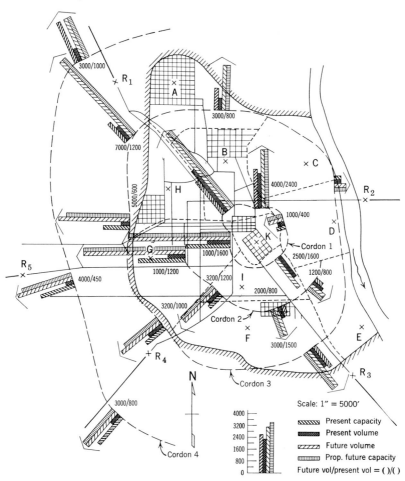

FIGURE AII-11. Capacity study for proposed street layout.

1, 2, 3, and 4. The data so obtained and developed are placed on a map of the city, Figure AII-11, for reference and analysis, being shown as fractions. The denominator represents present (1960) flow. The numerator is projected 1980 flow based on increase factors assumed to have been determined for each individual neighborhood. Note here that as a matter of simplification these neighborhood-increase factors have not been developed in this illustration but are accepted and used as having already been determined. The "fractional presentation" of traffic flow represents street capacities as determined by field-survey data and estimates for the future. The arrow indicates the direction of maximum peak flow.

Solution:

1. The check on individual-zone-increase factors is made by summating the individual peak flows for 1960 (denominators in the "fractions") and 1980 (numerators in the "fractions") and dividing the one by the other, that is, Σ_{1980} peak flow $\div \Sigma_{1960}$ peak flow = increase factor. Thus 328,400 $\div$ 120,550 = 2.72. This is a close check on the over-all 2.60 increase factor and gives the planner confidence that his general approach is reasonably accurate. Such cross checks should be performed wherever practicable.

2. The graphical presentation of 1960 and 1980 peak flows are next shown in Figure AII-11, at the cordon or screen-line-station location at which the data were collected, as bar graphs. Present major street capacities are also shown. These are the sums of capacities of existing routes serving the traffic under study at a given location. The final data shown in the bar graph are proposed 1980 street capacity. The thirtieth-highest-hour value may be inserted here (based on flow data from Figure AII-9 or on individual 24-hour flow taken at the cordon or screen-line station). Or, the maximum flow as projected and herewith graphically tabulated for each neighborhood and screen-line station may be used. Conservative traffic planning will possibly *increase* this value by 10 to 15 percent as a contingent and induced traffic-flow factor of safety. Conservative financial planning may *reduce* this value by the same amount (thereby bringing the value closer to the thirtieth-highest-hour estimate). Probably it is better to be conservative with money on the minor streets, where future increases are likely to be as estimated, and to be generous with street capacity and expenditures on major streets and expressways.

Once the future capacities have been determined, these are allocated to existing streets. The deficit in capacity must then be overcome by planning additional traffic lanes for existing streets (street widening) or by building an entirely new street facility, probably an expressway.

INDEX

(Boldface folios indicate principal references.)

Acceleration, 197, 231
  computation, **240, 241**
  curves, 265
  force, 241
  on gradients, **220**
  rate, 241
Adhesion, 241
Advantage, inherent, 157
Air Commerce Act of 1926, 64
Aircraft, balloons, 34, 56
  capacity, load, 236, 257, **260, 261**
  classification, 236
  dependability, 249, 250
  development, 23, 56
  dirigible, 56, 61, 63
  early, 34
  engine, 23
  flexibility, **236, 237**
  guidance, **162**
  helicopter, 237
  number of, 97, **102**
  safety, 24, **249, 250**
  speed, 24, **257**
  utility, **236, 237**
  weather vs., 249, 250
  Zeppelin, 56, 61, 63
  also see Airplane
Airfoil, 165, 166, 167, 168
  air density, 166
  angle of attack, **167, 171, 172, 180**
  aspect ratio, 180
  burble angle, 166, 167
  center of pressure, 49, **167, 168, 171, 172**
  characteristics, **166, 167**
  drag, **166, 179, 180, 181**

Airfoil, lift, **165, 166, 167, 168**
  N.A.C.A., 167
  slots, 168
Airlines, 80
  cost types, 365, 366
  service types, **80, 81**
Air mail, 64
Airplane, ceiling, **207, 208**
  chord, wing, 180
  climb, rate of, 206
  costs, 363
  development, **63, 64, 65**
  drag, **166, 179, 180, 181**
  efficiency, thermal, 199
  elevation vs., 224, 226
  engine performance, **206, 207, 263**
  jet, 168, 237
  lift, **165, 166**
  resistance, ground, **207, 208**
  stability, **171, 172**
  surveys, 451
  types, 65, 324, **459, 460**
  vertical take-off, 324
Airports, air space, **309**
  capacity, **278, 311**
  classification, **310**
  control, **352, 353, 354**
  elevation, 224, 225
  drainage, **130**
  facilities, **309, 311**
  land, **252, 309, 310**
  location, 224, 225, **309, 310**
  maintenance facilities, 312
  need for, 237
  runways, 23, 113, **115, 116, 117, 168, 224, 225, 307, 310**

Airports, safety, 249
    zoning, 352
Air Route Traffic Control, **340**
    block systems, **344**
    control centers, **340**
Airways, capacity, 278, 279
    elevation vs., 224, 448
    flexibility, **235, 236**
    land use, **253**
    mileage of, 105
    routes, **95, 97, 98, 99, 100, 101,** 105,
        448
    skyways, 97, **279**
    zones, 352
Alignment, 137
    rivers, **149**
Allen, Horatio, 43, 46
American Bureau of Shipping, load
    lines, **164**
American Petroleum Institute, **183,
    184**
American Railway Engineering As-
    sociation, recommendations, 267,
    269, 202, 391, 440
Asphalt Institute, 115
Association of American Railroads, 50,
    331, 412
Association of American State High-
    way Officials, standards of, 324,
    391, 441
Automobiles, accessories, 23, 54
    clutch, 54
    development, 53, 54
    efficiency, fuel, 284, 285
    flexibility, **235**
    number of, 61
    private, 12

Ballast, depth, **120, 122**
    pressure distribution, 119
    pressure intensity, 120
    purpose of, 113, 131
    resistance, 131
    size, 121
    tanks, **170**
Balloons, ascent, initial, 34
    buoyancy, 165
    Montgolfier brothers, 34
Barge, cost type, 365

Barge, design, 66, **235**
    integrated, 66
    life, 391
    number of, **93**
    terminals, 293
    tows, **235**
    utility, 236
Blanchard, Jean Pierre, 34
Benz, Carl, 54
Bernoulli's law, 165
Bicycles, 53
Bleriot, Louis, 63
Block coefficient, **163, 164, 165**
Bonrepos, Baron Paul de Riquot, 27
Boone, Daniel, 32
Boyle's law, 165
Brakes, air, 50, 58
    application time, 242
    dynamic, **220**
    regenerative, **220**
Branham, A. K., 284
Bryant, Gridley, 43
Buoyancy, Archimedes' principle, **163,
    165**
    block coefficient, **163, 164, 165**
    center of, **169, 170**
    ship's, **163, 164, 165**
Bureau of Public Roads, activities, 89
    formulas, 142
    resistance tests, 177
    standards, 91
    statistics, 411
    test roads, 400, 411
Buses, cost type, **365, 366**
    use, 78

Cableways, *see* Tramways, Aerial
Cacini, **21**
Canal, curvature, 445
    land use, **252**
    location, **444,** 445, 448
    locks, 21, 27, 41, 55
    operation, **154**
    soils, **124, 125**
    statistics, 441
    subgrades, **124, 125**
    traffic, 235
    types, 153
    water supply, 154, 450

Canals, Calumet Sag, 66
  Canal du Midi, 27
  Chesapeake and Ohio, 54
  early United States, 21, 27, **38**, 54
  Erie, 19, **37**, 38, 39, 54, 66
  European, 27
  Grand, 27
  Gulf Intracoastal, 92, 93, 96
  inland rivers, 66
  James River, 27
  Merrimac, 27
  Miami-Toledo, 37, 38
  New York State Barge, 19, 90, 91, 154
  Panama, 12, 19, 20, 21, 154, 399, 403
  Pennsylvania system, 38
  Portsmouth-Cleveland, **37**, 38
  Soo, 21, 22, **54**, **55**, 153, 154, 390, 391, 411
  Suez, 20, 403
  Welland, **41**, 54, 90, 91, 327
Capacity, carrier, **231**, **256**, **257**, **258**
  computation, **271**, **272**, **273**
  criteria, 263
  definition, **274**
  density vs., **274**
  driver reaction to, 271
  factors, **263**, **264**, **278**
  flexibility, 231
  hauling, 240
  headway, **271**, **272**, **273**, **274**, 278
  highway, 58, 256, 257, 271, **274**, **275**, **276**, **278**
  lane, **274**
  practical, **273**, **274**, 482
  saturated, 271, 272
  speed vs., 242, 243
  track, 58, **272**, 467
  transportation, 174
  values of, **277**
  vehicle performance, **264**, **265**, **266**, **267**, **268**, **269**, **270**
Car(s), accounting, 232
  air conditioning, 58
  early United States, **48**, **49**, **55**
  ferries, 327
  floats, 327
  improvements, 58
  interchange, 232, 318

Car(s), movements, 290, 291
  ore, 324, 326
  ownership, 83, **84**
  replacement, 238
  safety devices, 50, 51
  sleeping, 49
  standardization, 232
  steel, 57
  tank, 55
  terminal time, **290**, **291**
  variety of, 232
Cargo, bulk, 291, 292, 293
  general, 292, 293, 303
Carriage, electric, 53
  gas-powered, 53
  liquid-gas-driven, 54
Carriers, capacity types, 367
  contract, 75, 371
  cost groups, **367**
  exempt, **75**, **76**
  for-hire, 74, 75, 79
  freight, 73, 74, 75, 76, 77, 79
  passenger, 77, 78
  private, **74**, **76**, **79**, 357
Chariot, Roman, 28, 50
Chevalier, Michel, **18**
Civil Aeronautics Authority, 95
  classifications, 80
Civil Aeronautics Board, 64
  accident records, 413
  activities, 95, 278, **371**
  powers, 371
  regulation, 371
Clark, J. M., 367
Classification, carrier, 73
  C.A.B., 80
  I.C.C., **74**, **75**, **78**, **79**, **80**
  I.C.C. commodity, 77
  I.C.C. route, 76
  revenue, 74, 78, 79
  technological, **158**, **159**
Classification, Technological, assembled unit, **158**
  continuous flow, **159**
  single unit, **158**
Clock, 21, 22
Coach, 28
Communications, control, **338**, **339**, **340**, **341**

Communications, dispatching, **329**, **340**, **341**
  emergency, **339**
  inductive telephone, 341
  microwave, **338, 339**
  nondispatching, **342**
  pipeline, 68, 338
  radio, 338, 339, 340, 341
  ship-to-shore, **66**, **338**, **339**, **397**
  telephone, 338, 339, 340, 341
  teletype, 341
  television, 341
  truck, 365
  walkie-talkie, 341
  wire, 338, 339, 340
Competition, 23, 24
  cost vs., **368, 369**
  cutthroat, **53**
  rate, 368
  traffic assignment vs., 433
Computers, Electronic, applications, 241, 419
  Chicago study, 430
  for traffic surveys, **419, 435**
Construction, stage, 59, **397, 398, 399**
  surveys, 451
Containers, operation with, 331
  rehandling vs., 318
  size of shipment, **331**
Control, Centralized Traffic, capacity vs., 273, 274, 366, 433
  operation by, **342**
  pipeline, **342**
  systems of, **340, 341, 349**
Control, Centralized Transport, **349**
Control, Operational, 246, 273, 274, 278, 279, 342, 349
  airports, **352, 354**
  Air Route Traffic, 340
  for airways, **339, 340**
  block systems, **344**
  communications, **338, 339**
  defects, 343
  dispatching, **338, 413**
  factors, **337**
  functions, **337**
  headway vs., 343
  human engineering, 338
  instrument landing, 353

Control, Operational, interlockings, **350**
  interval, **342, 343, 344, 345**
  radio, train, 350, **351**
  railroad, **340, 341**
  schedules, 343
  see-and-be-seen, **343**, 351
  signals, **344, 345, 346, 347, 348**
  signal spacing, 344
  space-interval system, **344**
  supervising agencies, **338**
  systems, 342
  time intervals, 343
  time tables, 343
Conveyors, Belt, 24
  belt, 185, 186, 188, 189, **215, 216**
  belt tension, 187, 214, 215, 216
  capacity, 279
  cost type, 365
  curvature, 445
  dependability, 250
  flight, 186
  guidance, **159**
  horsepower, **214, 215, 216**
  idlers, 185, 186, 216
  land use, 253
  location, 452
  operation, 159, 215, **216**, 257
  performance, **255, 258, 262**
  pulley, **185, 186, 187, 188, 214**
  resistance, 185, 186, 188, 189, 214
  safety, 250
  speed, **192**
  utility, 104, **280, 283**
Coordination, 157, 315
  airlines-railroad, 324
  analysis, 468, 469
  cost of, 318
  definition, 315
  economics, 317, 321
  end-to-end, **322**
  equipment interchange, **320**
  establishing, **333, 334**
  extension of service, **323**
  factors, **316**
  intercarrier, 322
  joint use, **319**, 322
  limitations, **317, 318**
  occurrence, **333, 334**
  other types, 322

Coordination, piggy back, **298**
  rail-air, 324
  rail-ship, **295, 297, 298**, 316
  rail-truck, **296, 297, 298**
  Rail-Van service, **332, 333**
  rail-water, **324, 325, 326**
  reasons for, **316, 317**
  of right of way, **323, 324, 433**
  schedules, **320**
  significance, 315
  supplemental services, 323
  trackage, **321**
  types of, **318**
Costs, allocations, **399, 400, 401**
  alternatives, 381, **388**
  average, 361, **362**
  canal, 444
  capital, **360**, 390, 391, 392, 393
  collection, 410
  common carrier, 359
  comparisons, 381, 382
  demand vs., **358**
  direct, 363
  distance vs., **443, 444**
  estimates, 385, 386
  excess capacity, effect of, **366, 367**
  factors, 384
  fixed, **361**, 368
  gradients, effect on, **219**, 446
  importance of, 337
  incremental, 401
  indirect, 363
  investment, 391
  joint, **361, 362, 363, 370**
  location, 434, 444
  operating, **360, 361**, 392, 393
  out-of-pocket, 368
  overhead, **367**
  private carriers, 258, 259, **370, 371**
  rates vs., **358, 359**
  of service, 359, 369
  speed, 242, 243
  terminal, 290, 300
  ton-mile, 401, 402
  transportation, 25, 73
  typical, **386**
  unit, **366, 386**
  user, 389, 390, **399, 400**
  variable, **361**

Costs, variable-cost carriers, **363, 364, 366, 367**
  variations with traffic, 357, **366**
Couplers, automatic, 50, 58
  link and pin, 50
Coupling, electric, 197, 205
Cross ties, 113, **131**
  ballast pressures, 120
  load distribution, 119
  tie pressures, 120
Cugot, Nicholas Joseph, **28, 29**
Curvature, catenary, **442**
  degree of, **438**
  effects on stability, 162
  functions of, **438**
  geometrics of, **438, 439, 440, 441**
  limitations of, **444, 445, 446**
  location, effects of, **444, 445**
  maximum, **445**
  pipeline, 324
  river, 149
  superelevation, 136, **439**
  vertical, **440, 441**

Daimler, Gottlieb, 54, 61
Davis, W. J., **174, 175**
Deceleration, 8, 197, 220
  brake, application time, **242**
  braking, 241, 242
  computation of, 241, 242
  deceleration force, 241
  friction, coefficient, 240
  speed vs., 242
Decentralization, 8
Defense, National, 12
Dependability, 231, 246, 357
  aerial tramways, **250**
  airways, **249, 250**
  conveyors, **250**
  delays, 246
  highway, **248**
  importance, 246
  operational control vs., **337**
  pipeline, **250**
  railroad, 284
  safety, 246
  waterways, **249, 281**
Diesel, flexibility, 232, 241
  fuel economy, 284

Diesel, locomotive, 24
  trucks, 24
Dirigibles, 56, 61, 63
Dispatching, airline, **339, 340**
  communications, **338, 339**
  emergency, 339
  harbor master, 339
  pipeline, **342, 349, 350**
  purpose of, 338, 339
  radio, 339
  railroad, **340, 341**
  time interval, 343
  train sheet, 341
Dominico brothers, 27
Drag, 166, 171, 172
  airplane, 179, 180
  coefficient, 167, 177
  induced, **179, 180**
  parasitic, **179, 180**
  profile, **179, 180**
Drainage, capacity, **126**
  critical flow, **128**
  design, **126**
  empirical formula, 128, 130
  Manning's formula, **126**
  rainfall intensity, **129**
  rational method, **128**
  subdrainage, **127,** 130
Drake, Colonel, 55
Drive, aerial tramway, **212, 213**
  band, **212, 213**
  conveyor, **214, 215, 216**
  gear, **203**
Driver guidance, **160**
Dumont, Santos, 56, 63
Dunham, Edward B., 442
Duryea brothers, 54

Economic Justification, capital costs,
  391
  capital recovery, **390, 391, 392**
  capital-recovery factor, **390**
Economic life, **391, 392**
Edison, Thomas A., 53
Elasticity, 122, **131**
Elevation, aerial tramway, 238
  airplane, **224, 225**
  canal, 224

Elevation, horsepower, relation to,
  195, 211, 214, **217, 218, 219**
  location, 448
  pipeline, **222, 223**
  resistance, grade, **217**
  runways, 224, 225
  stratosphere, 224
Energy, kinetic, 221
  potential, 221
  rotative, 221
Engines, airplane, **205, 206**
  atomic, 198
  diesel, 199, **203,** 215
  internal-combustion, 196
  jet, 198
  marine, **204, 205**
  performance, **204, 205, 206, 207**
  solar, 196
  steam, **196, 197**
  supercharged, **206**
  water-powered, 196
Exploration, railway, 18, 20
Expressways, 397

Federal, aid, Highways Act of 1956, 59,
  60, 85
  airways, 95, **339, 340**
  Aviation Act, 64, 310, 409
  financing, road, 159
  highways, 85, 365
  interstate highways, 59, **402**
  Road Act, 59
  taxes, 89
Financing, 24
  bonds, 391, **393, 394, 395, 396, 397**
  borrowing, 396
  differential uses, **400, 401, 402**
  earnings, 393
  Federal interstate highway, 89
  government, 393, 394
  methods, 393, 394, 395, 396
  pay-as-you-go, 396, 397
  programs, **396, 397**
  savings, 393
  stage construction, 397
  stocks, 393
  tax support, **395, 402**
  tolls, **396, 399, 400, 403**
  urban transit, **403**

Financing, user payment, **399, 400**
Flexibility, 232, **239,** 280, 316, 357
aerial tramway, **238, 239**
aircraft, **236, 237, 239**
conveyor, **238, 239,** 280
highway, 282
motor truck, **233, 234, 239,** 282
pipeline, **237, 238, 239**
railroad, **231 232, 233, 239**
ship, **236, 239,** 281
water carrier, **235, 236, 239,** 281
Flow, Fanning's equation, **182, 183, 184, 185**
resistance, **182, 183, 184, 185,** 209
Reynolds number, 182, 184
streamlined, **182, 183**
turbulent, **182, 183**
Force, Propulsive, **174**
gradients vs., **219**
horsepower, **195,** 196, 212, **214**
speed, 240
tractive, **174, 200, 201, 202**
Ford, Henry, 23, 61, 62
Freight House, design, 301, **302**
floor area, 301
floor load, 301
function, 295, **296**
motor freight, 319
operation, 296
planning, 301
platform, 301, 302
tonnage factor, 302
also see Transit Shed; Terminals
Fuel, coal, 196
conservation, 200
consumption, 196, 219, 242
discovery, 9, 61
efficiency, comparative, **198, 199, 285, 286, 287**
energy in, **198**
elevation vs. airplane efficiency, 226
gasoline, 196
gradient, effect of, **219**
load vs., 262
nuclear, 196
octane, high, 65
prime movers, 196
Fulton, Robert, 39

Gage, of track, 20, 232
General Motors Corporation, air fleet, 80
cars, 62
Geometrics, aerial tramway, **441, 442**
alignment, **438**
curves, degree of, **438**
curves, horizontal, **438, 439**
curves, parabolic, **440, 441**
elements of, **437**
grade, change in, **440**
profiles, **439, 440**
sight distance, **440, 441**
Germany, 19
Gifford, Henri, 56
Goldbeck, 115, **144, 145**
Goodyear Tire and Rubber Company, dirigibles, 63
equation, conveyor, **187**
Grades, balancing of, 219
canal, **224,** 448
definition, 217
delay from, **220**
drifting, 220
economic effects, **219, 446, 447**
hydraulic, **222, 223**
length, **220, 221,** 440
limitations from, 446, 447
limiting, **218,** 446, 447
location vs., **218**
maintenance on, **219**
momentum, **221, 222**
profile, rolling, 222
rates of, **220, 221, 259**
resistance, **217,** 240, 241
ruling, **218, 446**
speed on, 243
traction on, 220, 221
Great Lakes, 22, 23, 24, 57, 90, 153
Arthur M. Anderson, **457, 458**
bulk-cargo ships (typical), **457, 458**
capacity on, **260, 261**
channel depths, **90**
communications, **338, 339**
coordination, **324, 325, 326**
costs, **326**
Erie, 90, 91
Griffin, 28
Huron, 54

Great Lakes, Michigan, 90, 91, 326, 327
  ore movement, **297**
  passenger, 67
  routes, **90, 91**
  Saint Clair, 90
  ships, **41**, 55, 170, 236
  speed, 243, 257
  time, terminal, **291**
Greyhound Bus Lines, 13
Guidance, aerial tramway, **160, 249**
  airways, 249, 250
  conveyor, **159**
  highway vehicle, **160, 248**
  pipeline, **159**
  railway, **159**
  tow, 149
  waterway, **160, 249**

Haenlein, Paul, 56
Harbor, 303
  depths, **303**
  lights, 345
  purpose, **302**
  tidal basins, **303**
Helicopter, capacity, 258
  flexibility, 237
  maneuverability, 162
  performance, **258**
  utility, 237
Hiawatha, **17**
Highway(s), Alaska, 21
  Aztec, 32
  Boston Post Road, 32
  Chinese, **29, 31**
  colonial, **32**
  cost types, 365
  curves, 445
  demand, level of, 435
  dependability, 248
  early, 29
  equipment, **89**
  European, 31
  gradients, **221**
  Lancaster Pike, 34
  land use, 252
  lanes, number of, 398
  location, 323, **443, 444, 445**
  Los Caminos Reales, 32
  MacAdam, **31, 32**

Highway(s), Mayan, 32
  Mediterranean, **29**
  mileage, 60, **85**, 105
  National, **35, 36**, 53
  pavement, 23, **137, 138, 139, 140, 141,
    142, 143, 144, 145**
  Roman, **29, 30**, 32
  routes, **85, 86, 87**
  safety, **248**
  signals, 345, **346**
  Spanish-American, 32, **33**
  statistics, **411**
  superhighway, 57, 60
  surfaces, 60
  technology, 23
  Telford, **31, 32**
  tramways, **33**
  Trisaguet, **31, 32**
  turnpikes, **35**
  vehicle stability, 163
  Wilderness Road, **32, 33**
Highway Research Board, **274**
  tests, **400, 401**
History, analysis, **17**
  economic factors, **17**
Hoover, President Herbert, 66
Horsepower, aerial tramway, **211, 212**
  airplane, **205, 206, 207**
  altitude vs., 207
  brake, 202
  conveyor, 214, 215, 216
  ship, **204, 205**
  speed vs., 240
  torque vs., 202, 203
  tractive effort vs., 201, 240
  use of, 195

Industrial park, 300
  location, **300, 301**
  zoning, 300
Integration, 157
Interlocking, Railroad, automatic, 350
  entrance-exit, 350
  types, 350
Interstate Commerce Commission, 53,
    237, 329
  accident reports, 413
  Act, **335, 359, 371**
  cost definition, **369**

Interstate Commerce Commission,
  cost of service vs., **369**
Dockett 32533, 329
Motor Carrier Act, 59, 335, 371
one-percent sampling, **409, 412, 413**
rebates, 55
reports, **408, 409**
subject carriers, **371**
terminal costs, **300**

Jackson, President Andrew, 36
Janey, Eli H., 50
Japan, 19
Jervis, John B., 43
  swivel trucks, **43**
Jessop, William, 34
Justification, Economic, alternative
  rate, **385**
annual costs, **388, 389**
attractive rate, 386
basis of, 382
benefit-cost ratio, **389, 390**
benefit, user, 390, **398, 400, 402**
cost estimates, **385, 386, 463, 464**
principles, guiding, **384, 385**
rate of return, **385, 387, 470**
type of project, **382, 383**

Kettering, 23, 61
Kelley Mail Act, 64
Kimball, E. E., **267, 268, 269**
Knot, definition, 178
Krebs, A. C., 56

Land Grant Act, 20, 46
Land Use, acquisition, 324
  highway needs, 252
  industrial parks, 300
  railroad needs, 252, 320, 433
  right of way, widths, 252
  scarcity, 251
  terminal needs, **300, 301, 302**
  transportation needs, 251, 252, 319, 320
  waterway needs, 252
  zoning, 300, **324**
Lang, Professor A. S., 268, 269
Langen, Eugene, 54
Langley, Dr. Samual P., 56

Latrobe, Benjamin, 46
League of American Wheelmen, 53
Legislation, Land Grant Act, 20, 46
  Gadsden Purchase, 20
Leland, Henry, 61
Lenoir, Jean Joseph Étienne, 53
Leonardo da Vinci, 27
Lift, **165, 166, 171, 172**
  center of pressure, 166
  coefficient, **166, 167, 168**
  fuel vs., **262**
Lincoln, Abraham, 49
Location (Factors), curvature, **444, 445**
  development, **447, 448**
  distance, **443**
  grades, **446, 447, 448**
  grade design, **447, 448**
  miscellaneous, 450
  procedures, **451, 452**
  soils, 449
  surveys, **451, 452**
  surveys, aerial, 451
  topography, 449
  water, 449
Location, Route, design factors, 46, **218, 219, 437**
  design, pioneer, 43, **437**
  economic, 437
  flexibility, **236**
  geographic, 19
  gradients, **218, 219**
  railroad routes (early), **47, 52**
  also see Location (Factors);
    Route(s)
Locks, Chain of Rocks, 153
  design, **151, 153, 224**
  dimensions, 153
  economics of, **224**
  operation, **151, 153**
  requirements, 149
  Soo, 153
  use, **151**
Locomotive, adhesion, 202, 241
  boiler, 43, 57
  brakes, **220**
  diesel, 19, 20, 24, 47, 58, **197**
  efficiency, 198, 199, 201, 284
  electric, 24, 53

Locomotive, engines, **205**
  first, **41, 42, 53**
  flexibility, **231, 232**
  gear ratios, 201, 202
  gradients vs., **220**
  improvements, 57
  life, 391
  performance, **259, 260**
  radio-controlled, 163
  side rod thrust, 136
  tractive effort, 200, 201, 202
  truck, swiveled, 43
  turbine, gas, 202
  typical, **455, 456**
  water, 449, 450
  also see Motive Power; Prime
    Movers
Locomotives, mid-century (19th), 46
  999, 53
  Rocket, 42
  Stourbridge Lion, 43
Loree, L. F., 273

MacAdam, 31, 32
MacKenzie, 54
MacKinder, Sir Halford, **11**
Mahan, Alfred Thayer, **10**
Markens of Vienna, 54
Markets, 8, 12, 13, 18
Momentum, **221, 222**
  airplane vs., **225**
  grades, **221, 222**
  velocity head, **221**
Monorails, resistance, 175
  stability, 163
  Wuppertal, 316
Montgolfier brothers, 34
Mostafa, Khalil K., 267
Motive Power, efficiency, thermal,
    198, 199
  improvements, 57
  also see Locomotives; Prime Mov-
    ers; Tractor
Motor Freight, guidance, **160**
  operation, 158
Motors, a-c series, 198
  d-c series, 197
  induction, 198, 216

Moving sidewalks, 13, 250
  also see Conveyors
Murdoch, Walter, 29

National Homes, 12
Navigation, aids, 23, 93, 224, 250, **351,
    353, 362**
  astrolabe, 21
  beacons, radio, 224, **353**
  charts, 224
  compass, 21
  compass, gyroscopic, **162**
  compass, radio, 353
  depths, 147
  direction finders, 351
  instrument landings, 278, 317
  lights, 345
  radio range, 95, 351, 353
  signals, 345
  sonar, 351
  also see Navigation Aids; Control,
    Operational
Navigation Aids, **351, 352, 353, 354**
  instrument landing systems, **353, 354**
  need, 351
  weather effects, 351
  also see Navigation; Control, Op-
    erational
Newton, Sir Isaac, 240
  laws of motion, 240
Nozzle, Kort, 206
  also see Towboats
Nuclear energy, 65, 196, 198

Older, Clifford, 143
  Older formula, 143, 144
Olds, Ransom E., 54
Operation, characteristics, 231
  driver reaction, 271
  also see Control, Operational
Operation, Railroad, 158, 246, 247, 255,
    256, 258
  capacity, **256, 259**
  equipment, interchange, **233**
  flexibility, **231, 232, 233**
  gradients, **219, 220, 221, 222**
  guidance, **159, 160**
  interchange, 234
  performance, 255, **256, 258, 262, 263**

Operation, Railroad, rack, 175
  train speeds, 242, 243, **256**
  also see Control, Operational
Operation, Trains, CTC, 58
  orders, 50
  rules, 50
  Standard Code, 50
  also see Control, Centralized
    Traffic; Signal(s)
Otto, Nikolaus, **53**
Outram, 34

Panama Canal, **12, 66**
Parking lots, drainage, 130
  also see Roads
Pavements, 113, **114**
  asphalt, 37, 53, 60
  binder material, 137, **140**
  brick, 60
  classifications, 137, 138, 140
  concrete, **138, 139, 141, 142, 143,
    144, 145, 146**
  cross sections, **138, 139**
  definition, 137
  elasticity, modulus of concrete, 142
  failure, 141
  flexible, **114, 115, 116, 117, 118, 140**
  lane width, **146**
  life, 391
  load, wheel, distribution, **114, 115,
    116,** 121, 137
  macadam, 141
  modulus of subgrade reaction, 142
  miles of, 58
  Poisson's ratio for concrete, 142
  rigid, **117, 141, 142, 143, 144**
  stresses, **141, 142, 143, 144, 145, 146**
  thermal effects, **145**
  thickness, **114, 143, 144**
  wearing course, 137
  wood block, 36, 37
  also see Roads; Highway(s); Soils
Performance, criteria, 231, **264,** 280,
    281, 284
  dead-load-to-pay-load, **262, 263**
  horsepower-per-net-ton, **259, 260,
    261, 262**
  optimum, **270, 271**

Performance, ton-miles-per-vehicle-
    hour, **255, 256, 257, 258, 259, 260,
    261, 262**
  vehicles, number of, **264, 265, 266,
    267, 268, 269, 270**
  vehicle-hour diagram, **267, 268, 269,
    270**
Petroleum, discovery of, 55, 61
Photogrammetry, 381
  also see Location (Factors); Loca-
    tion, Route
Piggy Back, advantages, 328
  costs, **329, 330**
  disadvantages, **331**
  economics, **329**
  efficiency, 331
  equipment, **331, 332, 333**
  facilities, **330, 331**
  ferry, 327
  movement, **298, 328, 330, 331**
  planning, **328, 329, 330**
  systems, **328, 329, 330**
  trailer-on-flatcar, 318, 323, 327
  types of, **327, 328**
Pipeline(s), Buckeye Pipeline Com-
    pany, 13
  Canol, 21
  capacity, **257, 258, 366**
  cathodic protection, **125**
  classification, 237
  communications, 237
  companies, 13, 80, 102
  corrosion, **125**
  curvature, 445
  dependability, 23, **55, 56, 68**
  dispatching, 342, **349, 350**
  flexibility, **237, 238**
  gas, 68, 80
  gradient, hydraulic, 222, **223, 224,**
    448
  gradients, 222, **223, 224**
  guidance, 159
  head, 223
  high pressure, 68
  installation, **263, 264**
  land use, **253, 264**
  location, **443, 444, 445,** 448, 456
  mileage, **105**
  performance, 255, **257,** 267
  Prairie Pipeline Company, 68

Pipeline(s), pumps, 68, **209, 210, 238, 250**
  pump stations, 197
  resistance, flow, **182, 183, 184, 185**
  rights of way, 238, 324
  routes, 102, **104, 105**
  safety, 250
  soils, **125**, 449
  solids, 68, 237
  speed, **257**
  submarine, **12**
  surveys, 452
  technology, 23, 56
  Tidewater Pipeline Company, 55
  traffic, **80**, 237
  types, 97
  utility, **280, 283**
  welded, 68
Pittsburgh Steamship Division, 12
Planes, inclined, 27, 43
Planning, construction standards, 380
  cost allocations, **399, 400**
  cost estimates, **385, 386**, 391
  data collection, **407, 413, 414**, 463, 464
  demand, level of, **345**
  design standards, 380
  economic, **381, 382, 383**
  financing, 391
  need, 361, 377
  pay-as-you-go, 397
  policies, local, **379**
  problem example, **461, 471**
  requisites, **377**
  stage construction, **397, 398, 399**
  steps, 378
  thirtieth highest hour, **435**
  time, 436
  tools, 379
  traffic data, **407, 408, 409, 410, 411**
  also see Justification, Economic
Plimsoll, Samuel, 164
Policy, Government, 157
Pollard, Wm. S., Jr., corridor analysis, **435**
Ports, 90, 91, **303**
  capacities, **305, 306**
  definition, **304**
  drydock, 311
  functions, **304**

Ports, harbors, 299, 303
  Lake, 292
  marine railways, 311
  operation, **305**
  piers, **305, 306**
  quays, **305**
  statistics, **410, 411**
  wharves, **304, 305, 306**
Port of New York Authority, 291, 319
Power transmission, 196, 197
Prime Movers, aircraft, 249
  conveyors, **216, 217**
  definitions, **196**
  diesel, coupling, **205**
  efficiency, thermal, **198**
  gear, reduction, 197
  pumps, 209, **210**
  steam, 196, 210
  types, **196, 197, 198**
Production, 15
Propeller, cavitation, **204**
  efficiency, **204, 205, 206**
  screw, 39, **40**, 66
  thrust, **204**
Public Roads, Bureau of, 53
Pullman, George M., 49
Pumps, centrifugal, **210**
  double-acting, **210**
  efficiency, **210**
  horsepower, **209, 210**
  pipeline, 68, **209, 210, 225**
  piston, **210**
  pressure, **209, 210, 223**, 443, 444
  reciprocating, **210**
  stations, 237, 238
  also see Pipeline(s)
Purdue University, 284

Radar, 23
  airplane, 65, 351, 354
  control, airways, 279, 340, 351
  control, railroad cars, 58
  transpounder, **340**
Radio, communication, 58, 338, 339, 340
  compass, 23
  control, 162, 163
  control of trains, **350, 351**
  guidance, 160

Radio, microwave, 58
  range, 95, 97
  telephone, 23
Rail(s), bending moment, **132**, 133,
  134
  bullhead, 43
  continuous welded, 131
  deflection, **131**, **132**, **133**, **134**
  designation, 131
  early, **34**, **43**, 44
  load distribution, 119
  modulus of elasticity, 134, 136
  moment of inertia, 134, 136
  plate, 34
  properties, **136**
  Stevens, 43
  stiffness, 135, 136
  tee-rail, 43, 46
  wear, 136
  weight, 136, 137, 398
Railway, Alpine, 497
  belt, 316, 321, 436, 437
  Canadian, 50, 57, 327
  capacity, excess, **366**
  capitalization, 85
  construction, 43, 51
  control, Federal, 57
  cost types, **366**
  curves, 445
  electric, 53
  equipment, 83
  extent of, **47**, 82
  installation, **364**, 398
  land use, **252**
  location, **322**, **443**, **444**, **445**, **446**
  mileage, **82**, 83, 84, 105
  plant, **81**, **82**, 83, 84
  rack, 447
  revenues, **84**, **85**
  routes, 47, 52
  safety, 50, 57
  speed, 57, **242**, **243**
  switching, 316, 321
  technology, 22
  traffic, 81
Railways, Atchison, Topeka and Santa
  Fe, 13, 49, 57, 74
  Baltimore and Ohio, 44
  Belt Railway of Chicago, 74, 321

Railways, Berlin to Bagdad, 19
  Bessemer and Lake Erie, 334
  Canadian Pacific, 50, 447
  Central of New Jersey, 57
  Central Pacific, 49
  Chesapeake and Ohio, 333
  Chicago, Burlington and Quincy, 50,
    57
  Chicago, Milwaukee, St. Paul and
    Pacific, 57
  Chicago and Northwestern, 48
  Chicago, Rock Island and Pacific,
    46, 333
  Cincinnati Union Terminal, 321
  Delaware and Hudson, 43
  Duluth, Missabe and Iron Range,
    334
  Erie, 50, 412
  Great Northern, 50, 57
  Illinois Central, 46, 57, 74
  Kansas City Terminal, 74, 321
  Korean, 20
  Liverpool and Manchester, 41
  New Orleans Public Belt, 74
  New York Central, 53, 57, 58
  New York City subways, 274
  New York, New Haven, and Hart-
    ford, 57, 334
  Northern Pacific, 50, 57
  Ohio Central, 58
  Pacific, 20
  Pacific Great Eastern, 317
  Pennsylvania, 13, 38, 44, 49, 57, 74,
    274, 285, 322, 329
  Port Terminal Railroad of Houston,
    74
  Quebec, North Shore and Labrador,
    237
  Société Nationale Chemin de Fer,
    57, 342
  South African, 273, 334
  South Manchurian, 273, 334
  Southern Pacific, 49, 57, 324
  Southern system, 43, 45
  Terminal Railway Association of St.
    Louis, 321
  Union, 321
  Union Pacific, 49, **50**, 57
Rapid Transit, 197

Rapid Transit, block systems, **271, 272**
  demand, level of, **435**
  traffic assignment, **433, 434, 435**
Rates, base, **359**
  competition, **368, 369**
  costs vs., **358, 359, 367, 368, 369**
  criteria, 359
  differential, **359, 369, 370**
  group action, **370**
  regulation, 359, **371**
  structure, 359
  subsidy, **370**
Reconnaissance, data, **380**, 381
  field, 462, 463
  Pacific railways, **380**
  photography, aerial, 381
Regulation, 246
  carriers subject to, 371
  Civil Aeronautics Board, **371**
  costs vs., **269**
  Interstate Commerce Commission, 371
  powers, **371**
  of rates, 359, **371**
  reasons for, **371, 372**
Renard, Charles, 56
Resistance, Propulsive, acceleration, 240
  aerial tramway, **210, 211**
  conveyor, **185, 186, 188, 189, 214, 215, 216**
  Durand's formula, 178
  Fanning's equation, **182**, 183
  flow, 174
  forces, 173
  fuel efficiency vs., 284
  grade, 192, 195, 211, 216, **217, 218**
  gravity, API, **183, 185**
  horsepower vs., 195, 196
  pipeline, **182, 183, 184, 185**
  residual, **178**, 179
  Reynolds number, **182**
  road, 173, **177, 178**
  ship, **178, 179**
  skin friction, 173, **178**
  summary, **190, 191**
  tire rim, 173, **175, 176, 177, 178**
  tractive, **173, 174, 175, 176**
  train, 173

Resistance, Propulsive, viscosity, 182, 183, 185
  also see Airfoil; Drag; Force, Propulsive
River, Army Engineers, U. S., Board of, 66
  canalization, 66, 93, **149, 150, 151, 152, 153**
  channel depths, **93**
  lights, navigation, 345
  revenue, **94, 95**
  Rivers and Harbors Act, 65
  traffic, **94, 95**, 235
  also see Navigation Aids; Waterway(s); Rivers, canalized
Rivers, Allegheny, 55
  Danube, 27, 41
  Delaware, 37
  Detroit, 54, 90, 91
  Dnieper, 41
  Hudson, 37, 39, 90, 91
  Illinois, 66
  James, 27, 37
  Merrimac, 27
  Mississippi, 46, 66, 147, 153
  Missouri, 66
  Mohawk, 37
  Monongahela, 41, 54, 65
  Niagara, 28, 29
  Nile, 24
  Ohio, 24, 41, 54, 65
  Oise, 41
  Potomac, 37
  Rhine, 27, 41
  Rhone, 27
  St. Mary's, 55, 90, 91
  Seine, 41
  Volga, 41
Rivers, canalized, **147, 149, 150, 151**
Roads, cross sections, **138, 139**
  drainage, **126**
  Federal Road Act, 58
  guidance on, **160**
  miles of, 58
  National, 17, 20, 53
  resistance, **177, 178**
  Roman, 17, 20, 29
  subgrade, **113**

Roads, superstructure, 113, **131**
    toll, 396
    also see Highway(s) ; Route(s)
Rockets, 21, 65, 162, 163
Route(s), African, 237
    air, 237
    belt lines, 436, 437
    bypass, 436
    caravan, **17**, 29, 31
    cost, 381
    Federal system of interstate high-
        ways, **87**
    gateways, 109
    geometrics, 437, 438
    highway, 7, 85, **86**
    land use, **300**
    location, 322, 437, 442, 443, 480
    mileage, **105**
    pipeline, 238
    profile, **439, 440**
    rail, 82
    reconnaissance, 380, 381
    terminal, 300
    time factor, **436**
    traffic assignment, **433, 434, 435**
    United States, **105, 106, 107, 108, 109**
    waterway, 91, 92, 93, 96
Route Design, allocation, carrier, 433,
    434
    allocation factors, **433, 434**
    allocation traffic, 432, 433, 434
    assignment, traffic, **434**, 435, **482, 483**
    demand, traffic, **424, 426, 432, 433**
Rozier, Jean Jacques Pilatre de, 34
Russia, 20

Safety, 231
    aerial tramways, **250**
    aircraft, **249, 250**
    control, operational, **237**
    conveyors, 250
    devices, railroad, 50
    highway, **248**, 281, 282
    pipeline, **250, 324**
    railroad, 57, 58, 247, 248
    records, **247**
    track, 137
    waterway, **249**
    weather, 248, 249

Saint Lawrence, Seaway, 18, 66, 90, 91,
    327
    ships, 236
    tolls, 95, 399
Schmidt, Dr. Edward C., 175
Schwartz, David, 56
Sea, Mediterranean, 26, 90
Sea power, British, 11
Seldon, George B., 54
Ship(s), Atwood formula, **169, 170**
    bireme, aphract, 25
    block coefficient, **163, 164, 165, 166,**
        178
    bulk cargo, 326
    buoyancy, **163, 164, 165, 166**
    capacity, **257, 260,** 261, **303**
    capacity, excess, **366**
    caravel, 26
    cargo, bulk, **326**
    cargo, general, **326**
    clipper, 39
    construction, 26
    cost types, **365 366**
    deep water, 236
    displacement, **163, 164, 165, 166**
    efficiency, thermal, 199
    flexibility, **236**
    galleon, 26
    galley, 25, 26
    Great Lakes, **41**
    great ship, 26
    guidance, **162**
    heel, angle of, **169**
    iron, 27
    life, 391
    load line, **164**
    metacenter, **169, 170**
    Norse boat, 26
    operation, **162**
    ore boat, 55, 67
    paddle wheel, 39
    performance, 255, 260, **261**
    prime mover, **197**
    resistance, 178, 179
    sizes, 205
    special purpose, 236
    speed, **243, 244,** 257
    stability, **169, 170**
    steam, **39**

Ship(s), stowage, **170**, **236**, 257
  time, terminal, 291
  tonnage, **164**, **165**
  trireme, 26
  typical, **457**, **458**
  also see Ships; Steamboats; Water-
    craft
Ships, *Alecto,* 39, 40
  Arthur M. Anderson, **457**, **458**
  Charlotte Dundas, 39
  Clermont, 39
  Great Republic, 39
  Griffin, 28
  J. M. White, **40**
  Rattler, 39, 40
  R. J. Hackett, 55
  Savannah, 139
  Seeandbee, 139
  Walk on the Water, 41
  Vandalia, 41
Signal(s), airway, 345
  aspects, 347, 348
  automatic, railroad, 57, 247
  block, **271**, **272**, **273**
  Centralized Traffic Control, 58
  circuits, track, **347**, **348**, **349**
  circuits, track, coded, **348**
  highway, **245**, **246**
  purpose of, 344
  railroad, **346**, **347**, **348**, 397
  systems, **345**
  types, 345
  waterway, 345
Sillcox, Dr. L. K., 241, **329**
Society of Automotive Engineers, 61
Soils, bearing capacity, 120, **122**, 123
  for canal, **125**
  engineering, 58
  index properties, **122**
  location vs., **449**
  for pipeline, **125**, **126**
  stability, **123**, **124**
  surveys, **123**
Specialization, regional, **8**
Speed, 231, **240**, **241**, **242**, **243**, **244**,
  245, **246**
  acceleration vs., 240, 241
  aerial tramway, **244**, **258**, 279
  aircraft, **244**, 250, **256**, **278**, **279**, 281
  average, highway, 243, **256**, **276**

Speed, capacity vs., **274**
  conveyor, **244**, **258**
  coordination in, **316**
  cruising, 266, 267
  distance, curves, 241
  effects, 242, 256
  fuel vs., 262
  gradient vs., 447
  horsepower vs., 95, 196
  optimum, **274**
  over-all, 246
  performance, **256**, **264**, **265**, **266**, **267**,
  268
  pipeline, **244**, **250**
  railroad, 57, 256
  resistance vs., 175
  summary, **245**
  time, curves, 241
  time intervals vs., 343
  train, 242, 243, 256
  typical, 242
  waterway, **243**, **244**, 281
Stability, aircraft, **171**, **172**
  Atwood's formula, **169**, **170**
  lateral, **173**
  longitudinal, **171**, **172**
  metacenter, **169**, **170**
  vertical, **172**
  yaw, **173**
Standard Code (railroad), 50
  also see Control, Operational
Starr, Millard O., 177
Steamboats, **40**, **41**
Stephanson, 22
  Rocket, 22, **42**
Stevens, John, 43
Stresses, allowable, 136, 143, 144
  Committee on, Track, 120, 132
  Foppi, 132
  master diagram, **135**
  Older formula, **143**
  pavement, concrete, **143**, **144**, **145**,
  146
  radius, of relative stiffness, 142
  rail, 136
  track, **119**, **120**
Subgrade, bearing capacity, 120, **122**,
  123
  canal, **125**
  design, 123, 124

Subgrade, drainage, **126,** 130
  functions, 113
  loading, 122
  requirements, **122**
  soils, 123, 124
  stability, **123, 124**
  also see Soils; Drainage
Submarines, 12, 162
Surveys, Traffic, Chicago Area Trans-
    portation Study, 419
  cordon counts, **414, 415**
  estimates, statistical, **418, 419, 434**
  mathematical studies, **418, 419**
  origin-destination, **424, 426**
  questionnaire forms, **416, 417**
  questionnaires, **414, 415, 417**
  screen lines, **414, 415**
  traffic counts, **414**
  waybill sampling, **409, 412, 413**
Symes, James M., 285
Symington, William, 29

Talbot, Dr. Arthur N., 119, 120
  Committee on Stresses in Track, 120
  runoff formula, 130
Taxes, gasoline, 59
Taxicabs, 28
Telford, 31, 32
Terminals, aerial tramways, 238, 240
  costs, **299, 300,** 365, 372
  definitions, 290
  delays, 299
  dependability, 246
  facilities, 291, 292, 293
  functions, **290, 291, 292, 293, 295**
  importance, **290, 291**
  location, 300, 301
  locomotive, 312
  railroad, **74**
  river, 66
  ship, 67, 68, **303, 304, 305**
  speed, 246
  warehousing, 303
Terminal Facilities, car ferries, 327
  mechanization, **306, 318, 319**
  unloading, 291, 326
  also see Freight House; Harbor,
    Ports; Terminals; Transit Shed;
    Yards

Terminal Functions, concentration,
    292, **293, 294,** 307, 316
  delivery, 293, **295, 296, 297,** 298
  freight handling, **318**
  interchange, **294** 295, 307, **317,** 318,
    320
  in-transit privileges, 293
  loading, 292
  mechanization, **306, 318,** 319
  pickup, 293, **295, 296, 297,** 298
  service and repair, **311, 312**
  unloading, 292, **299, 302, 303**
Terminal Operations, equipment
    abuse, 299
  inbound, 295
  interchange, 300
  line haul relation, **295, 296, 297**
  mechanization, **306, 318, 319**
  palletized loads, 319
  pickup and delivery, 323
  road movement, relation to, 296,
    297, **298, 299**
  turn-around time, **295, 299**
Thrust, propeller, airplane, **205, 206**
  ship, **204**
  also see Prime Movers; Force,
    Propulsive
Time, 21, 22
  cost of, **436**
  design factor, **436**
  terminal, **290, 291, 299**
  time-distance curves, 241
  traffic factor, **436**
Tissaudier, Gaston, 56
Tolls, river, 95
Towboats, design, **66**
  diesel, 66
  nozzle, Kort, 206
  number of, **93**
  operation, **158, 160**
  propellers, **205, 206**
  speed, **244**
  typical, **458, 459**
  also see Ships; Watercraft; Tows
Tows, capacity, **260, 261**
  consist, 235, 236
  operation, **236, 260, 261**
Track, 113, 114
  alignment, 137
  bending moment, **132, 133, 134**

Track, circuit, **347, 348**
  deflection, **131, 132, 133, 134**
  distribution, wheel load, **117, 121**
  double, 57
  early U. S., **43, 44**
  fastenings, **131**
  gage, 20, 46, 50, **131**
  improvements, 57
  life, 391
  loads, 117, 121
  mileage, 58
  modulus of elasticity, **132, 133, 134**
  network, 232
  stresses, 119
  surface, 137
  tamping, 137
  trackage rights, 321
Tractive Resistance, aerial tramways,
  189, 192
  components, 174
  Davis equation, **174, 175, 176**
  gradients vs., 219, **240, 241**
  also see Resistance, Propulsive
Tractor, highway, 234
  highway, typical, **456, 457**
  life, 391
  steam, 53
  trailer, 234
  also see Truck, Motor; Prime Movers
Trade Associations, American Trucking Association, 412
  American Waterways Operators, 92,
  96
  Association of American Railroads,
  412
  National Tank Truck Carriers, 412
Traffic, airway, 80, 97, 103, 236, 237
  canal, 94
  capacity, **265, 266**
  carload, **292, 297,** 317, 359
  carload, less than, 247, 248, 292, 293,
  296, 302, 323, **329,** 359
  congestion, 235
  control, air, **278, 279**
  costs, flow, **257, 258**
  delays, 247
  freight, volume, **71**
  Great Lakes, 236

Traffic, highway, 89
  interference, **266, 267, 268, 269, 270,**
  276
  movements, **293**
  passenger, 250, 293
  passenger, volume, **72**
  pickup and delivery, **293**
  pipeline, 80, 237
  railway, 81, 82, 84, 85
  requirements to move, **263**
  restrictions on, 278
  river, 94
  suitability for, 280, 281, 282, 283
  terminal requirements, **291, 292**
  types, **291**
Traffic Analysis, allocation, **432, 433,**
  434
  assignment, **434, 435**
  check questions, **429**
  demand, **424, 426, 432**
  forecasting, **424, 426, 427, 428**
  growth factor, 424, 426, 427, 428, 471,
  472, 473, 474, 475
  level of demand, **435**
  time factor, **436**
  zone patterns, **434**
  also see Traffic Data; Traffic Patterns
Traffic Data, accident reports, 413
  analysis, **424, 425, 426, 427, 428,**
  429, 430
  Carroll, Dr. J. Douglas, Jr., 420
  collection, **409, 412, 413, 414, 415,**
  416, 417, 418, 419, 420
  counts, **414, 415**
  dispatchers' records, 413
  passing reports, **412, 413**
  presentation, **420, 421, 422, 423, 424,**
  425
  published, **408, 409**
  required, **407, 408**
  sources, **408, 409**
  survey, field, **413**
  waybill sampling, **409, 412, 413**
  also see Traffic Patterns; Traffic
  Analysis
Traffic, Granular Bulk, coal docks, 292
  coordination, **317**
  economics, **326, 327**

Traffic, Granular Bulk, hazards, 393
  Hulett unloaders, **325, 326**
  ore docks, 292, **324, 325, 326**
  requirements, transport, 291, 292
  ship design, **326**
  surge pile, 293
  transfer facilities, 322
  types, traffic, 291, 327
Traffic, livestock, 291, 292
Traffic Patterns, 380
  analysis, **424, 425**
  data, 380, **407, 408**
  desire lines, **424, 426, 433**
  flow diagrams, **420, 421, 422, 423**
  future, **424, 426, 427, 428**
  origin-destination, **424, 426**
  questions involved, **407, 408, 429**
  traffic generation, **418, 419**
  use, **432, 433**
  yard location, 309
Traffic, perishable, 291
Trains, electric, 220
  make-up, 295
  Mistral, 57
  operation, 268
  orders, 50
  performance, **256, 259, 261**
  streamlined, 57
  Talgo, 262
Tramways, **33, 34**
  early U. S., 42, 43
  gage, 50
  Outram, 34
Tramways, Aerial, 113, 210, **211, 212,**
    213, 214
  cable, 189, 192, **211, 212,** 250, 442
  capacity, **258, 261, 279**
  catenary, 192
  classification, 238
  cost type, **365, 366**
  curvature, **445, 446**
  dependability, 250, 251
  design, geometric, **441**
  drive, band, **213, 214**
  flexibility, 238, 239, 240
  friction, bearing, **189, 192**
  gradients, 211
  guidance, **160**
  horsepower, **213**

Tramways, land use, **253**
  location, 452
  operation, 159, 239, **240,** 250, 258,
    261, 262
  propulsion, 189
  resistance, **189, 192,** 211
  routes, 105
  route selection, **357**
  safety, 250, 251
  speed, 258
  traffic, 238, 240
  trolley, 189
Transit Shed, 397, 301
  design, 303, 304, 305
  function, 302
  tonnage factors, 303
  also see Freight House; Terminals;
    Terminal Facilities
Transportation, agencies, 71
  by animals, 4, 25
  characteristics, 367, 368, 379
  Chicago Area Transportation Sur-
    vey, 420
  commodity movements, **6, 7,** 8, 9, 18,
    297
  culture vs., **11**
  dependability, 251
  economic functions, 5
  fleets, **73, 76**
  general effects, **3, 4, 5, 6, 7, 8, 9, 10**
  history, primitive, **25**
  individual vs., 13
  industry, 12, 379
  of iron ore, 5, 55, **297, 317, 324, 325,**
    326, 379
  by man, 4, 25
  need for, **73, 337**
  planning, 337
  political effects, **11**
  science vs., 14
  sociological effects, 10
  student vs., 14
  systems, 71, 329
Trevethick, Richard, 41
Trisaguet, 31, 32
Truck, Motor, capacity, **260, 261,** 278
  costs, **365, 366**
  dimensions, **233,** 302
  efficiency, 199

Truck, Motor, flexibility, **233, 234**
  gradients vs., 221
  life, 391
  loading, 293, 317
  maintenance, 312
  operation, 364, 365
  performance, **256, 257, 258, 260, 261, 282**
  service, 323
  speed, 243, **256, 257,** 278
  tractive force, **203, 204**
  trailers, 293
  utility, 59
Turbine, 196, 197
Turnpikes, **35**
Tuthill, John K., 175

Union Barge Lines, 13
United Air Lines, 13
United States, Agriculture, Department of, 53
  Air Defense Command, 340
  Air Force, 340
  Air Traffic Control Centers, 338, 339
  Army Corps of Engineers, 338
  Board of Army Engineers, 66
  Civil Aeronautics Board, 64, 95
  Coast and Geodetic Survey, 381
  Coast Guard, 338, 339, 413
  Commerce Department, 95
  Federal Aviation Authority, 64
  Geological Survey, 451
  Interior, Department of, 412
  Map Information Office, 451
  Navy, 63
  Petroleum Administration, 412
  Post Office Department, 64
  Senate, 285
United States Steel Corporation, 12
  Bessemer and Lake Erie Railroad, 334
  Duluth, Missabe and Iron Range Railroad, 334
  Oliver Mining Company, 334
  Pittsburgh Steamship Division, 334
Urban Transit, administration, **404**
  demand, level of, **435**
  financing, 403, 404
  management, 404

Urban Transit, traffic assignment, **433, 434**
  transport authority, **404**
Utility, 231, **279,** 292
  aerial tramways, **280, 283**
  airplane, **280, 281, 283**
  conveyor, **280, 283**
  highway, **281, 283**
  pipeline, **280, 283**
  place, **3**
  railroad, **282, 283, 284**
  time, 3, **9**
  waterway, **281, 282, 283**

Vehicle, adhesion, 241
  capacity, **256, 260, 263**
  classification, **233**
  costs, 401
  energy of rotation, 241
  gear ratio, 203
  highway, 28
  operating range, **234, 235, 256, 257, 260, 261, 262**
  parking, 235
  performance, **256**
  resistance, **177, 178**
  speed, **256, 257**
  torque, **202, 203**
  tractive effort, 202
  utility, **234, 235**
  also see Locomotive; Ship(s); Truck; Tractor; etc.
Viscosity, curve, **185**
  kinetic, **184**
  viscometer, Saybolt Universal, **183, 184**

Wagon, chariot, **28**
  four-wheeled, 28
  petroleum hauling by, 55
  steam, 28
War, Civil, 21, 49, 50, 53
  Franco-Prussian, 56
  World War I, 21, 57, 58, 59, 60, 61, 63, 66
  World War II, 21, 57, 58, 59, 65, 67
Warehousing, **303**
Watercraft, barge, 24, 40
  bireme, 24

Watercraft, boat, keel, 40
  guidance, **160**
  raft, 24
  also see Barge; Ships(s); Tows;
    Towboats
Waterway(s), alignment, **149**
  artificial, 27, **149**
  capacity, **278**
  Champlain, Lake, 39
  channel regulation, **147, 148**
  classification, 235
  coastal, **92, 96**
  cost types, 365
  crossing bars, **147, 148**
  dikes, spur, **148**
  early, 35
  flexibility, **235**
  International Convention, **65, 66**
  intracoastal, **92, 96**
  land use, **252**
  levee, 147
  natural, 27, **147**
  routes, **90, 91, 92, 93, 96**
  route mileage, **105**
  tows, 235
Watt, James, 22, 28, 29
Weather, 247, 248, 249, 250
Wellington, Arthur M., 384
Westergaard, H. M., 141, 143
  radius of relative stiffness, 142
Westinghouse, George, 50
Wheels, early, 28
  flanged, 34, 284

Wheels, flattening, **114, 116, 117**
  guidance, flange, **159, 160**
  load, **121, 131, 136, 137, 141**
  safety, 247
Whitney, Eli, 60
Whitney, Silas, 42
Woelfert, Dr., 56
Worley, William, 53
Wright brothers, 63, 64

Yards, 296
  automatic, **308**
  classification, 58, 293, **306, 307, 308**
  "clearing," 321
  communication, **308, 341, 342**
  drainage, 130
  electronic, **308**
  functions, **296**, 307
  gravity, **307**
  interchange, **295, 296**
  location, **308, 309**
  locomotive, 197
  manual operation, **307**
  ore, **326**
  speed through, 243
  switch runs, **293**
  television, **341**
  train make-up, 295, **296**
  types, **306**
  units, 307

Zeppelin, Count Ferdinand von, 56
  dirigible, **61, 63**